IG Macdonald

March 1974

REPRESENTATION THEORY OF THE SYMMETRIC GROUP

Representation Theory of the SYMMETRIC GROUP

G. DE B. ROBINSON
PROFESSOR OF MATHEMATICS
UNIVERSITY OF TORONTO

EDINBURGH
AT THE UNIVERSITY PRESS

CANADA: UNIVERSITY OF TORONTO PRESS

Agents
THOMAS NELSON AND SONS LTD
Parkside Works Edinburgh 9
36 Park Street London W1
312 Flinders Street Melbourne C1
302-304 Barclays Bank Building
Commissioner and Kruis Streets Johannesburg

SOCIÉTÉ FRANÇAISE D'ÉDITIONS NELSON
97 rue Monge Paris 5

PRINTED IN GREAT BRITAIN BY
ROBERT CUNNINGHAM AND SONS LTD
ALVA, SCOTLAND

PREFACE

THE ordinary representation theory of a finite group was largely developed by Frobenius, Burnside and Schur, and the modular theory by Dickson, Brauer and Nesbitt. In the first chapter of this book we shall try to provide the background for those parts of the subject which are necessary in the sequel. With regard to the ordinary theory, a fairly complete though brief account of these 'classical' ideas is given in Part 1. The case of the modular theory is somewhat different, since new and fundamental developments are still in progress. Our purpose in Part 2 is to present as clear a picture as possible of a complicated piece of mathematics. Though proofs are omitted in §§ 12.5 and 12.6, corresponding theorems will be proved later on for $\mathfrak{S}_n$ by quite different methods and in a more explicit form. Alternative approaches to these general ideas are available, and we have chosen that due to Osima and Nagao in which the ordinary and modular theories appear as different aspects of an integrated whole.

The ordinary representation theory of the symmetric group $\mathfrak{S}_n$ was first developed by Frobenius. Just a year later (1900-1) an independent approach was given by Alfred Young which was based on a study of the group algebra and its idempotents. Young was primarily interested in applications to projective invariants and his work on representation theory is scattered through a long series of papers. D. E. Rutherford has collected together this material and the reader is referred to his *Substitutional Analysis* for an account of Young's work. Young's Fundamental Theorem (2.17) giving the actual matrices which generate any given irreducible representation is quoted without proof, as is also his substitutional equation (2.23) which leads to the definition of the *raising operator*. From this point on the presentation is self-contained.

The interesting aspect of the theory is the crucial role played at every stage by the Young diagram $[\lambda]$. One may legitimately ask why so many concepts, often very involved when stated in general terms, become so simple when applied to $\mathfrak{S}_n$ and interpreted with reference to $[\lambda]$. That this is so provides the chief reason for the writing of the present book, since it is conceivable that a corresponding approach through the group algebra may lead to a simplification and clarification of the general theory. Some slight progress along these lines has already been made. Fundamentally, the problem is to derive the representation theory of a given group in terms of that of suitably chosen subgroups.

In the case of $\mathfrak{S}_n$ such suitable sub-groups are easily recognized to be of the form

$$\mathfrak{S}_{\lambda_1} \times \mathfrak{S}_{\lambda_2} \times \ldots \times \mathfrak{S}_{\lambda_h}, \quad \sum \lambda_i = n.$$

Many authors have contributed to the theory described here as a glance at the Bibliography will show. Particular mention should be made of the work of J. S. Frame, D. E. Littlewood, Masaru Osima and R. M. Thrall. Notes on the various sections with appropriate references will be found at the end of the book, but the method of presentation is often changed in an attempt to coordinate the work of different authors. The greater part of the material in Chapters VII and VIII is published here for the first time and is based on theses by O. E. Taulbee and Diane Johnson. The ideas are complicated and it may be that further work will lead to significant simplifications, but the general pattern of development is clear.

The chief feature of this account of the representations of $\mathfrak{S}_n$ is the use made of Young's *raising operator* which plays a major role in Chapters II and III and again in Chapters VI, VII and VIII. That it is possible to express the reduction of the appropriate permutation representations of $\mathfrak{S}_n$ in an explicit manner seems to be largely responsible for the completeness of the theory.

In conclusion, I would like to express my thanks to Professor J. S. Frame, Professor Masaru Osima, and to my colleague Professor A. J. Coleman for reading the manuscript and making many useful suggestions. I am particularly indebted to Professor Hirosi Nagao for his friendly interest and valuable criticism of Chapters I, VII and VIII. But above all I am indebted to my wife for her continued encouragement over many years.

G. de B. Robinson
University of Toronto

CONTENTS

To

ALFRED YOUNG

1873-1940

CHAPTER ONE

THE ORDINARY AND THE MODULAR REPRESENTATION THEORY OF A FINITE GROUP

PART 1: THE ORDINARY REPRESENTATION THEORY

Introduction. We propose to set out here those parts of the representation theory of a finite group over the complex field which are essential in what follows. While such a survey is necessarily incomplete, two aspects of the theory can be emphasized:

(*a*) It is important to make clear just how far character theory goes: that it is a *class* theory, providing an explicit criterion of irreducibility but no information concerning the irreducible representations beyond equivalence.

(*b*) The *subgroup structure* of a finite group $\mathcal{G}$ is largely untouched as yet by character theory. Yet certain connections can be made and Frobenius' reciprocity theorem is vital in this regard. The fact that we have so little knowledge of the irreducible components of a permutation representation of $\mathcal{G}$ stands out.

The significance of these deficiencies of the general theory is greatly clarified by a study of the representation theory of the symmetric group $\mathfrak{S}_n$. First developed by Alfred Young, it has been extended by many authors and these developments are brought together in this book with the view of describing a pattern to which any generalization of Young's theory must conform.

11.1 Permutation representations. Historically, the notion of a group arose early in the 19th century as a group of *permutations* on the roots of an algebraic equation. In this context Galois showed its usefulness in providing a criterion for the solvability of an equation by radicals. It was not till 1854 that Cayley defined an *abstract* group as a set $\mathcal{G}$ of elements G_i subject to a law of combination which we may take to be multiplication and such that:

(*a*) for every G_i, G_j in $\mathcal{G}$ there exists an element G_k in $\mathcal{G}$ such that

$$G_iG_j=G_k;$$

(*b*) $G_i(G_jG_k)=(G_iG_j)G_k$ (the associative law);

(*c*) there exists an *identity* G_1 $(=I)$ in $\mathcal{G}$ such that $G_iI=G_i=IG_i$;

(*d*) for each G_i there exists an *inverse* G_i^{-1} in $\mathcal{G}$ such that

$$G_iG_i^{-1}=I=G_i^{-1}G_i.$$

These simple properties find their realization in many different domains. For example: (i) the ordinary integers of arithmetic form a group with respect to addition, with zero as the identity element; (ii) the rotations and translations in a plane form a group as do the symmetries of a sphere (which leave the centre fixed). In what follows we shall always assume that the number of elements in $\mathcal{G}$ is *finite* and we shall call this number the *order* g of $\mathcal{G}$. In this section we propose to reverse the historical procedure and see how, with each element G_i of $\mathcal{G}$, we may associate a permutation P_i such that $P_iP_j = P_k$ as in (*a*). Such a set of permutations is said to form a *permutation representation* of $\mathcal{G}$.

To this end consider a subgroup $\mathcal{H}$ of $\mathcal{G}$ of order h. If we gather together those elements of $\mathcal{G}$ which may be written in the form HG_i, where H is any element of $\mathcal{H}$ and G_i is fixed, we may denote them $\mathcal{H}G_i$, called a right *coset* of $\mathcal{H}$. Any two such cosets of $\mathcal{H}$ are entirely distinct or coincide, so that we may write

11.11 $$\mathcal{G} = \mathcal{H} + \mathcal{H}G_2 + \mathcal{H}G_3 + \ldots + \mathcal{H}G_n\,,$$

with $n = g/h$. It follows readily that the corresponding left cosets $G_i^{-1}\mathcal{H}$ are also distinct so that

11.12 $$\mathcal{G} = \mathcal{H} + G_2^{-1}\mathcal{H} + G_3^{-1}\mathcal{H} + \ldots + G_n^{-1}\mathcal{H}.$$

Now let us multiply every coset $\mathcal{H}G_i$ in 11.11 on the right by some element of $\mathcal{G}$. The effect will be to leave $\mathcal{H}G_i$ unchanged or to change it into some other coset, thus yielding a *permutation* of the n cosets which we may denote by

$$G \to \begin{pmatrix} \mathcal{H}, & \mathcal{H}G_2, & \ldots \mathcal{H}G_n \\ \mathcal{H}G, & \mathcal{H}G_2G, & \ldots \mathcal{H}G_nG \end{pmatrix} = \begin{pmatrix} \mathcal{H}G_i \\ \mathcal{H}G_iG \end{pmatrix}.$$

Since

$$\begin{pmatrix} \mathcal{H}G_i \\ \mathcal{H}G_iG \end{pmatrix} \begin{pmatrix} \mathcal{H}G_iG \\ \mathcal{H}G_iGG' \end{pmatrix} = \begin{pmatrix} \mathcal{H}G_i \\ \mathcal{H}G_iGG' \end{pmatrix},$$

these permutations form a *representation* $\mathcal{G}^{\mathcal{H}}$ of $\mathcal{G}$.

Of course it may happen that $\mathcal{H}G_iG = \mathcal{H}G_i$ for all i, in which case $G_iGG_i^{-1} \in \mathcal{H}$ and $\mathcal{H}$ contains a largest subgroup $\mathcal{K}$ which is normal in $\mathcal{G}$. The mapping $\mathcal{G} \to \mathcal{G}^{\mathcal{H}}$ is a *homomorphism* with $\mathcal{G}^{\mathcal{H}}$ *isomorphic to the factor group* $\mathcal{G} \mid \mathcal{K}$.

If we multiply the cosets in 11.12 on the left by G^{-1} we similarly obtain a permutation

$$G \to \begin{pmatrix} \mathcal{H}, & G_2^{-1}\mathcal{H}, & \ldots & G_n^{-1}\mathcal{H} \\ G^{-1}\mathcal{H}, & G^{-1}G_2^{-1}\mathcal{H}, & \ldots & G^{-1}G_n^{-1}\mathcal{H} \end{pmatrix} = \begin{pmatrix} G_i^{-1}\mathcal{H} \\ G^{-1}G_i^{-1}\mathcal{H} \end{pmatrix}.$$

and so again a representation of $\mathcal{G}$. In view of the isomorphism

$$\text{11.13} \qquad \begin{pmatrix} G_i^{-1}\mathcal{H} \\ \mathcal{H}G_i \end{pmatrix} \begin{pmatrix} \mathcal{H}G_i \\ \mathcal{H}G_iG \end{pmatrix} \begin{pmatrix} \mathcal{H}G_i \\ G_i^{-1}\mathcal{H} \end{pmatrix} = \begin{pmatrix} G_i^{-1}\mathcal{H} \\ G^{-1}G_i^{-1}\mathcal{H} \end{pmatrix},$$

these right and left permutation representations are *formally equivalent*. Just as we replaced each group element by its inverse, and the coset $\mathcal{H}G_i$ by $G_i^{-1}\mathcal{H}$ in 11.13, so we may replace $\mathcal{H}$ by any conjugate subgroup $G^{-1}\mathcal{H}G$ and arrive at a formally equivalent permutation representation. Thus we may speak of the permutation representation $\mathcal{G}^{\mathcal{H}}$ of $\mathcal{G}$ *induced* by the subgroup $\mathcal{H}$.

If $\mathcal{H}=I$ we have a particularly important permutation representation of $\mathcal{G}$ of degree g called the *regular* representation, since no symbol remains fixed except under the identity and every cycle in any permutation is of equal length. The left regular representation has the remarkable property of containing all permutations which commute with every permutation of the right regular representation and *vice versa*, since

$$\begin{pmatrix} G \\ GG_i \end{pmatrix}\begin{pmatrix} G \\ G_j^{-1}G \end{pmatrix} = \begin{pmatrix} G \\ G_j^{-1}GG_i \end{pmatrix} = \begin{pmatrix} G \\ G_j^{-1}G \end{pmatrix}\begin{pmatrix} G \\ GG_i \end{pmatrix}.$$

There is a second way of constructing a permutation representation of $\mathcal{G}$ which is important in the sequel. If $G^{-1}\mathcal{K}G=\mathcal{K}$ then the totality of such elements constitutes the *normalizer* $\mathcal{N}(\mathcal{K})$ of $\mathcal{K}$ and it can easily be seen that the number of distinct conjugate subgroups of $\mathcal{K}$ is equal to the index of $\mathcal{N}(\mathcal{K})$ in $\mathcal{G}$. If we now *transform* these conjugate subgroups by G they will be permuted amongst themselves according to the permutation

$$G \rightarrow \begin{pmatrix} G_i^{-1}\mathcal{K}G_i \\ G^{-1}(G_i^{-1}\mathcal{K}G_i)G \end{pmatrix}.$$

Again, such permutations form a representation of $\mathcal{G}$ which is equivalent to $\mathcal{G}^{\mathcal{H}}$ if we set $\mathcal{H}=\mathcal{N}(\mathcal{K})$. If $\mathcal{K}$ is normal in $\mathcal{G}$ (e.g. if $\mathcal{K}=I$) this representation by transformation collapses. However, in the case of the symmetric group $\mathfrak{S}$ we shall always be considering subgroups of the form

$$\mathcal{K} = \mathfrak{S}_p \times \mathfrak{S}_q \times \ldots \times \mathfrak{S}_r \qquad p+q+\ldots+r = n,$$

where $\times$ indicates the 'direct product' and each factor affects different symbols. By keeping track of the order of the factors and the symbols involved we can obtain a permutation representation equivalent to $\mathcal{G}^{\mathcal{K}}$. These ideas will be developed in detail in the following chapter.

Of course, one can conclude from these constructions that *every* finite group is isomorphic to a subgroup of $\mathfrak{S}_n$ for some value of n, but this does not seem to be a very fruitful line of thought.

From any permutation representation $\mathcal{G}^{\mathcal{H}}$ we obtain immediately a *linear* representation of $\mathcal{G}$ by permutation matrices (G) having one 1 in each row and column and zeros elsewhere. The rule for constructing (G) depends on our convention for multiplying permutations. Since permutations are operators we shall multiply them from *right to left* and place 1 at the intersection of the ith row and jth column of (G), when $\mathcal{H}G_iG=\mathcal{H}G_j$. One may, however, multiply permutations from left to right; with such a convention the matrix (G) would be replaced by its transpose $(G)'$, where

$$(G)' = (G)^{-1} = (G^{-1}).$$

The number of 1's in the diagonal of (G) is called the *permutation character* of G and written $\chi^{\mathcal{H}}(G)$. If g_G is the number of conjugates of G in $\mathcal{G}$ and $g_G^{\mathcal{H}}$ the number of these that lie in $\mathcal{H}$:

11.14 $$\chi^{\mathcal{H}}(G) = \frac{g g_G^{\mathcal{H}}}{h g_G}.$$

Proof. For each 1 in $\chi^{\mathcal{H}}(G)$ we must have $\mathcal{H}G_iG=\mathcal{H}G_i$ so that $G_iGG_i^{-1}\in\mathcal{H}$. If G_i runs over *all* elements of $\mathcal{G}$ we obtain a given conjugate in $\mathcal{H}$ counted g/g_G times; but there are $g_G^{\mathcal{H}}$ such conjugates in $\mathcal{H}$ so we must multiply g/g_G by $g_G^{\mathcal{H}}$. On the other hand if $G_iGG_i^{-1}\in\mathcal{H}$ so also $(HG_i)G(HG_i)^{-1}\in\mathcal{H}$ for every $H\in\mathcal{H}$; if each such solution to the problem is to be counted once only we must divide $gg_G^{\mathcal{H}}/g_G$ by h, proving the theorem.

We state the following two relations between permutation characters:

11.15 $$\sum_G \chi^{\mathcal{H}}(G) = g,$$

11.16 $$\sum_G \chi^{\mathcal{H}}(G)\,\chi^{\mathcal{K}}(G) = tg,$$

where t is the number of double cosets in the decomposition

$$\mathcal{G} = \mathcal{H}\mathcal{K} + \mathcal{H}G_2\mathcal{K} + \ldots + \mathcal{H}G_t\mathcal{K}.$$

It is an interesting and easy exercise to construct the proof of 11.15 but that of 11.16 is more difficult.

11.17 *Example.* By way of illustration we take $\mathcal{G}=\mathfrak{S}_4$ and list below a representative set of subgroups.

TABLE I

$\mathscr{H}$	*Subgroup*	h
$\mathscr{H}_1$	I	1
$\mathscr{H}_2$	I, (12)	2
$\mathscr{H}_3$	I, (12) (34)	2
$\mathscr{H}_4$	I, (123), (132)	3
$\mathscr{H}_5$	I, (1324), (12) (34), (1423)	4
$\mathscr{H}_6$	I, (12) (34), (14) (23), (13) (24)	4
$\mathscr{H}_7$	I, (12), (34), (12) (34)	4
$\mathscr{H}_8$	I, (12), (13), (23), (123), (132)	6
$\mathscr{H}_9$	I, (12), (34), (12) (34), (14) (23), (13) (24), (1324), (1423)	8
$\mathscr{H}_{10}$	$\mathfrak{A}_4$	12
$\mathscr{H}_{11}$	$\mathfrak{S}_4$	24

In particular, we may write the cosets of the subgroup $\mathscr{H}_9$ in the form

11.171 $$\mathfrak{S}_4 = \mathscr{H}_9 + \mathscr{H}_9\,(23) + \mathscr{H}_9\,(24).$$

Since $\mathscr{H}_9 \supset \mathscr{H}_6$ which is normal in $\mathfrak{S}_4$, the permutation representation $\mathscr{G}_9$ (cf. Table II) is isomorphic to $\mathfrak{S}_4 / \mathscr{H}_6 \sim \mathfrak{S}_3$. Denoting the three cosets of $\mathscr{H}_9$ by b, c, d respectively, we have

$$(23) \to (bc) \sim \begin{bmatrix} 0 & 1 & 0 \\ 1 & 0 & 0 \\ 0 & 0 & 1 \end{bmatrix}, \quad (34) \to (cd) \sim \begin{bmatrix} 1 & 0 & 0 \\ 0 & 0 & 1 \\ 0 & 1 & 0 \end{bmatrix},$$

which generate the representation.

The permutation characters are listed in Table II below, in which $\mathscr{G}_i$ is used as an abbreviation for $\mathscr{G}^{\mathscr{H}_i}$.

TABLE II—$\chi_i^{\mathscr{H}_j}$

Class	(1^4)	$(2, 1^2)$	(2^2)	$(3, 1)$	(4)
g_i	1	6	3	8	6
$\mathscr{G}_1$	24	.	.	.	.
$\mathscr{G}_2$	12	2	.	.	.
$\mathscr{G}_3$	12	.	4	.	.
$\mathscr{G}_4$	8	.	.	2	.
$\mathscr{G}_5$	6	.	2	.	2
$\mathscr{G}_6$	6	.	6	.	.
$\mathscr{G}_7$	6	2	2	.	.
$\mathscr{G}_8$	4	2	.	1	.
$\mathscr{G}_9$	3	1	3	.	1
$\mathscr{G}_{10}$	2	.	2	2	.
$\mathscr{G}_{11}$	1	1	1	1	1

The headings indicate the cycle structure of each *class* of permutations followed by the number g_i of elements in the class. Using 11.14 it is easy to check the construction of the table.

11.2 The group algebra over a field F. If we take the elements $G_1(=I)$, $G_2, \ldots, G_g$ of the group $\mathscr{G}$ as basis elements of a *group algebra* $\mathscr{A}$ with coefficients in a given field F, we can define addition and multiplication in the algebra as follows:

11.21
$$\begin{aligned}(\sum x_iG_i)+(\sum y_iG_i) &= \sum (x_i+y_i)G_i,\\ (\sum x_iG_i)\,(\sum y_jG_j) &= \sum (x_iy_j)G_iG_j.\end{aligned}$$

Such a group algebra is clearly associative with a unity element. If we denote any element of $\mathscr{A}$ by

11.22
$$a = \sum_{i=1}^{g} x_iG_i,$$

then

11.23
$$a\,.\,G_i = \sum_{j=1}^{g} s_{ji}G_j, \qquad G_i\,.\,a = \sum_{j=1}^{g} r_{ij}G_j,$$

and the matrices (s_{ji}) and $(r_{ij})'$ constitute the *left* and *right regular* representations of $\mathscr{A}$ where $(r_{ij})'$ denotes the transpose of (r_{ij}). A different choice of basis elements leads to an *equivalent* regular representation. In general, if the two regular representations are equivalent the algebra is called a *Frobenius algebra*; this condition is certainly satisfied in the case of a group algebra, since

$$G_i^{-1}\,.\,a = \sum_{j=1}^{g} s_{ij}G_j^{-1}$$

for a choice of new basis elements G_i^{-1} $(i=1, 2, \ldots, g)$.

The *centre* of an algebra $\mathscr{A}$ is made up of all those elements which commute with every element of $\mathscr{A}$. To describe such elements, let us denote the classes of conjugate elements of $\mathscr{G}$ by

$$C_1\ (=I),\ C_2, \ldots, C_k,$$

where there are g_i elements in C_i and $g=g_1+g_2+\ldots+g_k$. No confusion will arise if we use the same symbol C_i to denote the *sum* of conjugate elements in $\mathscr{A}$.

11.24 *The necessary and sufficient condition that an element a belongs to the centre of $\mathscr{A}$ is that it have the form*

$$a = \sum_{i=1}^{k} y_iC_i.$$

Proof. If $ab=ba$ for all b then $G_i a=aG_i$ for all i, so all conjugates of a given group element must appear in a with the same coefficient. Clearly, the condition is sufficient.

Multiplication of the sets C_i is also important, and a similar argument leads to the relation

11.25 $$C_l C_m = C_m C_l = \sum_{n=1}^{k} c_{lmn} C_n.$$

where the $c_{lmn}=c_{mln}$ are integers.

If we set all $x_i=0$ in 11.22 we obtain the *zero element* 0 of $\mathscr{A}$. If $a^n=0$ for some index n then a is *nilpotent*. On the other hand, an element a' of $\mathscr{A}$ is said to be *properly nilpotent* if aa', and so $a'a$, is nilpotent for every a in $\mathscr{A}$. Thus the properly nilpotent elements of $\mathscr{A}$ form an *ideal* of $\mathscr{A}$ called the *radical*. It is customary to denote the radical by $\mathscr{N}$ so that the quotient algebra $\mathscr{A} / \mathscr{N}$ is *semi-simple*, i.e. can be written as the direct sum of *simple* algebras $\mathscr{A}_i$

$$\mathscr{A} / \mathscr{N} \sim \mathscr{A}_1 + \mathscr{A}_2 + \dots$$

11.26 *Example.* Consider the algebra $\mathscr{A}$ of all 3×3 matrices (a_{ij}) with $a_{12}=a_{13}=a_{23}=0$, the remaining coefficients being arbitrary elements of the field F. Then

$$\mathscr{N}: \begin{bmatrix} 0 & 0 & 0 \\ a_{21} & 0 & 0 \\ a_{31} & a_{32} & 0 \end{bmatrix}, \qquad \mathscr{N}^2: \begin{bmatrix} 0 & 0 & 0 \\ 0 & 0 & 0 \\ a_{31} & 0 & 0 \end{bmatrix},$$

where $\mathscr{N}^2$ is defined to be the set of all products of any two elements of $\mathscr{N}$. $\mathscr{A} / \mathscr{N} \sim \mathscr{A}_1 + \mathscr{A}_2 + \mathscr{A}_3$, where

$$\mathscr{A}_1: \begin{bmatrix} a_1 & 0 & 0 \\ 0 & 0 & 0 \\ 0 & 0 & 0 \end{bmatrix}, \quad \mathscr{A}_2: \begin{bmatrix} 0 & 0 & 0 \\ 0 & a_2 & 0 \\ 0 & 0 & 0 \end{bmatrix}, \quad \mathscr{A}_3: \begin{bmatrix} 0 & 0 & 0 \\ 0 & 0 & 0 \\ 0 & 0 & a_3 \end{bmatrix}.$$

In this case $\mathscr{N}^3=0$, i.e. the product of any element of $\mathscr{N}$ by any element of $\mathscr{N}^2$ must be the zero matrix.

The following Theorem is of fundamental importance:

11.27 *If the field F is of characteristic zero, the group algebra $\mathscr{A}$ is semi-simple.*

Proof. From the *anti-isomorphism* of $\mathscr{A}$:

$$a = \sum_i x_i G_i \qquad a' = \sum x_i^{-1} G_i^{-1},$$

where $x_i^{-1}=0$ if $x_i=0$, we conclude that if $a \in \mathscr{N}$ then so also is a', and conversely. From the definition it follows that for any $a \neq 0$ in $\mathscr{N}$

there exists an integer m such that $a \in \mathcal{N}^m$ and $a' \in \mathcal{N}^m$, with $\mathcal{N}^{2m}=0$. But the coefficient of I in aa' can never vanish so that $aa' \neq 0$, which is a contradiction. Thus no $a \neq 0$ exists in $\mathcal{N}$ and $\mathcal{A}$ is semi-simple.

If F is of characteristic different from zero this proof fails and the group algebra may possess a radical, as we shall see.

There is one other important idea which we must introduce here: if $e_1^2=e_1$ then e_1 is said to be *idempotent*. If e_2 is also an idempotent such that $e_1e_2=e_2e_1=0$, then

$$(e_1+e_2)^2 = e_1+e_2$$

so that e_1+e_2 is an idempotent. Continuing thus, we may construct in at most g steps a *principal idempotent* e for which no further e' exists. That this principal idempotent is unique is easily seen. For,

$$eI = e = Ie, \quad (I-e)\,e = e\,(I-e) = 0,$$

and $e+(I-e)=I$ is also idempotent. But, by assumption, this can only happen if $I-e=0$ so that $e=I$. Thus:

11.28 *The only principal idempotent in a group algebra is the identity.*

11.3 Character theory. Consider a group $\mathcal{G}$ of finite order and a group (G) of nonsingular matrices or linear transformations of a vector-space V with coefficients in a field F, which we shall assume is algebraically closed. If (G) is homomorphic to $\mathcal{G}$, every element of a normal subgroup $\mathcal{H}$ is mapped on the identity matrix of (G); if $(G_i)(G_j)=(G_iG_j)$ for all i, j, (G) is called a *representation* of $\mathcal{G}$, and $\mathcal{G} \,/\, \mathcal{H}$ is isomorphic to (G). From such a representation of $\mathcal{G}$ we obtain a representation of the group algebra $\mathcal{A}$ by replacing G_i by its representative matrix (G_i) in 11.22. If we interpret the x_i in 11.22 as independent variables the matrix

11.31
$$G = \sum_{i=1}^{g} x_i(G_i)$$

is called the *group matrix* of the representation (G).

A representation (G) is said to be *decomposable* if the vector space V is the direct sum of two subspaces V_1 and V_2 *both* of which are invariant under (G). Adapting the coordinate system in V to this decomposition we have

11.32
$$(G) = \begin{bmatrix} (G)_1 & 0 \\ 0 & (G)_2 \end{bmatrix},$$

where $(G)_1$ operates in V_1 and $(G)_2$ in V_2. If such reduction be continued we finally obtain a splitting of (G) into *indecomposable components* $(G)_i$ which are uniquely determined up to a linear transformation. Each $(G)_i$ is also a representation of $\mathcal{G}$.

While the representation (G) may be indecomposable it may still be *reducible*, in which case the vector-space V contains a subspace V_1 which is invariant under (G), although the complementary subspace V_2 is not. Again, adapting the coordinate system in V, we have

11.33 $$(G) = \begin{bmatrix} (G)_{11} & 0 \\ (G)_{21} & (G)_{22} \end{bmatrix}$$

where $(G)_{11}$ and $(G)_{22}$ are representations of $\mathcal{G}$. If $(G)_{11}$ and $(G)_{22}$ are irreducible then clearly the *radical* of the group algebra is obtained by setting $(G)_{11}=(G)_{22}=0$ in 11.33. If the field F has characteristic zero, in particular if F is the complex field, $(G)_{21}=0$ and (G) is *completely reducible* by 11.27; in this case the concepts of indecomposability and irreducibility coincide.

The following theorem is fundamental in the theory:

11.34 SCHUR'S LEMMA. *If* X *and* X' *are two irreducible group matrices of* $\mathcal{G}$ *degrees* f *and* f' *and* P *is a constant* $f \times f'$ *matrix such that* $XP=PX'$, *then (i)* $P=0$ *or (ii)* $f=f'$ *and* $|P| \neq 0$.

Proof. Let us assume that P is a non-zero matrix of rank $r>0$, and set

$$f-r = s, \quad f'-r = t,$$

so that there exist non-singular matrices A, B such that $APB=Q$ where

$$Q = \begin{bmatrix} I & 0_{rt} \\ 0_{sr} & 0_{st} \end{bmatrix}.$$

In this matrix Q, I_{rr} is the identity matrix of degree r while 0_{rt} is the zero matrix having r rows and t columns. If we write $AXA^{-1}=X_1$, $B^{-1}X'B=X_1'$, then the relation $XP=PX'$ becomes

$$X_1Q = QX_1',$$

so that, by suitably partitioning X_1 and X_1' we may write

$$X_1Q = \begin{bmatrix} X_{rr} & X_{rs} \\ X_{sr} & X_{ss} \end{bmatrix}\begin{bmatrix} I_{rr} & 0_{rt} \\ 0_{sr} & 0_{st} \end{bmatrix} = \begin{bmatrix} I_{rr} & 0_{rt} \\ 0_{sr} & 0_{st} \end{bmatrix}\begin{bmatrix} X'_{rr} & X'_{rt} \\ X'_{tr} & X'_{tt} \end{bmatrix} = QX_1',$$

or

$$\begin{bmatrix} X_{rr} & 0_{rt} \\ X_{sr} & 0_{st} \end{bmatrix} = \begin{bmatrix} X'_{rr} & X'_{rt} \\ 0_{sr} & 0_{st} \end{bmatrix},$$

from which we conclude that $X_{sr}=0_{sr}$, $X'_{rt}=0_{rt}$. But if $r<f$ or $r<f'$ this would imply that X or X' is reducible, contrary to supposition. Thus if $P\neq 0$, $r=f=f'$ and $|P|\neq 0$, so that

$$P^{-1}XP = X'$$

and X and X' are said to be *equivalent*.

This definition of the equivalence of the group matrices X, X' includes in particular the change of basis elements introduced in § 11.2.

There is a remarkable corrollary of Schur's Lemma namely:

11.341 *If X is irreducible and $P^{-1}XP=X$ then $P=aI_f$.*

Proof. If a is a characteristic root of P then $|P-aI_f|=0$. But clearly

$$X(P-aI_f) = (P-aI_f)X$$

so that the matrix $(P-aI_f)$ must be the zero matrix by 11.34, and $P=aI_f$ as required.

This conclusion enables us to dispose of the representation theory of Abelian groups once and for all:

11.342 *Every irreducible representation of an Abelian group is of degree* 1.

Proof. If $X=\sum x_i(G_i)$ for any representation (G) of the Abelian group $\mathcal{G}$, it follows immediately that

$$X(G_i) = (G_i)X,$$

so that $(G_i)=\rho I_f$ for every i. But this is just the condition above, that every irreducible representation must be of degree 1.

There is one further application of Schur's Lemma which gives explicit information concerning the matrices of an irreducible representation.

11.343 *If $X=(x_{ij})$ and $X'=(x'_{mn})$ are the group matrices of two irreducible representations $G\rightarrow(a_{ij}^G)$ of degree f and $G\rightarrow(b_{mn}^G)$ of degree f' of $\mathcal{G}$, where:*

$$x_{ij} = \sum_G a_{ij}^G x_G, \qquad x'_{mn} = \sum_G b_{mn}^G x'_G,$$

then

(i) $$\sum_G a_{ij}^{G^{-1}} a_{kl}^G = \frac{g}{f}\,\delta_{il}\,\delta_{jk} \qquad (i, j, k, l = 1, \ldots, f),$$

(ii) $$\sum_G a_{ij}^{G^{-1}} b_{mn}^G = 0 \qquad (m, n = 1, \ldots, f').$$

Proof. If we set $A^R=(a_{ij}^R)$ and $B^R=(b_{mn}^R)$ and let $U=(u_{ij})$ be an arbitrary non-singular $f\times f$ matrix, then if

$$V = \sum_R A^{R^{-1}} U A^R, \qquad R \in \mathcal{G},$$

we see that

$$A^{S^{-1}} V A^S = \sum_R A^{S^{-1}R^{-1}} U A^{RS} = V, \qquad S \in \mathcal{G}.$$

Thus, $V^{-1}XV=X$ and by 11.341 V must be of the form vI_f, where v is a linear function of the u_{ij}:

$$v = \sum_{i,j} k_{ij} u_{ij}.$$

Thus

$$\sum_R \sum_{j,k} a_{ij}^{R^{-1}} u_{jk} a_{kl}^R = \delta_{il} \sum_{j,k} k_{jk} u_{jk}$$

so that

$$\sum_R a_{ij}^{R^{-1}} a_{kl}^R = \delta_{il} k_{jk}.$$

If we set $i=l$ and sum for $i=1, 2, \ldots, f$ we have

$$f k_{jk} = \sum_R \Big(\sum_i a_{ki}^R a_{ij}^{R^{-1}}\Big) = \sum_R a_{kj}^I = g\delta_{jk}$$

which yields 11.343 (i).

Again, if $W=(w_{im})$ is an arbitrary $f\times f'$ matrix and we set

$$T = \sum_R A^{R^{-1}} W B^R,$$

then $XT=TX'$ and so $T=0$ by Schur's Lemma. Thus

$$\sum_R \sum_{j,m} a_{ij}^{R^{-1}} w_{jm} b_{mn}^R = 0$$

and since the w_{jm} are arbitrary, we have 11.343 (ii).

The following two Theorems express the inherent properties of the group matrix which are not obvious but follow readily from 11.343 and enable us to prove the Principal Theorem 11.36.

11.351 *If X, X', . . . are non-equivalent irreducible group matrices of $\mathcal{G}$ of degrees $f, f', \ldots$ then the*

$$f^2+f'^2+\ldots$$

homogeneous linear functions of the x_G are linearly independent.

Proof. In fact, suppose a relation existed of the form

$$\sum_{i,j} c_{ij} x_{ij} + \sum_{m,n} c'_{mn} x'_{mn} + \ldots = 0.$$

Since the x_G are arbitrary it follows that

$$\sum_{i,j} c_{ij}\, a_{ij}^G + \sum c'_{mn}\, b_{mn}^G + \ldots = 0.$$

Multiplying by $a_{kl}^{G^{-1}}$ and summing over G we conclude from 11.343 (i) and (ii) that $c_{ij} = c'_{mn} = \ldots = 0$.

11.352 *The determinant of an irreducible group matrix* $\boldsymbol{X}$ *is an irreducible function of the g variables* x_G. *Two irreducible group matrices are equivalent if and only if their determinants are equal.*

Proof. The first statement is merely a consequence of the fact that a determinant whose elements can take arbitrary values cannot be factored. Again, the linear independence of the elements of X and X' when these are non-equivalent implies that $|X| \neq |X'|$. Thus X and X' are equivalent if and only if $|X| = |X'|$.

This last result enables us to prove the *uniqueness* of the reduction of an arbitrary representation of $\mathcal{G}$. If $\boldsymbol{X}$ is the group matrix of such a representation we may assume that each irreducible component equivalent to $\boldsymbol{X}_\rho$ has the same form so that we may write

11.353 $$X \sim \sum_{\rho=1}^{k} r_\rho X_\rho$$

from which we conclude that

11.354 $$|X| = \prod |X_\rho|^{r_\rho}.$$

Since the determinant of the group matrix is invariant under transformation, the $\boldsymbol{X}_\rho$ are uniquely determined except for the order of their appearance. Finally we have the

11.36 Principal Theorem. *Every irreducible representation* ρ *of* $\mathcal{G}$ *of degree* f^ρ *over the complex field appears as an irreducible component of the regular representation of* $\mathcal{G}$ *with multiplicity* f^ρ. *Moreover, the number of non-equivalent irreducible representations of* $\mathcal{G}$ *is equal to the number of classes of conjugate elements of* $\mathcal{G}$.

Proof. Let $\boldsymbol{X}$ be the group matrix of, say, the right regular representation of $\mathcal{G}$, so that we may write 11.353 and 11.354. Since the number of linearly independent x_G is g we have, by 11.351

(i) $$g = f_1^2 + f_2^2 + \ldots + f_k^2,$$

but also

(ii) $$g = f_1 r_1 + f_2 r_2 + \ldots + f_k r_k.$$

The most general matrix P such that $XP=PX$, can be partitioned so that $P=(P_{\rho\sigma})$ where

$$X_\rho P_{\rho\sigma} = P_{\rho\sigma} X_\sigma,$$

and by 11.341, $P_{\rho\sigma}=pI_\rho$ if $\rho=\sigma$ while $P_{\rho\sigma}=0$ if $\rho\neq\sigma$. Thus we may write

11.361 $$P = \sum_{\rho=1}^{k} P_\rho \times I_\rho \qquad \text{(direct sum)},$$

where $P_\rho=(p_{ij}^\rho)$ is an arbitrary matrix with $i, j=1, \ldots, r_\rho$ and $P_\rho \times I_\rho$ denotes the Kronecker product of the two matrices P_ρ and I_ρ.

In discussing the right and left regular representations of $\mathcal{G}$ we observed that every permutation of the right regular representation commutes with every permutation of the left regular representation. In terms of the group algebras

$$R'(\mathscr{A})\, S(\mathscr{A}) = S(\mathscr{A})\, R'(\mathscr{A}),$$

so that the number of linearly independent matrices P must also be g.

(iii) $$g = r_1^2+r_2^2+\ldots+r_k^2,$$

and it follows from 11.36 (i), (ii), (iii) that

$$\sum_1^k (f_\rho - r_\rho)^2 = 0,$$

so that $f_\rho=r_\rho$ as required and every irreducible representation is accounted for, by 11.351.

Finally, if we look for the most general matrix Q such that $XQ=QX$ and also $QP=PQ$, we conclude that Q must have the form of P but must be further specialized so that $Q_\rho P_\rho=P_\rho Q_\rho$. Again, by 11.341 $Q_\rho=q_\rho I_{f_\rho} \times I_{f_\rho}$ so that the number of linearly independent matrices Q_ρ is equal to k. By 11.24 this number must be equal to the number of conjugate sets in $\mathcal{G}$, proving the second statement of 11.36.

One of the most interesting and elusive problems of group theory has to do with the equality of the *number* of irreducible representations ρ and the *number* of classes C_i referred to in 11.36. Is it possible to set up a 1-1 correspondence between them in the general case? This question will be answered in the affirmative for the symmetric group $\mathfrak{S}_n$ in Chapter II, but the more one considers this correspondence the more it appears to concern certain *subgroups* (direct products of symmetric groups) of $\mathfrak{S}_n$, which are uniquely defined by the C_i, rather than the C_i themselves. Indeed, any success which we shall achieve in studying the representation theory of $\mathfrak{S}_n$ depends solely on our knowledge of the representation theory of these subgroups. Lacking such knowledge of the subgroup structure of a general group $\mathcal{G}$, we turn to *characters*, whose theory we shall now briefly survey.

If $A=(a_{ij})$ be any non-singular matrix of degree f then the characteristic equation $|A-\lambda I| = 0$ has f characteristic roots whose sum $\chi(A)$ is the *trace* of A:

$$\text{(iv)} \qquad \chi(A) = \sum_{i=1}^{f} a_{ii}.$$

If B is another non-singular matrix of degree f then the trace of AB is given by

$$\chi(AB) = \sum_{i,j} a_{ij} b_{ji} = \sum_{i,j} b_{ji} a_{ij} = \chi(BA),$$

and replacing A by $B^{-1}A$ we conclude that

$$\text{(v)} \qquad \chi(B^{-1}AB) = \chi(A)$$

for any nonsingular matrix B. Considered with reference to the matrices of a representation (G) of $\mathcal{G}$, the trace function is called the *character* χ of $\mathcal{G}$; because of (v), it is a *class function* taking the same value for every element of C_i. We denote by $\chi_\rho(G)$ the value of this function in the irreducible representation ρ, and we call $\chi^\rho(G)$ an *irreducible* character of $\mathcal{G}$. It will often be convenient to write

$$\chi^\rho(G) = \chi_i^\rho \text{ for } G \in C_i.$$

Since they were first introduced by Frobenius and Burnside towards the end of the 19th century, *group characters* have played an ever increasing role in the applications of representation theory, particularly to the subtle problems of physics and chemistry whose solutions depend on the recognition of an underlying symmetry. From the abstract point of view they do not tell the whole story as we shall see in the sequel, but in general they yield a great deal of information regarding the structure of an abstract group.

A table of group characters is best thought of as a square matrix χ with certain orthogonality relations, which we shall proceed to derive from 11.343 (i) and (ii).

A preliminary observation is necessary. If $G \in C_i$, we shall denote the class containing G^{-1} by $C_{i'}$. Since

$$R^{-1}G_iR = G_j \to R^{-1}G_i^{-1}R = G_j^{-1}$$

we conclude that the inverse of every element of C_i lies in $C_{i'}$ and we call $C_{i'}$ the *inverse class* of C_i. Similarly, with each irreducible representation ρ we may associate an irreducible representation ρ'. Since $G^g = I$, every characteristic root is a gth root of unity, so that $(\overline{G})$ yields the representation ρ' and

(vi) $$\chi^{\rho'}(G) = \chi^{\rho}(G^{-1}) = \overline{\chi^{\rho}(G)}$$

for every $G \in \mathcal{G}$. Of course, $C_{i'}$ may coincide with C_i as in the case of $\mathfrak{S}_n$.

Let us now write 11.343 (i) in the form

$$\sum_R a_{rj}^{R^{-1}} a_{kl}^{R} = \frac{g}{f} \delta_{rl} \delta_{kj},$$

multiply by a_{ir}^S and sum over r to yield

(vii) $$\sum_R a_{ij}^{SR^{-1}} a_{kl}^{R} = \frac{g}{f} a_{il}^{S} \delta_{kj}.$$

If now we set $i = j$, $k = l$, with $S = I$ in (vii) and sum over i and k we have

(viii) $$\sum_R \chi^{\rho}(R^{-1}) \chi^{\rho}(R) = g$$

for any irreducible representation ρ of $\mathcal{G}$. By a similar argument, we deduce from 11.343 (ii) that

(ix) $$\sum_R \chi^{\rho}(R^{-1}) \chi^{\sigma}(R) = 0, \qquad \sigma \neq \rho.$$

Using (vi) we may combine (viii) and (ix) into the convenient form:

11.371 $$\sum_{i=1}^{k} g_i \chi_i^{\rho'} \chi_i^{\sigma} = \begin{cases} g, & \sigma = \rho, \\ 0, & \sigma \neq \rho. \end{cases}$$

If we divide by g, 11.371 implies that $\chi\overline{\psi}' = I$, where ψ is the matrix obtained from χ by multiplying each column by g_i/g. Since χ is non-singular

$$\overline{\psi}'\chi = \chi^{-1} \cdot \chi\overline{\psi}' \cdot \chi = I,$$

so that we also have the relations:

11.372 $$g_i \sum_{\rho=1}^{k} \chi_{i'}^{\rho} \chi_j^{\rho} = \begin{cases} g, & j = i, \\ 0, & j \neq i. \end{cases}$$

Taking $\sigma = \rho$ in 11.371 *we have a criterion in terms of the characters for the irreducibility of the representation* ρ. Moreover, given any representation of $\mathcal{G}$ we can determine (cf. Example 11.39) the multiplicity in it of each irreducible representation ρ. Thus:

11.38 *The necessary and sufficient condition that two representations of $\mathscr{G}$ over the complex field be equivalent is that they have the same characters.*

No ambiguity will arise if we denote equivalence of representations by $=$ and the direct sum of representations by $+$.

Finally, it can be proved that the degree $f^\rho = \chi^\rho(I)$ is a divisor of the order g of $\mathscr{G}$ for any irreducible representation ρ of $\mathscr{G}$. The quotient g/f^ρ has great significance in our application of this general theory to the symmetric group $\mathfrak{S}_n$ (cf. 2.37).

11.39 *Example.* In example 11.17 we gave all the subgroups of $\mathfrak{S}_4$ and a table of the characters of the corresponding permutation representations. It would seem natural now to complete the story by giving their complete reduction into irreducible components. To this end the character Table 4.24 of $\mathfrak{S}_4$ is given here:

TABLE III—χ_i^λ

Class	(1^4)	$(2, 1^2)$	(2^2)	$(3, 1)$	(4)
g_i	1	6	3	8	6
$[4]$	1	1	1	1	1
$[3, 1]$	3	1	-1	0	-1
$[2^2]$	2	0	2	-1	0
$[2, 1^2]$	3	-1	-1	0	1
$[1^4]$	1	-1	1	1	-1

We have introduced in Table III the notation $\lambda = [\lambda_1, \lambda_2, \ldots, \lambda_h]$, $\lambda_i \geqq \lambda_{i+1}$ and $\sum \lambda_i = n$, for the irreducible representations of $\mathfrak{S}_n$ which will be used throughout this book. If we assume the reduction of the permutation representation $\mathscr{G}^{\mathscr{H}j}$ to have character

11.391 $$\chi_i^{\mathscr{H}_j} = \sum_\lambda m_j^\lambda \chi_i^\lambda,$$

then, multiplying by χ_i^λ and summing over i we obtain

11.392 $$m_j^\lambda = \frac{1}{g} \sum_i g_i \chi_i^{\mathscr{H}_j} \chi_i^\lambda = \frac{1}{h_j} \sum_R \chi_R^\lambda \qquad R \in \mathscr{H}_j$$

by 11.371 and 11.14. We list the multiplicities m_j^λ in the following Table.

TABLE IV—m_j^λ

λ	[4]	[3, 1]	[2^2]	[2, 1^2]	[1^4]
$\mathscr{G}_1$	1	3	2	3	1
$\mathscr{G}_2$	1	2	1	1	.
$\mathscr{G}_3$	1	1	2	1	1
$\mathscr{G}_4$	1	1	.	1	1
$\mathscr{G}_5$	1	.	1	1	.
$\mathscr{G}_6$	1	.	2	.	1
$\mathscr{G}_7$	1	1	1	.	.
$\mathscr{G}_8$	1	1	.	.	.
$\mathscr{G}_9$	1	.	1	.	.
$\mathscr{G}_{10}$	1	.	.	.	1
$\mathscr{G}_{11}$	1	.	.	.	.

11.4 Applications. Consider now the sum C_i of the elements of the ith class as an element of the group algebra $\mathscr{A}$. As in 11.24, we have $C_iG = GC_i$ for all $G \in \mathscr{G}$ so that $C_i = \gamma_i^\rho I$ in any irreducible representation ρ, from 11.341. If the degree of ρ is f^ρ, the character of C_i is $f^\rho \gamma_i^\rho$, so that

11.41 $$\gamma_i^\rho = g_i \chi_i^\rho / f^\rho;$$

γ_i^ρ is called the *class multiplier* of C_i in ρ. By 11.25

11.42 $$\gamma_l^\rho \gamma_m^\rho = \sum_{n=1}^{k} c_{lmn} \gamma_n^\rho,$$

and these equations can be solved for the c_{lmn} in terms of the characters.

There is an interesting application of these ideas in the construction of the idempotents of the group algebra (11.2). In fact, if we define

11.43 $$T^\rho = \frac{f^\rho}{g} \sum_{i=1}^{k} \chi_i^\rho C_i,$$

then

11.44 $$I = \sum_{\rho=1}^{k} T^\rho, \quad T^\rho T^\sigma = \begin{cases} T^\rho, & \sigma = \rho, \\ 0, & \sigma \neq \rho. \end{cases}$$

The proof of these relations is involved but requires no more than repeated applications of 11.371 and 11.372.

If we consider the special case of 11.392 in which λ is the identity representation of $\mathscr{G}$ we conclude that

11.45 $$m_j^I = \frac{1}{h_j} \sum_R 1 = 1,$$

for every subgroup $\mathscr{H}_j$.

Certainly each of the permutation representations $\mathcal{G}^{\mathcal{H}_j}$ is transitive in the sense that every symbol can be transformed into every other symbol. Conversely, if this property holds, then those permutations which leave a given symbol fixed form a subgroup $\mathcal{H}$ and the representation is isomorphic to $\mathcal{G}^{\mathcal{H}}$. Thus (cf. Table IV of Example 11.39):

11.46 *A transitive permutation representation of $\mathcal{G}$ contains the identity representation of $\mathcal{G}$ once and once only.*

In a similar manner, if we set $\mathcal{H}=\mathcal{K}$ and substitute from 11.391 in 11.16 we have:

11.47 $$\sum_{R\in\mathcal{G}} (\chi^{\mathcal{H}}(R))^2 = g(1+\ldots+(m_p^{\mathcal{H}})^2+\ldots) = tg;$$

and if $\mathcal{G}^{\mathcal{H}}$ is doubly transitive (i.e. if any two symbols can be transformed into any other two), $t=2$, so that:

11.48 *A doubly transitive permutation representation of $\mathcal{G}$ contains the identity representation and one other.*

Clearly character theory is inadequate to give any deep insight into the irreducible components of a permutation representation of $\mathcal{G}$. The following example is chosen to show that, even in the simplest possible case, such information involves a knowledge of the properties of the *group ring*, or more generally, of the group *algebra* $\mathcal{A}$.

11.49 *Example.* Let us take the group $\mathcal{G}$ to be the symmetric group $\mathfrak{S}_2$ so that $G_1=I$ and $G_2=(12)$, and the group matrix of the regular representation is

11.491 $$\mathbf{G} = \begin{bmatrix} x_1 & x_2 \\ x_2 & x_1 \end{bmatrix}.$$

If we set $T=\frac{1}{2}(I+(12))$ and $T'=\frac{1}{2}(I-(12))$ then the conditions 11.44 are satisfied and $I=T+T'$ with $TT'=T'T=0$. Knowing the idempotents we obtain the complete reduction of the group matrix $\mathbf{G}$ by setting

11.492 $$U = \begin{bmatrix} 1 & 1 \\ 1 & -1 \end{bmatrix}, \qquad U^{-1} = \tfrac{1}{2}\begin{bmatrix} 1 & 1 \\ 1 & -1 \end{bmatrix},$$

so that

11.493 $$U\,\mathbf{G}\,U^{-1} = \begin{bmatrix} x_1+x_2 & 0 \\ 0 & x_1-x_2 \end{bmatrix}.$$

This transformation of $\mathbf{G}$ *is valid so long as the characteristic of the field F is not* 2. In this excluded case the sum of the variables still remains invariant so we may transform by

11.494 $$U_1 = \begin{bmatrix} 1 & 1 \\ 0 & 1 \end{bmatrix}, \qquad U_1^{-1} = \begin{bmatrix} 1 & -1 \\ 0 & 1 \end{bmatrix}$$

to yield

11.495 $$U_1 G U_1^{-1} = \begin{bmatrix} x_1+x_2 & 0 \\ x_2 & x_1-x_2 \end{bmatrix} \equiv \begin{bmatrix} x_1+x_2 & 0 \\ x_2 & x_1+x_2 \end{bmatrix} \pmod 2.$$

The element $G_1+G_2=I+(12)$ is nilpotent and is represented by the matrix

$$\begin{bmatrix} 0 & 0 \\ 1 & 0 \end{bmatrix}$$

in 11.495. In this modular case there is only one irreducible representation, namely the identity representation, and the group algebra does have a radical. Thus the regular representation of $\mathfrak{S}_2$ is indecomposable.

11.5 Induced representations. In order to generalize the idea of a permutation representation, let us consider the relationship of the irreducible representations of $\mathscr{G}$ to those of a subgroup $\mathscr{H}$. If we denote the irreducible representations of $\mathscr{H}$ by λ with character ψ^λ, then we may limit consideration to those matrices of the irreducible representation ρ of $\mathscr{G}$ associated with elements of $\mathscr{H}$. By such a *restricting* process we obtain a representation of $\mathscr{H}$ which is in general reducible, and we may write:

11.51 $$\chi^\rho(R) = \sum_\lambda k_{\rho\lambda}\psi^\lambda(R), \qquad R \in \mathscr{H}.$$

If we multiply by $\psi^\lambda(R^{-1})$ and sum over R we have by 11.371:

$$\sum_{R\in\mathscr{H}} \chi^\rho(R)\psi^\lambda(R^{-1}) = k_{\rho\lambda}h, \qquad R \in \mathscr{H};$$

multiplying by $\chi^\rho(S)$ and summing over ρ we have:

11.52 $$\sum_\rho k_{\rho\lambda}\chi^\rho(S) = \frac{g g_S^{\mathscr{H}}}{h g_S}\psi^\lambda(S) = \chi^{\mathscr{H}}(S)\psi^\lambda(S),$$

by 11.372 and 11.14.

Consider now the group matrix $\boldsymbol{G}$ of the right-regular representation $\mathscr{G}^I$ of $\mathscr{G}$, and let us collect its rows and columns in sets of h according to 11.11. We can write

11.53 $$\boldsymbol{G} = (x_{P^{-1}Q}) = (G_i^{-1}\boldsymbol{H}G_j) \qquad (i, j, = 1, 2, \ldots, g/h),$$

where G_i^{-1} operating on the left and G_j on the right affect the *subscripts* of

$$\boldsymbol{H} = (x_{R^{-1}S}) \qquad R, S \in \mathscr{H},$$

so that

$$\boldsymbol{G} = (G_i^{-1}\boldsymbol{H}G_j) = (x_{G_i^{-1}R^{-1}SG_j}).$$

If we replace $\boldsymbol{H}$ by Σx_i, where the x_i are the independent variables associated with the elements of $\mathscr{H}$, we have the group matrix of the permutation representation $\mathscr{G}^{\mathscr{H}}$ of $\mathscr{G}$, which we have called the representation of $\mathscr{G}$ *induced* by the identity representation of $\mathscr{H}$. If we replace $\boldsymbol{H}$ by the group matrix of *any* representation λ of $\mathscr{H}$ we obtain the group matrix of the representation of $\mathscr{G}$ *induced* by the representation λ of $\mathscr{H}$. In order to calculate its character, which uniquely determines it by 11.38, it is sufficient to observe that the $G_i^{-1}\mathscr{H}G_i$ are all conjugate in $\mathscr{G}$ and the character of S is $\psi^{\lambda}(S)$ for each such matrix appearing in the diagonal of the induced representation. Thus this character is $\chi^{\mathscr{H}}(S)\psi^{\lambda}(S)$, and 11.51 and 11.52 yield

11.54 FROBENIUS' RECIPROCITY THEOREM. *The frequency with which an irreducible representation λ of $\mathscr{H}$ appears as an irreducible component when the irreducible representation ρ of $\mathscr{G}$ is restricted to $\mathscr{H}$ is equal to the frequency with which ρ appears as an irreducible component of the representation of $\mathscr{G}$ induced by the irreducible representation λ of $\mathscr{H}$.*

We conclude this survey of the ordinary representation theory of a finite group $\mathscr{G}$ with two definitions which will play a significant role in its application to the symmetric group $\mathfrak{S}_n$.

11.55 *Definition.* If $(G_i)^{\rho}$ and $(G_i)^{\sigma}$ are matrices representing G_i in two irreducible representations ρ and σ of G, then the Kronecker products of these matrices:

$$(G_i)^{\rho} \times (G_i)^{\sigma}$$

yield a representation of G which we shall call the *inner product* $\rho \times \sigma$.

Since the character of $\rho \times \sigma$ is $\chi^{\rho}\chi^{\sigma}$, it follows from 11.38 that $\rho \times \sigma$ is equivalent to $\sigma \times \rho$.

Let us utilize these ideas to prove a simple lemma which will be of importance in Chapter III. To this end *we denote the inducing process by an upward arrow* ($\uparrow$) *and the restricting process by a downward arrow* ($\downarrow$). Also, we write the representation ρ of $\mathscr{G}$ in the form $\rho\mathscr{G}$.

11.56 LEMMA. $\quad (\lambda\mathscr{H}\uparrow\mathscr{G}) \times \rho\mathscr{G} = ((\rho\mathscr{G}\downarrow\mathscr{H}) \times \lambda\mathscr{H})\uparrow\mathscr{G}.$

Proof. Since the character of the induced representation $(\lambda\mathscr{H}\uparrow\mathscr{G})$ is the product of the permutation character 11.14 and that of the representation $\lambda\mathscr{H}$, we have the character on each side of 11.56 to be

$$\frac{gg_Q^{\mathscr{H}}}{hg_Q}\,\psi^{\lambda}(Q)\,\chi^{\rho}(Q),$$

where $\psi^\lambda(Q)$ is defined only for $Q \in \mathscr{H}$. This does not raise any difficulty, however, since $g_Q^{\mathscr{H}} = 0$, if Q is not an element of $\mathscr{H}$.

The significance of 11.56 is that the problem of constructing the inner product of representations of $\mathscr{G}$ on the left is shifted to the same problem for the subgroup $\mathscr{H}$, followed by inducing. In particular, if we take λ to be the identity representation I of $\mathscr{H}$, 11.56 becomes

11.57 $$(I\mathscr{H}\uparrow\mathscr{G}) \times \rho\mathscr{G} = (\rho\mathscr{G}\downarrow\mathscr{H})\uparrow\mathscr{G}.$$

Consider now the Kronecker product of the matrices $(G_i)^\rho$ *and* $(G_j')^{\rho'}$:

$$(G_i)^\rho \times (G_j')^{\rho'}$$

where $\mathscr{G}$ and $\mathscr{G}'$ are distinct groups. Clearly such matrices yield a representation of the direct product $\mathscr{G} \times \mathscr{G}'$ which we may denote $\rho \times \rho'$, where multiplication again is commutative. By analogy, we shall call $\rho \times \rho'$ the *direct product* of ρ and ρ'. The following theorem is an immediate consequence of the character relations 11.37.

11.58 *Every irreducible representation of the direct product* $\mathscr{G} \times \mathscr{G}'$ *is of the form* $\rho \times \rho'$ *where* ρ *is an irreducible representation of* $\mathscr{G}$ *and* ρ' *an irreducible representation of* $\mathscr{G}'$.

11.59 *Definition.* If the direct product $\mathscr{G} \times \mathscr{G}'$ is a subgroup of a finite group $\mathscr{G}''$, we shall call the representation of $\mathscr{G}''$ induced by the irreducible representation $\rho \times \rho'$ of $\mathscr{G} \times \mathscr{G}'$ an *outer product* $\rho \,.\, \rho'$.

In general the group $\mathscr{G}''$ is not well defined but if we set $\mathscr{G} = \mathfrak{S}_m$ and $\mathscr{G}' = \mathfrak{S}_n$ we may take $\mathscr{G}'' = \mathfrak{S}_{m+n}$ (cf. Chapter III). The character of an outer product is defined as in the proof of 11.56 so that $\rho \,.\, \rho'$ is equivalent to $\rho' \,.\, \rho$.

PART 2: THE MODULAR REPRESENTATION THEORY

Introduction. The study of the representation of a group $\mathscr{G}$ by matrices with coefficients in a modular field was begun by Dickson, who proved that the ordinary theory remains valid provided the characteristic p of the field is prime to the order g of $\mathscr{G}$. A systematic study of the situation which arises when p divides g was initiated in 1937 by Brauer and Nesbitt. The difficulties involved are formidable but subsequent work has clarified many of the ideas. In this Part 2 of Chapter I we shall summarize those parts of the theory which are essential to our purpose, basing the development on a recent approach by Nagao and Osima.

Perhaps the most significant aspect of the application of representation theory, ordinary and modular, to the symmetric group $\mathfrak{S}_n$, is the small role played by character theory. As a substitute we shall utilize the deeper insight into properties of the group-ring provided by the Young diagram. Thus we shall emphasize here the general structural relations between blocks, modular irreducible representations and the indecomposables of the regular representation. No attempt will be made to develop the properties of the Cartan matrix C which depend on the general structure theory of algebras. In view of the relation $C = D'D$ which holds for a group algebra we shall concentrate attention on the decomposition matrix D.

12.1 The decomposition matrix D. In Part 1 we assumed that the field containing the coefficients of every absolutely irreducible representation of $\mathcal{G}$ had characteristic zero; we now consider the representation of $\mathcal{G}$ with coefficients in a field Σ of characteristic p, where p divides g.

If $\wp$ is a fixed prime ideal divisor of p in Σ, we may assume that the coefficients of all the chosen set of non-equivalent irreducible representations of $\mathcal{G}$ are $\wp$-integers, i.e. numbers of the form α/β where α and β are integers in Σ and β is prime to $\wp$. If we denote the ring of $\wp$-integers of Σ by σ, and the residue class field of σ (mod $\wp$) by $\bar{\Sigma}$, then an ordinary irreducible representation ρ_i $(i = 1, 2, \ldots, k)$ may be written in the form:

12.11 $$\rho_i \sim \bar{\rho}_i \simeq \begin{bmatrix} F_1 & & & & & & & \\ & \cdot & & & & 0 & & \\ & & F_1 & & & & & \\ & & & F_2 & & & & \\ & & & & \cdot & & & \\ & & & & & F_2 & & \\ & * & & & & & \cdot & \\ & & & & & & & F_{k'} \end{bmatrix} \begin{matrix} \left.\vphantom{\begin{matrix}a\\a\\a\end{matrix}}\right\} d_{i1} \\ \left.\vphantom{\begin{matrix}a\\a\\a\end{matrix}}\right\} d_{i2} \\ \\ \\ \end{matrix}$$

where the F_i $(i = 1, 2, \ldots, k')$ are modularly irreducible and the part below the diagonal indicated by $*$ yields the radical $\mathcal{N}$ of the group algebra A over $\bar{\Sigma}$. Ignoring this part below the diagonal we write:

12.12 $$\bar{\rho}_i \leftrightarrow \sum_{j=1}^{k'} d_{ij} F_j$$

and the matrix $D = (d_{ij})$ is called the *decomposition matrix* of $\mathcal{G}$ over Σ.

Let us consider the special case in which Σ is the rational field, proving that:

12.13 *If an irreducible representation ρ of $\mathcal{G}$ has rational coefficients then there exists a linear transformation L such that $\rho_1 = L\rho L^{-1}$ has rational integral coefficients.*

Proof. Let us suppose that the transformations of ρ operate in a vector space V with coordinates $(v_1, v_2, \ldots, v_f)$. If γ is the least common denominator of the coefficients of all transformations of ρ, we may apply these transformations to γv_1 and obtain a set of g linear forms L_i in $v_1, v_2, \ldots, v_f$, of which f are linearly independent. Moreover, the coefficients of each form are rational integers. Our problem is to find a basis in terms of which all the transformations of ρ also have integral coefficients.

If the L_i are transformed amongst themselves by $\mathcal{G}$, so also are their sums and differences, so that we have a *module M* over the integers. Since the system is finite we can apply the Euclidean algorithm and find a form

$$L_1 = l_{11}v_1 + l_{12}v_2 + \ldots + l_1 v_{ff}$$

such that l_{11} divides the coefficient of v_1 in every form L' belonging to M. Thus we can find an integer l such that $L' - lL_1$ does not involve the variable v_1 of V. Proceeding thus we can find a basis

$$\begin{aligned} L_1 &= l_{11}v_1 + l_{12}v_2 + \ldots + l_{1f}v_f \\ L_2 &= \qquad\quad l_{22}v_2 + \ldots + l_{2f}v_f \\ &\qquad\qquad \cdots \\ L_f &= \qquad\qquad\qquad\quad l_{ff}v_f \end{aligned} \qquad 12.14$$

of L such that if we choose these L_i as coordinate hyperplanes in V all the transformations of $\rho_1 = L\rho L^{-1}$ will have integral coefficients. The equations 12.14 define the non-singular transformation L.

In 2.17 we shall give Young's seminormal form of the matrices of any irreducible representation of $\mathfrak{S}_n$, and these are clearly rational. One would expect that a transformation should exist which would be more explicit than 12.14 and would give also the modular reduction 12.11. We shall return to this problem later.

12.15 *Example.* Referring to Chapter II, we take variables v_1, v_2, v_3, v_4, v_5 associated with the standard tableaux

123	,	124	,	134	,	125	,	135
45		35		25		34		24

of the irreducible representation [3, 2] of $\mathfrak{S}_5$. Applying 2.17 we have the following matrices for the transpositions:

$$(12) = \begin{bmatrix} 1 &&&& \\ & 1 &&& \\ && -1 && \\ &&& 1 & \\ &&&& -1 \end{bmatrix} \qquad (23) = \begin{bmatrix} 1 &&&& \\ & -\frac{1}{2} & \frac{3}{4} && \\ & 1 & \frac{1}{2} && \\ &&& -\frac{1}{2} & \frac{3}{4} \\ &&& 1 & \frac{1}{2} \end{bmatrix}$$

12.151

$$(34) = \begin{bmatrix} -\frac{1}{3} & \frac{8}{9} &&& \\ 1 & \frac{1}{3} &&& \\ && 1 && \\ &&& 1 & \\ &&&& -1 \end{bmatrix} \qquad (45) = \begin{bmatrix} 1 &&&& \\ & -\frac{1}{2} && \frac{3}{4} & \\ && -\frac{1}{2} && \frac{3}{4} \\ & 1 && \frac{1}{2} & \\ && 1 && \frac{1}{2} \end{bmatrix}.$$

In order to transform these into integral form we note that

12.152 $$\begin{bmatrix} 1 & -\lambda_n \\ 0 & 1 \end{bmatrix} \begin{bmatrix} -\rho_n & \rho_n\lambda_n \\ 1 & \rho_n \end{bmatrix} \begin{bmatrix} 1 & \lambda_n \\ 0 & 1 \end{bmatrix} = \begin{bmatrix} -\dfrac{1}{\rho_n} & -\dfrac{\lambda_n}{\rho_n} \\ 1 & \dfrac{1}{\rho_n} \end{bmatrix},$$

where $\rho_n = 1/n$ and $\lambda_n = \rho_n/\rho_{n-1}\rho_{n+1}$. Transforming the matrices 12.151 by

$$L = \begin{bmatrix} 1 & -\lambda_3 & 0 & 0 & 0 \\ & 1 & -\lambda_2 & -\lambda_2 & +\lambda_2^2 \\ && 1 & 0 & -\lambda_2 \\ &&& 1 & -\lambda_2 \\ &&&& 1 \end{bmatrix}, \quad L^{-1} = \begin{bmatrix} 1 & \lambda_3 & \lambda_2\lambda_3 & \lambda_2\lambda_3 & \lambda_2^2\lambda_3 \\ & 1 & \lambda_2 & \lambda_2 & \lambda_2^2 \\ && 1 & 0 & \lambda_2 \\ &&& 1 & \lambda_2 \\ &&&& 1 \end{bmatrix},$$

we obtain the matrices:

$$(12) = \left[\begin{array}{c|ccc|c} 1 & 0 & 0 & 0 & 0 \\ \hline 0 & 1 & 3 & 0 & 0 \\ 0 & 0 & -1 & 0 & 0 \\ 0 & 0 & 0 & 0 & 3 \\ \hline 0 & 0 & 0 & 0 & -1 \end{array}\right] \qquad (23) = \left[\begin{array}{c|ccc|c} 1 & 4 & 4 & 6 & 6 \\ \hline 0 & -2 & -3 & 0 & 0 \\ 0 & 1 & 2 & 0 & 0 \\ 0 & 0 & 0 & -2 & -3 \\ \hline 0 & 0 & 0 & 1 & 2 \end{array}\right]$$

$$(34) = \left[\begin{array}{c|ccc|c} -3 & -8 & -12 & -12 & -18 \\ \hline 1 & 3 & 3 & 3 & 0 \\ 0 & 0 & 1 & 0 & 3 \\ 0 & 0 & 0 & 1 & 3 \\ \hline 0 & 0 & 0 & 0 & -1 \end{array}\right] \qquad (45) = \left[\begin{array}{c|ccc|c} 1 & 4 & 6 & 4 & 6 \\ \hline 0 & -2 & 0 & -3 & 0 \\ 0 & 0 & -2 & 0 & -3 \\ 0 & 1 & 0 & 2 & 0 \\ \hline 0 & 0 & 1 & 0 & 2 \end{array}\right]$$

in which the reduction modulo 2 or 3 is evident.

12.2 Modular characters. When we come to extend the notion of character to the modular theory we encounter difficulties because of the fact that the characteristic roots of a matrix $(B)^\rho$ representing an element B of order p are pth roots of unity. In general, we can write any element G of $\mathcal{G}$ as a product of two elements A, B which commute, so that $G=AB=BA$, where A has order prime to p and B has order $p^\beta(\beta\geqq 0)$. We call G *p-regular* for $\beta=0$ and *p-singular* for $\beta>0$. In the field Σ the characteristic roots of $(B)^\rho$ are all 1's since

$$x^{p^\beta}-1 \equiv (x-1)^{p^\beta} = 0 \pmod{p},$$

and $(G)^\rho$ and $(A)^\rho$ have the same characteristic roots.

If σ is a representation of $\mathcal{G}$ different from ρ we can ensure that σ and ρ have the same characteristic roots by requiring that this be true for the p-regular elements of $\mathcal{G}$.

12.21 *Let ρ and σ be two representations of a finite group $\mathcal{G}$. If ρ and σ have the same characteristic roots for all $G \in \mathcal{G}$, then ρ and σ have the same irreducible constituents and conversely.* (12.21 implies 11.38 for a field of characteristic zero.)

Proof. Equality of characteristic roots implies that the degrees f of ρ and σ are equal. If we denote the multiplicity of F_j in ρ and σ by $d_{\rho j}$ and $d_{\sigma j}$, then since the F_j are linearly independent

$$d_{\rho j} \equiv d_{\sigma j} \pmod{p},$$

though these need not necessarily be equal. We assume the theorem to be true for representations of degree less than f. If we replace ρ by ρ_0 and σ by σ_0, where ρ_0 and σ_0 are completely reducible (i.e. we omit the radical in each case) and omit a common F_i, then the remainders ρ_1 and σ_1 satisfy our inductive hypothesis and must have the same irreducible constituents.

There remains the case when $d_{\rho j}\equiv d_{\sigma j}\equiv 0 \pmod{p}$ for every j, but not all are zero. Denote by ρ_2 and σ_2 the completely reduced representation which contains F_j with multiplicity $d_{\rho j}/p$ and $d_{\sigma j}/p\,(j=1, 2, \ldots, k')$. But the degrees of ρ_2 and σ_2 are less than f and so $d_{\rho j}=d_{\sigma j}$ originally. The converse of the theorem follows easily.

12.22 *Two modular representations of $\mathcal{G}$ have the same irreducible components if and only if the p-regular elements have the same characters.*

The only part that requires clarification is the word *character*. In proving 12.21 we considered the characteristic roots in Σ and we could call their sum the *trace* of (G). In the ordinary theory the characteristic roots are roots of unity and it is desirable to define the character of ρ

so that this property still holds. If $g = p^a g'$, then the ordinary character of a p-regular element is a sum of g'th roots of unity, and since $(p, g') = 1$, no two of these roots are congruent modulo $\wp$. Let us extend the coefficient field Σ of characteristic p to Σ_1 by adjoining these g'th roots of unity $1, \delta, \ldots, \delta^{g'-1}$ and let $\wp_1$ be a prime ideal divisor of p in Σ_1; let $\bar{\Sigma}_1$ be the field of integers of Σ_1 taken modulo $\wp_1$. Then $\bar{\Sigma}_1$ is an extension field of $\bar{\Sigma}$ which contains the g'th roots of unity $1, \bar{\delta}, \ldots, \bar{\delta}^{g'-1}$ which are the residues of $1, \delta, \ldots, \delta^{g'-1}$ (mod $\wp_1$). We have here a 1-1 correspondence between the powers of δ and of $\bar{\delta}$, since $\delta^\alpha \not\equiv \delta^\beta$ if $\delta^\alpha \neq \delta^\beta$.

We define the *character* of a p-regular element G of $\mathscr{G}$ to be the sum of the residues $\bar{\delta}^\alpha$ instead of δ^α which appear in the trace. Equality of roots δ^α implies equality of $\bar{\delta}^\alpha$, proving 12.22. Thus the character is again a complex valued function, as in the ordinary theory. Taking the character of ρ_i to be χ^i and that of F_j to be ϕ^j, 12.12 yields

12.23 $$\chi^i = \sum_{j=1}^{k'} d_{ij}\,\phi^j \qquad (i = 1, 2, \ldots, k).$$

12.3 Indecomposable and modularly irreducible representations. Consider the left- and right-regular representations $S(a)$ and $R(a)$ of the group algebra $\mathscr{A}$, writing the defining equations 11.23 in the matrix form:

12.31 $$\begin{aligned} a(G_1, G_2, \ldots, G_g) &= (G_1, G_2, \ldots, G_g)\, S(a),\\ (G_1, G_2, \ldots, G_g)b &= (G_1, G_2, \ldots, G_g) R'(b), \end{aligned}$$

so that

12.32 $$a(G_1, G_2, \ldots, G_g)b = (G_1, G_2, \ldots, G_g)\, S(a) R'(b).$$

If $\mathscr{G}'$ is anti-isomorphic with $\mathscr{G}$ we have a correspondence

$$a = \sum_{i=1}^{g} x_i G_i \quad \leftrightarrow \quad a' = \sum_{i=1}^{g} x_i G_i^{-1},$$

so that $a' \to R(a)$ is the left-regular representation of $\mathscr{G}'$. Since

$$S(a)\, R'(b) = R'(b)\, S(a)$$

for every a, b in $\mathscr{A}$, $a \times b \to S(a)\, R'(b)$ is a representation of the direct product $\mathscr{G} \times \mathscr{G}'$. If the modular irreducible components of R are F_i, then these are also the modular irreducible components of S, since R and S are equivalent. As in 11.58, the modular irreducible representations of $\mathscr{G} \times \mathscr{G}'$ are all of the form $F_i(a) \times F_j'(b)$ so that:

12.33 $$S(a)\, R'(b) \leftrightarrow \sum_{i,j} c_{ij}(F_i(a) \times F_j(b)),$$

where the c_{ij} are the *Cartan invariants* of $\mathscr{A}$.

Consider now the reduction of $S(a)$ and $R'(b)$ into their indecomposable constituents U_i and V_j, where the correspondence between the U_i and F_i is *uniquely* determined (cf. 12.44 and 12.45). We take the following theorem as the basis of our development of the modular theory:

12.34 *If* c_{ij} *is the multiplicity of* $F_i(a) \times F_j'(b)$ *in* $S(a)\,R'(b)$ *then*

(i) $$U_j(a) \leftrightarrow \sum_i c_{ij} F_i(a);$$

(ii) $$V_i(a) \leftrightarrow \sum_j c_{ij} F_j(a);$$

(iii) $$S(a)\,R'(b) \leftrightarrow \sum_j U_j(a) \times F_j'(b) \leftrightarrow \sum_i F_i(a) \times V_i'(b).$$

For the proof of this theorem the reader is referred to the paper by Osima (3) on which this discussion is based.

The Cartan invariants may be introduced otherwise and we give three alternative definitions:

(*a*) In general, if ρ and σ are two representations of an algebra $\mathscr{A}$ which associates $\rho(a)$ and $\sigma(a)$ with each element a of $\mathscr{A}$, the representation ρ is *intertwined* with σ if there exists a matrix $X \neq 0$ such that

12.35 $$\rho(a)X = X\sigma(a)$$

for all $a \in \mathscr{A}$. The representation ρ is h times intertwined with σ if there are exactly h linearly independent matrices X satisfying 12.35. If we write $h = I(\rho, \sigma)$ then it can be shown that

$$c_{ij} = I(U_i, V_j) = I(U_j, U_i) = I(V_j, V_i).$$

This definition leads directly to 12.34 (i) and (ii) via Schur's Lemma, and 12.34 (iii) then implies 12.33.

(*b*) If $\mathscr{N}$ is the radical of the group algebra $\mathscr{A}$, $\mathscr{A} \,/\, \mathscr{N}$ is semi-simple and the direct sum of simple algebras $\mathscr{A}_i$ associated with F_i. The unit element ε_i of $\mathscr{A}_i$ is associated with a matrix having the identity matrix in place of each F_i with zeros elsewhere. Thus

$$\varepsilon_i^2 = \varepsilon_i, \quad \varepsilon_i\,\varepsilon_j = 0 \quad (i \neq j).$$

The number of linearly independent a's in $\mathscr{A}$ for which $\varepsilon_i a \varepsilon_j = a$ is given by $c_{ij}\phi_1^i\phi_1^j$ where ϕ_1^i is the degree of F_i.

(*c*) Finally, we may define the c_{ij} by means of the equation 12.34 (i). This was the original procedure of Brauer and Nesbitt. It has the advantage of straightforwardness up to the stage of relating the c's to the decomposition numbers d_{ij}, but relies on a difficult theorem of Frobenius.

In the present version of the theory the required character relations follow directly from 12.34, 12.35 and the following theorem on the ordinary characters of $S(G_r)\, R'(G_r)$:

12.36 *If* $\chi(G_r \times G_s)$ *is the ordinary character of the representation* $S(G_r)\, R'(G_s^{-1})$ *of* $\mathscr{G} \times \mathscr{G}$ *then*

$$\chi(G_r \times G_s) = g\delta_{ij}/g_i, \qquad G_r \in C_i,\ G_s \in C_j.$$

Proof. From 12.32 we have

$$G_r \times G_s \to G_r(G_1, G_2, \ldots, G_g)G_s^{-1} = (G_1, G_2, \ldots, G_g)\, S(G_r)\, R'(G_s^{-1}),$$

so that to have the desired character we must consider those scalar products of rows of $S(G_r)$ with columns of $R'(G_s^{-1})$ which yield a contribution to the trace of the product matrix. Since both are permutation matrices with one 1 in each row and column, with zeros elsewhere, the necessary and sufficient condition that 1 appear in the t, t position in the product is that

$$G_r G_t = G_k, \qquad G_k G_s^{-1} = G_t,$$

or

$$G_t^{-1} G_r G_t = G_s.$$

Thus, if $i=j$ we have

$$\begin{aligned} S(G_r)\, R'(G_s^{-1}) &= S(G_r)\, R'(G_t^{-1})\, R'(G_r^{-1})\, R'(G_t) \\ &= R'(G_t^{-1}) \cdot S(G_r)\, R'(G_r^{-1}) \cdot R'(G_t), \end{aligned}$$

so we may assume that $r=s$ and $G_t^{-1} G_r G_t = G_r$. But then G_t belongs to the centralizer of G_r of order g/g_i, and every such element G_t contributes 1 to $\chi(G_r \times G_s)$, proving the result.

In this case of the ordinary representations over a field of characteristic zero $U_i = F_i$ in 12.34 (iii), so by 11.58

12.361
$$\chi(G_r \times G_s) = \sum_{\rho=1}^{k} \chi_i^\rho \chi_j^\rho = \begin{cases} g/g_i, & j = i', \\ 0, & j \neq i'. \end{cases}$$

This is 11.372 from which 11.371 can be derived, as before.

Combining 12.33 and 12.36 we have

12.37
$$\sum_{i,j} c_{ij}\, \phi_r^i \phi_s^j = g\delta_{rs'}/g_r.$$

But also by 12.34

12.38
$$\sum_i \eta_r^i \phi_s^i = g\delta_{rs'}/g_r.$$

If we set $\Phi = (\phi_r^i)$, $H = (\eta_r^i)$ where i refers to the row and r to the column, then 12.38 may be written

$$H'\Phi = (g\delta_{rs'}/g_r) = T.$$

Since T is non-singular, the columns of Φ, which we may suppose is a (k^*, k') matrix, are linearly independent so $k^* \geq k'$, where k' is the number of p-regular classes of $\mathcal{G}$. On the other hand, the rows of T are linearly independent so that $k^* = k'$. Thus we have proved that:

12.39 *The number of modular irreducible representations of $\mathcal{G}$ is equal to the number k' of p-regular classes of $\mathcal{G}$.*

12.4 Character relations. The decomposition numbers d_{ij} were defined in 12.23 with reference to the *rows* of the matrix D. We now prove the following important property of the *columns*:

12.41 $$\eta^j = \sum_i d_{ij} \chi^i \qquad (H = D'X)$$

Proof.
$$\sum_i \chi_r^i \chi_s^i = \sum_i \chi_r^i (\sum_j d_{ij} \phi_s^j)$$
$$= \sum_j (\sum_i d_{ij} \chi_r^i) \phi_s^j = \sum_j \eta_r^j \phi_s^j$$

by 11.372, 12.23 and 12.38. Since the ϕ's are linearly independent this yields 12.41 by equating coefficients.

There is a corollary of this result which is interesting and easy to derive, and which will be significant for us later on. If we suppose that A is a p-regular and B a p-singular element of $\mathcal{G}$, then 11.372 requires that
$$\sum_i \chi^i(A) \chi^i(B) = 0,$$

since B and A^{-1} cannot be conjugate in G. Substituting from 12.23 we have
$$\sum_i \sum_j d_{ij} \phi^j(A) \chi^i(B) = \sum_j \eta^j(B) \phi^j(A) = 0$$

by 12.41. Since the ϕ's are linearly independent we have:
$$\eta^j(B) = 0,$$

or,

12.42 *The ordinary character of any p-singular element must vanish in an indecomposable component of the regular representation of $\mathcal{G}$.*

Using 12.41 we have:
$$\eta^j = \sum_i d_{ij} \chi^i = \sum_i d_{ij} (\sum_t d_{it} \phi^t) = \sum_t (\sum_i d_{it} d_{ij}) \phi^t,$$

but by 12.34 (i)

$$\eta^j = \sum_t c_{tj}\,\phi^t \qquad (H = C\Phi),$$

thus $c_{tj} = \sum_i d_{it}\,d_{ij} = c_{jt}$ and we may write

12.43 $$C = D'D.$$

Our argument is all but complete. Referring to 12.34 (i) and (ii) we see that $U_i \leftrightarrow V_i$. But the argument used in proving 12.34 (loc. cit.) requires that

12.44 $$U_i \simeq \begin{bmatrix} F_i & 0 \\ * & * \end{bmatrix}, \qquad V_i \simeq \begin{bmatrix} * & 0 \\ * & F_i \end{bmatrix}.$$

Since the left and right regular representations are equivalent we conclude that U_i and V_i are equivalent, so that we may speak of U_i as an indecomposable of the regular representation of $\mathcal{G}$ and we must have

12.45 $$U_i \simeq \begin{bmatrix} F_i & & 0 \\ & \ddots & \\ * & & F_i \end{bmatrix},$$

so that $c_{ii} \geqq 2$, unless $U_i = F_i$ when $c_{ii} = 1$.

There are two further character relations which are significant. If we rewrite 12.38 in the form

12.46 $$\Phi T^{-1} H' = (\delta_{rs})$$

and multiply through by $C^{-1} = (\gamma_{rs})$ on the right, then, since $H' = \Phi' C$,

$$\Phi T^{-1} H' C^{-1} = C^{-1} = \Phi T^{-1} \Phi'$$

so that

12.47 $$\sum_{r=1}^{k} g_r\,\phi_r^i\,\phi_{r'}^j = \gamma_{ij}\,g \qquad (\Phi T^{-1}\Phi' = C^{-1}).$$

Similarly, multiplying 12.46 by C on the left we have

12.48 $$\sum_{r=1}^{k} g_r\,\eta_r^i\,\eta_{r'}^j = c_{ij}\,g \qquad (H T^{-1} H' = C).$$

These last two formulae 12.47 and 12.48 are to be compared with 11.371 but there is an important difference. Due to the presence of the Cartan invariants on the right side, *neither the modular characters nor the characters of the indecomposables alone are sufficient to provide a criterion of irreducibility or indecomposability.*

We conclude this section on the modular characters by proving a result which will be important later on:

12.49 *If m is a rational integer and $m\mathcal{J}$ is an indecomposable or sum of indecomposables of $\mathfrak{S}_n$ then so also is $\mathcal{J}$.*

Proof. Denote by χ the character of $\mathcal{J}$, so that

$$m\chi = \sum_i a_i \eta^i$$

with non-negative integers a_i. It follows from 12.42 that $\chi(B)=0$ for any p-singular element B of $\mathfrak{S}_n$ which implies that

$$\chi = \sum_i b_i \eta^i.$$

Since the η's are linearly independent it follows that $mb_i = a_i$ and the b_i are non-negative, proving the result.

12.5 Blocks. The structure of the decomposition matrix D is significant in all that follows. Indeed, our principal problem with reference to the application of this general theory to $\mathfrak{S}_n$ will be to construct D.

12.51 *Definition.* Two ordinary representations ρ and σ of $\mathcal{G}$ belong to the same *block* **B** if and only if the class multipliers γ_i^ρ and γ_i^σ are congruent (mod $\wp$) for all i.

The effect of this definition is best illustrated by means of the following

12.52 *Example.* We give the decomposition matrices of $\mathfrak{S}_5$ for $p=2, 3$, as they appear in Tables 2-5 and 3-5 in the Appendix, with the addition of the degrees of the ordinary representations down the left hand side and those of the modular representations across the top.

		1	4	4
1	[5]	1	0	
5	[3, 2]	1	1	
6	$[3, 1^2]$	2	1	
5	$[2^2, 1]$	1	1	
1	$[1^5]$	1	0	
4	[4, 1]			1
4	$[2, 1^3]$			1

$p = 2$

		1	4	4	1	6
1	[5]	1	0			
5	$[2^2, 1]$	1	1			
4	$[2, 1^3]$	0	1			
4	[4, 1]			1	0	
5	[3, 2]			1	1	
1	$[1^5]$			0	1	
6	$[3, 1^2]$					1

$p = 3$

The columns yield the indecomposables of the regular representation by 12.41, and the rows the modular irreducible components of the ordinary representations of $\mathfrak{S}_5$. For example, the degrees of the indecomposables for $p=2$ are 24, 16 and 8 and $24.1+16.4+8.4=120$ according to 12.38 for $r=s=1$ and similarly for $p=3$.

In Example 12.15 we actually carried out the reduction of [3, 2] as given in the tables. One may verify that the character of a p-singular element is zero in each indecomposable, according to 12.42.

Since the number k' of p-regular classes C_i of $\mathcal{G}$ is equal to the number of modularly irreducible representations of $\mathcal{G}$ and so equal to the number of columns of the decomposition matrix, it would seem natural to establish a correspondence between the C_i and the blocks **B**. To this end we make the following

12.53 *Definitions.* If G_i is an element of the p-regular class C_i of $\mathcal{G}$ and $\mathcal{N}(G_i)$ of order n_i is the normalizer of G_i in $\mathcal{G}$, then the *defect group* D_i of C_i is a p-Sylow subgroup of $\mathcal{N}(G_i)$ of order p^{d_i}.

If $g=p^\alpha g'$, where $(p, g')=1$, and we set $e(g)=\alpha$ then

$$g_i = g/n_i, \quad e(g_i) = \alpha - d_i,$$

and d_i is called the *defect* of the class C_i.

The three following theorems summarize a complicated situation and form the basis of the general theory of blocks. We give them here without proof, and we shall use them in Chapter V with reference to $\mathfrak{S}_n$.

12.54 (i) *Each p-regular class can be associated with a unique block* **B**.

(ii) *If $C_1, C_2, \ldots C_\beta$ are thus associated with* **B** *then they may be arranged so that*

$$d_1 > d_i \qquad i = 2, 3, \ldots \beta.$$

(iii) *If we set $D_1=\mathcal{D}$ and $d_1=\delta$, then p^δ is the highest power of p dividing one of the numbers g/f^ρ for $\rho\subset$* **B**, *so that*

$$e(f^\rho) = \alpha - \delta + \varepsilon, \qquad \varepsilon \geqq 0.$$

One could say more concerning the p-regular classes associated with the block **B**, e.g. the elementary divisors of the Cartan matrix of **B** are precisely the p^{d_i}, but it would carry us too far afield.

12.55 *Definition.* We shall call the uniquely defined defect group $\mathcal{D}=D_1$ of C_1 the *defect group* of the block **B**, and $d_1=\delta$ the *defect* of **B**.

The following criteria are important.

12.56 *An irreducible representation ρ belongs to a block of defect $\geqq\delta$ if and only if*

$$\gamma_j^\rho \equiv 0 \qquad (\text{mod } p),$$

for all p-regular classes C_j with $d_j<\delta$.

12.57 *Two ordinary irreducible representations* ρ *and* σ *of* $\mathcal{G}$ *belonging to blocks of defect* δ *belong to the same block* **B** *if and only if*

$$\gamma_j^\rho \equiv \gamma_j^\sigma \qquad \text{(mod } p\text{)},$$

for all p-regular classes C_j *with* $d_j = \delta$.

While 12.56 distinguishes between blocks of different defect, 12.57 distinguishes between blocks of the same defect, yielding a refinement of the original condition 12.51.

It should be observed that this association of the p-regular classes with the blocks is *numerical.* When we come to apply the theory to $\mathfrak{S}_n$ we shall replace the notion of *defect* by that of *weight* (§ 5.351) which has a natural interpretation with respect to the Young diagram. As in the case of the ordinary theory, one would like to see some way of generalizing these ideas to apply to an arbitrary group. The following important conclusion follows immediately from 12.54–12.57:

12.58 *The necessary and sufficient condition that an ordinary irreducible representation* ρ *constitutes a block by itself is that* $\delta = 0$. *In such a case* ρ *is irreducible modulo* $\wp$ *and constitutes an indecomposable of the regular representation of* $\mathcal{G}$.

It is easy to verify in Example 12.52 that $[3, 1^2]$ for $p=3$ satisfies 12.58 while $[4, 1]$ for $p=2$ does not.

Much deep and detailed work has been done along the lines indicated above. For example, if we associate with each ordinary irreducible representation ρ of $\mathcal{G}$ a dot P_ρ we may join P_ρ to P_σ if ρ and σ have a modular component in common (i.e. if ρ and σ contribute to the same column of D). The linear graph so obtained characterizes completely the matrix D and for $\delta = 1$ it has been proved that this graph must be a tree. This property provided the basis for Nakayama's first application of the general theory to $\mathfrak{S}_n$.

12.6 The Nakayama reciprocity formulae. Just as in the ordinary theory, the notions of inducing and restricting are of great importance and are defined in a similar manner. In the modular theory, however, reducibility does not imply complete reducibility so that we must distinguish between the processes of inducing and restricting as they apply to modular irreducible representations F and indecomposables U of the regular representation.

If $\mathcal{H}$ is any subgroup of $\mathcal{G}$ let us denote the modular irreducible representation of $\mathcal{H}$ by $\tilde{F}$ and the indecomposables of the regular representation of $\mathcal{H}$ by $\tilde{U}$. As in § 11.5, we denote inducing by an upward arrow (↑) and restricting by a downward arrow (↓) yielding the following important generalization of Frobenius' reciprocity theorem:

(12.61) $$\tilde{U}^i \uparrow \sum a_{ij}\, U^j, \quad F^j \downarrow \sum a_{ij}\, \tilde{F}^i,$$

(12.62) $$\tilde{F}^i \uparrow \sum b_{ij}\, F^j, \quad U^j \downarrow \sum b_{ij}\, \tilde{U}^i,$$

where $i=1, 2, \ldots, \tilde{k}'$ for $\mathscr{H}$ and $j=1, 2, \ldots, k'$ for $\mathscr{G}$. The method of proof is essentially the same as before.

CHAPTER TWO

ORDINARY REPRESENTATION THEORY OF $\mathfrak{S}_n$ AND YOUNG'S RAISING OPERATOR

Introduction. The development of the representation theory of $\mathfrak{S}_n$ as presented here is largely the work of Alfred Young. Curiously enough, the results were incidental to his study of invariants and were rarely separated from such applications in his published papers. Since a co-ordinated account of the basis of Young's theory has already been given by D. E. Rutherford we shall only summarize these ideas in § 2.1 and state the principle theorem 2.17 which gives the connection between a Young diagram $[\lambda]$ and the matrices of the corresponding irreducible representation of $\mathfrak{S}_n$.

Associated with the right diagram $[\lambda]$ is the subgroup P^λ of $\mathfrak{S}_n$ consisting of the direct product of the symmetric groups on $\lambda_1, \lambda_2, \ldots \lambda_h$ symbols where $\lambda_1+\lambda_2+\ldots\lambda_h=n$. Young recognized the importance of the permutation representation of $\mathfrak{S}_n$ induced by the identity representation of P^λ and we devote § 2.2 to developing the theory of the *raising operator* in terms of which the reduction of this permutation representation may be expressed. Though implicit in Young's work, the importance of a *hook* (§ 2.3) was not realized until Nakayama drew attention to it in connection with the modular theory. To properly understand its significance, we introduce in § 2.5 the notion of a *skew diagram* $[\alpha]-[\beta]$ which consists of those nodes of $[\alpha]$ not contained in $[\beta]$, where $\beta_i \leqq \alpha_i$ for all i. Such a skew diagram yields a representation of $\mathfrak{S}_{n-m}$, which, in general, is reducible.

The idea of a *standard tableau* in which the arrangement of the symbols $1, 2, \ldots, n$ in the diagram $[\lambda]$ follows the natural order in each row and column is the cornerstone of Young's theory. Thus it is not surprising that a considerable part of this and subsequent chapters is devoted to studying the implications of the standardness condition. It is important to realize that this is, fundamentally, a 'constructibility condition' which relates the representations of $\mathfrak{S}_n$ to those of $\mathfrak{S}_{n+1}$.

2.1 Young's representation theory of $\mathfrak{S}_n$. Each class of conjugate elements of the symmetric group $\mathfrak{S}_n$ is defined by means of a partition $(\lambda)=(\lambda_1, \lambda_2, \ldots, \lambda_h)$, where

$$\lambda_1+\lambda_2+\ldots+\lambda_h = n.$$

Since the cycles in a substitution can be arranged in any order, there is no restriction in assuming that $\lambda_1 \geqq \lambda_2 \geqq \ldots \geqq \lambda_h$.

Corresponding to each class of conjugates (λ), Young showed that there exists a uniquely determined irreducible representation defined in terms of the *Young diagram*

$$
2.11 \qquad [\lambda]: \quad
\begin{array}{l}
\cdot \;\; \cdot \;\; \cdot \;\; \cdot \;\; \cdot \;\; \cdot \;\; \cdot \quad (\lambda_1 \text{ nodes}) \\
\cdot \;\; \cdot \;\; \cdot \;\; \cdot \;\; \cdot \;\; \cdot \quad (\lambda_2 \text{ nodes}) \\
\cdot \;\; \cdot \;\; \cdot \\
\cdot \;\; \cdot \;\; \cdot \quad (\lambda_h \text{ nodes})
\end{array}
$$

We shall sometimes refer to such a diagram as a *right* diagram in contrast to a *skew* diagram to be defined later. If the number of nodes appearing in the *i*th column of $[\lambda]$ is λ_i' we shall call the diagram $[\lambda']$ obtained by interchanging the rows and columns of $[\lambda]$ the *conjugate* of $[\lambda]$.

In establishing the ordinary representation theory of $\mathfrak{S}_n$, Young made no use of characters, and worked wholly with elements of the group algebra. The problem was to determine the idempotents and in particular the basis units of each irreducible representation.

To this end consider the Young diagram $[\lambda]$ with the n symbols $1, 2, \ldots, n$ replacing the nodes. There will be $n!$ such arrangements of the symbols or *tableaux* associated with each $[\lambda]$, which we may denote by

$$t_1^\lambda, t_2^\lambda \ldots t_{n!}^\lambda.$$

These $n!$ tableaux may be arranged in *dictionary order* by assuming that $[\lambda]_i$ *precedes* $[\lambda]_j$ if the symbols in the first r rows of each tableau are the same and the first s symbols in the $(r+1)$th rows are the same but the $(s+1)$th symbol in the $(r+1)$th row of $[\lambda]_i$ *precedes* the $(s+1)$th symbol in the $(r+1)$th row of $[\lambda]_j$. Such a *dictionary order* may also be established between the diagrams by assuming that $[\lambda]$ *precedes* $[\mu]$ if

$$\lambda_1 = \mu_1, \quad \lambda_2 = \mu_2, \ldots \lambda_r = \mu_r, \quad \lambda_{r+1} \geqq \mu_{r+1}.$$

Let us denote the symmetric group on the symbols appearing in the rth row of t_i^λ by $\mathfrak{S}_{\lambda_r}^i$. Forming the direct product and adding the resulting elements of $\mathfrak{S}_n$ over the group algebra we obtain a sum which we may write

$$2.12 \qquad P_i^\lambda = \{\mathfrak{S}_{\lambda_1}^i \times \mathfrak{S}_{\lambda_2}^i \times \ldots \times \mathfrak{S}_{\lambda_h}^i\}.$$

Similarly, we may form the direct product of the symmetric groups of the columns of t_i^λ but now let us affix a minus sign to every odd permutation of $\mathfrak{S}_n$, writing

2.13 $$N_i^\lambda = \{\mathfrak{S}^i_{\lambda'_1} \times \mathfrak{S}^i_{\lambda'_2} \times \ldots \times \mathfrak{S}^i_{\lambda'_{h'}}\}',$$

where λ'_s nodes appear in the sth column of $[\lambda]$. Finally, we construct the elements of the group algebra of $\mathfrak{S}_n$:

2.14 $$T^\lambda = \left(\frac{f^\lambda}{n!}\right)^2 \sum_i P_i^\lambda N_i^\lambda \qquad i = 1, 2, \ldots, n!$$
$$= \left(\frac{f^\lambda}{n!}\right) \sum_i P_i^\lambda N_i^\lambda \qquad i = 1, 2, \ldots, f^\lambda$$

Much is involved in these equations which we shall not attempt to explain here. Suffice it to say that T^λ in 2.14 is an *idempotent* of the group algebra of $\mathfrak{S}_n$ over the field of rationals, satisfying the relations 11.44. In general, the symbols $1, 2, \ldots, n$ will not follow their natural order in the rows and columns of a tableau, but when this is the case, i.e., when the symbol in the (i, j) position *precedes* that in the (k, l) position for all $i \leqq k$, $j \leqq l$, the tableau t^λ is said to be *standard.* The second sum in 2.14 is taken over these f^λ standard tableaux. We shall obtain an explicit expression for f^λ in § 2.3.

2.15 *Example.* It is worth illustrating 2.14 in the simple case $[\lambda] = [2, 1]$. We list the 3! tableaux and their associated expressions $P_i^\lambda N_i^\lambda$ in the following table.

	12 3	13 2	21 3	23 1	31 2	32 1	$\sum P_i^\lambda N_i^\lambda$
I	1	1	1	1	1	1	6
(12)	1	−1	1	−1			0
(13)	−1	1			1	−1	0
(23)			−1	1	−1	1	0
(132)	−1			−1	−1		−3
(123)		−1	−1			−1	−3

Note that the sum of the elements in the first two columns which correspond to the *standard tableaux* yield

$$T^{2,1} = \left(\frac{2}{3!}\right)^2 (6I-3(123)-3(132))$$

$$= \left(\frac{2}{3!}\right) (2I-(123)-(132)),$$

as in 2.14. We see easily that

$$T^3 = \left(\frac{1}{3!}\right) (I+(12)+(13)+(23)+(123)+(132)),$$

$$T^{1^3} = \left(\frac{1}{3!}\right) (I-(12)-(13)-(23)+(123)+(132)),$$

and the relations 11.44 are clearly satisfied.

Having shown how to construct the idempotents T^λ, Young passed in a natural though complicated manner to the actual matrices of the irreducible representation which we may also denote by the symbol $[\lambda]$. Clearly, it is sufficient to construct those matrices representing the transpositions $(r, r+1)$ for $r=1, 2, \ldots, n-1$. To this end we define the *graph* $\mathbf{G}[\lambda]$ of $[\lambda]$, obtained by replacing the (i, j)-node of $[\lambda]$ by

2.16 $$g_{ij}(x) = x+j-i,$$

where x is a variable parameter which can be set equal to zero since it does not enter into Young's.

2.17 Fundamental Theorem. *To construct the matrix representing* $(r, r+1)$ *in the irreducible representations* $[\lambda]$, *arrange the* f^λ *standard tableaux* $\ldots t_u^\lambda, \ldots, t_v^\lambda \ldots$ *in dictionary order and set*

(i) 1 *in the leading diagonal where* t^λ *has* r, *and* $r+1$ *in the same row.*
(ii) -1 *in the leading diagonal where* t^λ *has* r, *and* $r+1$ *in the same column.*
(iii) *a quadratic matrix*

$$(a) \quad \begin{matrix} & t_u^\lambda & t_v^\lambda \\ \begin{matrix} t_u^\lambda \\ t_v^\lambda \end{matrix} & \multicolumn{2}{c}{\begin{pmatrix} -\rho & 1-\rho^2 \\ 1 & \rho \end{pmatrix}} \end{matrix} \quad or \quad (b) \quad \begin{matrix} & t_u^\lambda & t_v^\lambda \\ \begin{matrix} t_u^\lambda \\ t_v^\lambda \end{matrix} & \multicolumn{2}{c}{\begin{pmatrix} -\rho & \sqrt{1-\rho^2} \\ \sqrt{1-\rho^2} & \rho \end{pmatrix}} \end{matrix}$$

at the intersection of the rows and columns corresponding to t_u^λ *and* t_v^λ *where* $u<v$ *and* t_v^λ *is obtainable from* t_u^λ *by interchanging* r *and* $r+1$.

If r appears in the (i,j) position and $r+1$ in the (k,l) position of t_u^λ with $i<k, j>l$, then

$$\frac{1}{\rho} = g_{ij}-g_{kl} = (j-i)-(l-k).$$

(iv) *zeros elsewhere.*

The matrices (*a*) lead to Young's *rational* 'semi-normal' form and the matrices (*b*) lead to his orthogonal form. Example 12.15 illustrates the application of 2.17.

2.2 Young's raising operator R_{ik}. If instead of arranging the rows of $[\lambda]$ above one another as in (2.11) we arrange them *disjointly*, i.e. so no overlapping takes place, we have a special case of a *skew diagram*:

$$\begin{array}{lll} \cdot\ \cdot\ \cdot\ \ldots\ \lambda_1 \text{ nodes} & & \\ & \cdot\ \cdot\ \cdot\ \ldots\ \lambda_2 \text{ nodes} & \\ & & \cdot\ \cdot\ \cdot\ \ldots\ \lambda_h \text{ nodes} \end{array} \tag{2.21}$$

which we shall designate by the symbol

2.211 $$[\lambda_1]\cdot[\lambda_2]\ldots[\lambda_h].$$

The arrangement of the disjoint rows in 2.21 *and the order of the 'factors' in* 2.211 *is immaterial.* For such a skew diagram N^λ is the identity. The number of standard skew tableaux 2.21 is easily seen to be

2.22 $$f_\lambda = \frac{n!}{\lambda_1!\,\lambda_2!\ldots\lambda_h!}$$

which is the degree of the (permutation) representation 2.211 of $\mathfrak{S}_n$ induced by the identity representation of the subgroup

$$P^\lambda = \mathfrak{S}_{\lambda_1}\times\mathfrak{S}_{\lambda_2}\times\ldots\times\mathfrak{S}_{\lambda_h}.$$

The actual matrices of the transpositions $(r, r+1)$ in 2.211 are given by 2.17 if in (iii) we take $\rho=0$. Note that (ii) is inoperative (cf. 3.12).

As the basis of an operator theory we take the following substitutional equation due to Young:

2.23 $$\frac{\Sigma' P^\lambda}{\lambda_1!\,\lambda_2!\ldots\lambda_h!} = \sum(\Pi R_{ik})\,\frac{n!}{f^\lambda}\,T^\lambda,$$

where Σ' indicates summation over all $n!$ arrangements of the symbols in the skew diagram 2.21, and R_{ik} is an operator which, for $i<k$, represents the raising of a node from the kth row to the ith row of $[\lambda]$ to yield a new diagram $[\mu]$. ΠR_{ik} represents successive raisings of nodes in $[\lambda]$ where $i=1, 2, \ldots, h-1$; $k=2, 3, \ldots, h$.

If we arrange the partitions in dictionary order then the $[\mu]$'s so obtained will all *precede* $[\lambda]$. Formula 2.23 gives the reduction of the permutation representation 2.21 in the form

2.24 $$[\lambda_1]\cdot[\lambda_2]\cdot\ldots\cdot[\lambda_h] = \Sigma\,(\Pi R_{ik})\,[\lambda] = [\lambda]+\ldots+[n],$$

where $[\lambda]$ and the identity representation $[n]$ each appear once and once only (cf. 11.46). In applying the operator ΠR_{ik} to the tableau $[\lambda]$ it is understood that *the result is to be disregarded* (i) *if any row contains more symbols than a previous row, or* (ii) *if two symbols from the same row appear in the same column.*

It is possible to systematize the application of the operator R_{ik} in the following manner. Let us suppose that the λ_1 symbols in the first row of $[\lambda]$ are a_1's, the λ_2 symbols in the second row are a_2's, etc. First of all we add the a_2's in succession from the left to $[\lambda_1]$ some in the first row and the remainder in the second row according to the operator:

$$(1-R_{12})^{-1} = 1+R_{12}+R_{12}^2+\ldots+R_{12}^{\lambda_2}+\ldots.$$

Clearly, no operator R_{12}^t with $t>\lambda_2$ has a meaning when applied to $[\lambda]$. To each of the resulting diagrams we add the a_3's in all possible ways subject to (i) and (ii). Each diagram thus obtained is associated with an allowable operator from the product

$$(1-R_{12})^{-1}\,(1-R_{13})^{-1}\,(1-R_{23})^{-1}.$$

Continuing thus we may rewrite 2.24 in the form

2.25 $$[\lambda_1]\cdot[\lambda_2]\ldots[\lambda_h] = \Pi(1-R_{ik})^{-1}\,[\lambda]$$

which can be inverted to yield the significant result

2.26 $$[\lambda] = \Pi(1-R_{ik})\,[\lambda_1].[\lambda_2]\ldots[\lambda_h].$$

Since each operator raises a symbol from a specified row and these rows are disjoint, the restrictions (i) and (ii) do *not* apply to 2.26.

So far, we have induced on the identity representation of the subgroup P^λ to obtain the representation 2.24 of $\mathfrak{S}_n$. Instead we could induce on the irreducible representation

$$[1^{\lambda'_1}]\times[1^{\lambda'_2}]\times\ldots$$

of $\mathfrak{S}_{\lambda'_1}\times\mathfrak{S}_{\lambda'_2}\ldots$ which corresponds to N^λ in 2.13. Instead of R_{ik} which *raises* a symbol from the kth row of $[\lambda]$ to the ith row we would use an operator S_{ik} which would similarly raise a symbol in the conjugate diagram $[\lambda']$. Alternatively, we could describe S_{ik} as *lowering* a symbol from the kth column to the ith column of $[\lambda]$ with appropriate restrictions. Thus corresponding to 2.25, we have

2.27 $$[1^{\lambda'_1}]\cdot[1^{\lambda'_2}]\cdot\ldots = \Pi(1-S_{ik})^{-1}\,[\lambda],$$

and corresponding to 2.26 we have

2.28 $$[\lambda] = \Pi(1-S_{ik})\,[1^{\lambda'_1}]\cdot[1^{\lambda'_2}]\cdot\ldots$$

In the application of these ideas we shall usually confine our attention to 2.25 and 2.26, but it should be borne in mind that an exactly analogous argument can be based on 2.27 and 2.28. Indeed this dual theory will be required in § 3.6. Since successive terms on the right side of 2.25 are *higher* and on the right side of 2.27 are *lower* than $[\lambda]$, we conclude that

2.29 $$[\lambda] = [\lambda_1]\cdot[\lambda_2]\cdot\ldots\cap[1^{\lambda'_1}]\cdot[1^{\lambda'_2}]\cdot\ldots$$

This expression of an irreducible representation in terms of permutation representations is suggestive for the generalization of these ideas to an arbitrary group $\mathcal{G}$.

2.291 *Example.* Let us take $[\lambda]=[3, 2]$ and determine the irreducible component of the permutation representation $[3]\cdot[2]$ of degree 10 by 2.22. Writing a_1's in to first row we add a_2's in all possible ways, subject to (i) and (ii), to yield the following tableaux:

$$\begin{matrix} a_1a_1a_1, \\ a_2a_2 \end{matrix} \qquad \begin{matrix} a_1a_1a_1a_2, \\ a_2 \end{matrix} \qquad \begin{matrix} a_1a_1a_1a_2a_2, \\ \end{matrix}$$

and the reduction:

$$[3]\cdot[2] = [3, 2]+[4, 1]+[5];$$

corresponding to 2.27 we have

$$[1^2]\cdot[1^2]\cdot[1] = [3, 2]+[3, 1^2]+2[2^2, 1]+2[2, 1^3]+[1^5],$$

of degree 30. These reductions have only the representations $[3, 2]$ in common so we may write (2.29):

$$[3, 2] = [3]\cdot[2]\cap[1^2]\cdot[1^2]\cdot[1].$$

2.3 The degree f^λ and the hook graph H$[\lambda]$. Knowing the degree f_λ of a permutation representation $[\lambda_1]\cdot[\lambda_2]\cdot\ldots\cdot[\lambda_h]$ we can use 2.26 to calculate the degree of $[\lambda]$, or the number f^λ of standard tableaux t^λ. We begin by considering the cases $h=2$ and $h=3$ in detail.

2.31 *Case* $h=2$. If $r \geqq s$ and $r+s=n$, then by 2.26

$$\begin{aligned}[r, s] &= (1-R_{12})\ [r]\cdot[s] \\ &= [r]\cdot[s]-[r+1]\cdot[s-1]\end{aligned}$$

so that

$$[r, s] = \begin{vmatrix} [r] & [r+1] \\ [s-1] & [s] \end{vmatrix}^{\cdot}, \quad f^{r,s} = n!\begin{vmatrix} \dfrac{1}{r!} & \dfrac{1}{(r+1)!} \\ \dfrac{1}{(s-1)!} & \dfrac{1}{s!} \end{vmatrix},$$

where the $\cdot$ indicates what type of multiplication is to be used. The expression for $f^{r,s}$ follows immediately from 2.22.

2.32 *Case* $h=3$. If $r \geqq s \geqq t$ and $r+s+t=n$, then similarly:

$$\begin{aligned}[r, s, t] &= (1-R_{12})(1-R_{13})(1-R_{23})\quad [r]\cdot[s]\cdot[t] \\ &= (1-R_{12}-\underline{R_{13}}-R_{23}+R_{12}R_{13}+R_{13}R_{23}+\underline{R_{12}R_{23}} \\ &\qquad -R_{12}R_{13}R_{23})\quad [r]\cdot[s]\cdot[t] \\ &= [r]\cdot[s]\cdot[t]-[r+1]\cdot[s-1]\cdot[t]-\underline{[r+1]\cdot[s]\cdot[t-1]} \\ &\quad -[r]\cdot[s+1]\cdot[t-1]+[r+2]\cdot[s-1]\cdot[t-1] \\ &\quad +[r+1]\cdot[s+1]\cdot[t-2]+\underline{[r+1]\cdot[s]\cdot[t-1]} \\ &\quad -[r+2]\cdot[s]\cdot[t-2],\end{aligned}$$

so that, noting that the underlined terms cancel, we may write

$$[r, s, t] = \begin{vmatrix} [r] & [r+1] & [r+2] \\ [s-1] & [s] & [s+1] \\ [t-2] & [t-1] & [t] \end{vmatrix}^{\cdot},$$

$$f^{r,s,t} = n!\begin{vmatrix} \dfrac{1}{r!} & \dfrac{1}{(r+1)!} & \dfrac{1}{(r+2)!} \\ \dfrac{1}{(s-1)!} & \dfrac{1}{s!} & \dfrac{1}{(s+1)!} \\ \dfrac{1}{(t-2)!} & \dfrac{1}{(t-1)!} & \dfrac{1}{t!} \end{vmatrix}.$$

We prove now the following Theorem which will serve to coordinate many of the ideas which we shall develop in subsequent chapters.

2.33 THEOREM. *If f^{λ} is the degree of the irreducible representation of $\mathfrak{S}_n$ then we may write*

$$[\lambda] = |\,[\lambda_i-i+j]\,|^{\cdot} \quad \textit{with} \quad f^{\lambda} = n!\left|\frac{1}{(\lambda_i-i+j)!}\right|,$$

where $[m]$ *and* $1/m!$ *are to be replaced by* 0 *if* $m<0$ *and by* 1 *if* $m=0$.

Proof. If we set

$$F(\lambda) = \Pi(1-R_{ik})\ [\lambda_1]\cdot[\lambda_2]\cdot\cdots,\quad \Delta = |\,[\lambda_i-i+j]\,|^{\cdot}$$

we must prove that $F(\lambda)=\Delta$.

To begin with, the operator R_{ik} changes $[\lambda_i]\cdot[\lambda_k]$ into $[\lambda_i+1]\cdot[\lambda_k-1]$. In general,

$$\Pi\, R_{ik}^{a_{ik}}\,[\lambda_1]\cdot[\lambda_2]\cdot\ldots = [\lambda_1+y_1]\cdot[\lambda_2+y_2]\cdot\ldots \qquad (a_{ik}=0,1)$$

where

$$\sum_k a_{ik}-\sum_l a_{li} = y_i \qquad (1<l<i<k)$$

with $\Sigma y_i=0$. The following relation should be noted:

2.331 $$(1-R_{s,\,s+1})\,R_{s+1,\,s} = -(1-R_{s+1,\,s}).$$

Also, we recall that in the definition in § 2.2 of the skew diagram $[\lambda_1]\cdot[\lambda_2]\cdot\ldots$, *the order of writing the factors is immaterial.*

Now, let us consider the effect on $F(\lambda)$ of:

2.332 *Interchanging the sth and* $s+1$*th rows of* Δ. Such a change would imply that $F(\lambda)$ should be written in the form:

$$\Pi(1-R_{ik})\ [\lambda_1]\cdot[\lambda_2]\cdot\ldots[\lambda_s-1]\cdot[\lambda_{s+1}+1]\cdot\ldots$$
$$= \Pi(1-R_{ik})R_{s+1,\,s}\ [\lambda_1]\cdot[\lambda_2]\cdot\ldots\cdot[\lambda_s]\cdot[\lambda_{s+1}]\cdot\ldots$$
$$= -F(\lambda),$$

by 2.331, with the operator $R_{s+1,\,s}$ replacing $R_{s,\,s+1}$ in $\Pi(1-R_{ik})$.

Since any permutation of the rows of Δ can be expressed in terms of the transpositions 2.332 we conclude that $F(\lambda)$ changes sign if, and only if, such a permutation is odd.

Finally, in 2.32 we saw that certain 'non-determinantal' terms will, in general, arise in the expansion of $F(\lambda)$. Such a term will contain at least two elements from the same row or column of Δ and interchanging these, the sign will not change. Thus *all non-determinantal terms in* $F(\lambda)$ *must cancel.* Since the coefficient of $[\lambda_1]\cdot[\lambda_2]\cdot\ldots$ is unity in both $F(\lambda)$ and in Δ we conclude that the two functions must be identical. The expression for f^λ follows immediately, proving 2.33.

From 2.28 we have a second determinantal expression for $[\lambda]$ so that

2.34 $$[\lambda] = |\,[\lambda_i-i+j]\,|^{\cdot} = |\,[1^{\lambda'_i-i+j}]\,|^{\cdot}.$$

Let us now make the following

2.35 *Definitions.*

(i) The (i, j)-*hook* of $[\lambda]$ will consist of the (i, j)-node along with the $\lambda_i - i$ nodes to the right, which we shall call the *arm* of the hook, and the $\lambda'_j - j$ nodes below, which we shall call the *leg* of the hook.

(ii) Thus the *length* of the (i, j)-hook is

$$\boldsymbol{h}_{ij} = (\lambda_i - i) + (\lambda'_j - j) + 1,$$

where λ'_j is the number of nodes in the jth column of $[\lambda]$.

(iii) If we replace the (i, j)-node of $[\lambda]$ by the number $\boldsymbol{h}_{ij}$ we obtain the *hook graph*

$$\boldsymbol{H}\,[\lambda] = (\boldsymbol{h}_{ij}).$$

We shall denote the product of all the $\boldsymbol{h}_{ij}$'s in $\boldsymbol{H}[\lambda]$ by $\boldsymbol{H}^\lambda$.

We have the following two corollaries of 2.33:

2.36
$$f^\lambda = n!\,\frac{\prod\limits_{i<k} (\boldsymbol{h}_{i1} - \boldsymbol{h}_{k1})}{\prod\limits_{i} \boldsymbol{h}_{i1}!}.$$

Proof. If we factor out the elements in the last column of the determinantal expression for f^λ in 2.33, we have the required denominator. The remaining determinant is easily recognized as the alternating function of the $\boldsymbol{h}_{i1}$'s.

Secondly, we have the striking result 2.37 involving the product $\boldsymbol{H}^\lambda$ of the hook lengths, which is of fundamental importance, particularly in our development of the modular theory in Chapters V-VIII:

2.37
$$f^\lambda = n!\;/\;\boldsymbol{H}^\lambda = f^{\lambda'}.$$

Proof. To derive 2.37 it is only necessary to observe that the factors $(\boldsymbol{h}_{i1} - \boldsymbol{h}_{j1})$ in the numerator of 2.36 do *not* represent the lengths of hooks in $[\lambda]$, while every factor in the denominator, other than these, *is* the length of a specified hook. Cancellation yields the desired result.

Since a standard tableau is also standard when its rows and columns are interchanged and a hook remains a hook, we conclude that $\boldsymbol{H}^\lambda = \boldsymbol{H}^{\lambda'}$, so that

$$f^\lambda = f^{\lambda'}.$$

It is worth remarking that 2.22 is a special case of 2.37.

One may well ask why the notion of a hook is significant in calculating f^λ. We start with the permutation representation

$$[\lambda_1]\cdot[\lambda_2]\cdot[\lambda_3]\cdot\,\ldots\,\cdot[\lambda_h]$$

whose standard skew tableaux are row-ordered. The superposition of two rows $[\lambda_1]$ and $[\lambda_2]$ to yield $[\lambda_1, \lambda_2]$ changes the hook structure by (i) introducing a *gap* corresponding to a hook of length $(\lambda_1 - \lambda_2 + 1)$ which has been obliterated, and (ii) adding 1 to the leg length of λ_2 other hooks. Analytically, these changes are described by means of the operator $1 - R_{12}$ and effected by means of the determinantal equation 2.33.

This combination of obliterating hooks and adding to the leg length of others arises with the superposition of succeeding rows to yield $[\lambda]$. In 2.36 the obliterations correspond to the cancellations to yield 2.37 and these occur at each step down in the rim of $[\lambda]$. In fact, it follows readily from 2.35 that:

2.38 *The leg length of the (i, j) hook in $[\lambda]$ is the number of missing integers less than $\mathbf{h}_{ij}$ and to the right of it in the hook graph $\mathbf{H}[\lambda]$.*

2.4 Lattice permutations. Instead of describing the reduction of the permutation representation $[\lambda_1] \cdot [\lambda_2] \dots [\lambda_h]$ of $\mathfrak{S}_n$ in terms of the operator R_{ij} we may be even more explicit and give a means of associating each of the f_λ standard skew tableaux t_λ of $[\lambda_1] \cdot [\lambda_2] \dots [\lambda_h]$ with a standard *right* tableau of an irreducible component. The first step in this association is to superimpose the rows of $[\lambda_1] \cdot [\lambda_2] \dots [\lambda_h]$ to obtain f_λ tableaux t^λ of $[\lambda]$, of which only f^λ are standard.

If we denote each symbol appearing in the ith row of t^λ by a_i as in 2.291, then any arrangement of $1, 2, \dots, n$ in t^λ will define a unique permutation π of the a_i, and this same permutation will be defined by the $\lambda_1! \, \lambda_2! \dots \lambda_h!$ tableaux obtained by rearranging the symbols in the rows of t^λ. If t^λ is standard then amongst the first r terms of π the number of a_i's is not less than the number of a_{i+1}'s for all i and all r; such a permutation π is said to be *lattice*. Conversely, each lattice permutation π defines a unique standard tableau t^λ.

Example. The lattice permutation corresponding to the standard tableau

$$\begin{array}{ll} 135 \text{ ——— } & a_1 \\ 24 \text{ ——— } & a_2 \end{array}$$

is $a_1 a_2 a_1 a_2 a_1$, and the equivalence of the lattice property with standardness is clear.

Let us now add a second suffix to each a_i according to the order of its appearance in a given permutation π. Considering first only the a_1's and the a_2's, if a_{2s} follows a_{1t} and precedes $a_{1,\,t+1}$ we define its *index*

$$i_{12s} = s - t,$$

which may be positive, zero or negative. A permutation of $a_1^{\lambda_1} \, a_2^{\lambda_2}$ is lattice, according to our definition, if and only if no $i_{12s}>0$. Similarly we may define indices i_{23s}, i_{34s} etc., and

2.41 *Any permutation of the symbols*

$$a_1^{\lambda_1}\, a_2^{\lambda_2} \ldots a_h^{\lambda_h}$$

is lattice if and only if no $i_{x,\,x+1,\,s}>0$ $(x=1, 2, \ldots, k-1)$.

We are now ready to show how to associate a given non-lattice permutation π arising from a standard skew tableau t^λ of $[\lambda_1]\cdot[\lambda_2]\ldots[\lambda_h]$ with a lattice permutation or standard tableau t^μ belonging to an irreducible component $[\mu]$. The steps in the process are as follows:

2.421 Consider only the a_1's and the a_2's in π. Take the first a_2 with the greatest position index i_{12s} and change it into an a_1. Reallocating the second suffixes, repeat the process until the a_1's and a_2's are lattice; π has become π'.

2.422 Considering only the a_2's and a_3's in π'. Take the first a_3 with the greatest positive index i_{23s} and change it into a_2. If this change upsets the 1-2 lattice property, correct for it by changing an a_2 into an a_1 according to 2.421; *this may or may not be the new* a_2. Reallocating the second suffixes, repeat this process until all the a_1's, a_2's, a_3's are lattice and π' has become π''.

2.423 Making use of the indices i_{34s}, i_{45s}, ... proceed as above, continuing until the resulting permutation $\bar{\pi}$ is lattice as regards all its terms and defines a standard tableau $[\mu]$ higher than $[\lambda]$ in dictionary order.

Let us consider these changes in terms of the raising operator R_{ij}.

2.424 Changing an a_2 into an a_1 is described by means of the operator R_{12}.

2.425 If changing an a_3 into an a_2 does *not* spoil the 1-2 lattice property it is described by means of the operator R_{23}. If changing an a_3 into an a_2 *does* spoil the 1-2 lattice property, forcing us to change an a_2 into an a_1, then it is described by means of the operator R_{13}.

2.426 Similarly, changing an a_4 is described by means of R_{34}, R_{24}, or R_{14} as further changes are necessary, etc. Thus:

2.43 *With each non-lattice permutation of the symbols* 2.41 *is associated by* 2.421-2.423 *a lattice permutation belonging to one of the irreducible components* $[\mu]$ *on the right of* 2.25, *along with the appropriate operator according to* 2.424-2.426. *Moreover, all* f^μ *lattice permutations associated with* $[\mu]$ *arise in this way and the necessary changes are described by the same operator.*

The last statement follows from the fact that all possible f_λ permutations of the symbols 2.41 are available.

2.44 *Example.* In order to illustrate these ideas we carry out the reduction of [2] · [1] · [1] in detail, obtaining

$$[2]\cdot[1]\cdot[1] = [2, 1^2]+[2^2]+2[3, 1]+[4],$$

with the associated operators:

$$(1-R_{12})^{-1}(1-R_{13})^{-1}(1-R_{23})^{-1}\equiv 1+R_{23}+(R_{13}+R_{12}R_{23})+R_{12}R_{13}.$$

Superposing the rows of the 12 standard skew tableaux $t_{2,\,1,\,1}$ we obtain the lattice permutations and the associated operators as follows:

$$\begin{array}{ccc} 12 & 13 & 14 \\ 3 & 2 & 2 \\ 4 & 4 & 3 \end{array} \xrightarrow[1]{} a_1a_1a_2a_3,\ a_1a_2a_1a_3,\ a_1a_2a_3a_1 \quad : \quad [2, 1^2]$$

$$\begin{array}{cc} 12 & 13 \\ 4 & 4 \\ 3 & 2 \end{array} \xrightarrow[R_{23}]{} a_1a_1a_2a_2,\ a_1a_2a_1a_2 \quad : \quad [2^2]$$

$$\begin{array}{ccc} 23 & 24 & 14 \\ 4 & 3 & 3 \\ 1 & 1 & 2 \end{array} \xrightarrow[R_{13}]{} a_1a_1a_1a_2,\ a_1a_1a_2a_1,\ a_1a_2a_1a_1 \quad : \quad [3, 1]$$

$$\begin{array}{ccc} 23 & 24 & 34 \\ 1 & 1 & 1 \\ 4 & 3 & 2 \end{array} \xrightarrow[R_{12}\,R_{23}]{} a_1a_1a_1a_2,\ a_1a_1a_2a_1,\ a_1a_2a_1a_1 \quad : \quad [3, 1]$$

$$\begin{array}{c} 34 \\ 2 \\ 1 \end{array} \xrightarrow[R_{12}\,R_{13}]{} a_1a_1a_1a_1 \quad : \quad [4]$$

One thing which stands out in connection with our proof of 2.33 and its corollaries is the lack of reference to the original standardness condition. In Young's proof the condition is used as the basis of an unpleasant induction.

Consider the f_λ standard skew tableaux of the permutation representation $[\lambda_1]\cdot[\lambda_2]\cdot\ldots[\lambda_h]$. We have seen how each of these which is non-lattice may be associated uniquely with a standard tableau of an irreducible component. When we state 2.26 we are essentially setting up a sequence of such correspondences which lead to sets of irreducible components, all of which cancel out except for $[\lambda]$. The usual argument of combinatorial logic is in fact applicable and precisely expresses the successive introduction and cancellation of irreducible components.

2.5 Skew diagrams. So far we have considered *right* Young diagrams, or *skew* diagrams having right diagrams as disjoint constituents, but it is not difficult to see that all these are special cases of a still more general type of skew diagram.

Consider a diagram $[\alpha]$ and a diagram $[\beta]$ which we shall suppose is superimposed upon $[\alpha]$, upper left hand corner upon upper left hand corner, and such that $[\beta]$ is contained entirely within $[\alpha]$. The residuum of $[\alpha]$ *not* covered by $[\beta]$ will be called a *skew diagram* and denoted $[\alpha]-[\beta]$. In particular that part of the rim of $[\alpha]$ beginning with the last node of any row and ending with the last node of an earlier column will be called a *skew hook*. Clearly, the description of $[\alpha]-[\beta]$ in terms of $[\alpha]$ and $[\beta]$ is by no means unique. Moreover, it may consist of one or more disjoint constituents which may themselves be skew diagrams.

Let us now introduce the operator B^{-1} which will *annihilate* those nodes of $[\alpha]$ belonging to $[\beta]$, setting

2.51 $$[\alpha]-[\beta] = B^{-1}[\alpha] = B^{-1}\,|\,[\alpha_i-i+j]\,|^{\cdot},$$

by 2.34, where

$$B^{-1} = (R_{01})^{\beta_1}(R_{02})^{\beta_2}(R_{03})^{\beta_3}\ldots.$$

As in the proof of 2.33, the operator $(R_{01})^{\beta_1}$ corresponds to *subtracting* β_1 nodes from each term in the first column of $|\,[\alpha_i-i+j]\,|^{\cdot}$, $(R_{02})^{\beta_2}$ to *subtracting* β_2 nodes from each term in the second column, and so on. The result of making these changes can be expressed again as a determinant and we have

2.52 $$[\alpha]-[\beta] = |\,[\alpha_i-i-\beta_j+j]\,|^{\cdot},$$

so that the degree of $[\alpha]-[\beta]$ is given by

2.521 $$f^{\alpha-\beta} = n!\left|\frac{1}{(\alpha_i-i-\beta_j+j)!}\right|,$$

with the same conventions as in 2.33.

But we can go one step farther by inverting 2.51 and using 2.52 to obtain the identity

2.53 $$[\alpha] = B\,|\,[\alpha_i-i-\beta_j+j]\,|^{\cdot},$$

in which we may suppose that the operator affects *only* the factors arising from the first column. We obtain a significant result if we choose $[\beta]$ to be the (1, 1)-hook consisting of the first row and the first column of $[\alpha]$.

As we have already seen, the irreducible representations of $\mathfrak{S}_n$ are in 1-1 correspondence with the Young diagrams $[\alpha]$. But such a diagram could equally well be defined by its *diagonal hooks*, setting, as in 2.35,

$$h_{ii} = a_i+b_i+1 \qquad (i = 1, 2, \ldots, s),$$

where $a_1>a_2>\ldots>a_s\geqq 0$, $b_1>b_2>\ldots>b_s\geqq 0$ and a_i and b_i are the number of nodes to the right of and below the (i, i) position. Moreover,

$$a_1+a_2+\ldots+a_s+b_1+b_2+\ldots+b_s+s = n.$$

Frobenius used the symbol

2.54 $$\begin{pmatrix} a_1a_2\ldots a_s \\ b_1b_2\ldots b_s \end{pmatrix}$$

to define $[\alpha]$. We prove the following interesting

2.55 THEOREM. $[\alpha] = |\,[1+a_i, 1^{b_j}]\,|^{\cdot} \qquad (i, j = 1, 2, \ldots, s).$

Proof. Let us choose $[\beta] = [1+a_1, 1^{b_1}]$ as suggested above, so that

$$[\alpha] = B\,|\,[\alpha_i-i-\beta_j+j]\,|^{\cdot} = |\,[\alpha_i-i-\beta_j+j]\,|^{\cdot} + [1+a_1, 1^{b_1}]$$

defining *addition*, which like subtraction, may not always be allowable. Since i refers to the row and j to the column, and since

$$(\alpha_i-i-\alpha_1+1)+\alpha_1 = 1+a_i,$$

we can write

$$[\alpha] = \left|\begin{matrix} [1+a_1, 1^{b_1}]\ldots[\alpha_1-1+(j-1)]\ldots \\ [1+a_2, 1^{b_1}]\ldots\ [\alpha_2-2+(j-1)]\ldots \\ \ldots \qquad\qquad \ldots \\ [1+a_s, 1^{b_1}]\ldots \\ 0 \quad\ldots[\alpha_h-h+(j-1)]\ldots \end{matrix}\right|^{\cdot}$$

where the number of zero elements in the first column is h-s. Moreover, the minors of the non-zero elements are determinantal expansions of certain $[\alpha']$'s containing at most h-1 rows, according to 2.33. Repeating the process, we take $[\beta]$ to be the second diagonal hook

$$[1+a_2, 1^{b_2}]$$

which can be removed and added again to the first column of each of the $[\alpha']$'s. After s repetitions we have the required determinant

$$\left| [1+a_i, 1^{b_r}] \right|^{\cdot} \qquad i, j = 1, 2, \ldots, s,$$

appearing in the upper left corner with 0's to the right and 1's in the rest of the diagonal, which proves 2.55.

It should be remarked that while two dual forms of the determinant appear in 2.34, 2.55 is self-dual. Moreover it is in general of smaller dimension ($s \leqq h$). On the other hand, it is of less fundamental significance in view of 2.29. We shall see how to reduce the products which arise in the expansion of 2.55 in § 3.3 of the following chapter.

2.56 *Example.* The skew diagram $[3^2, 1]-[2, 1]$ is equally well defined as $[4^2, 2, 1]-[3, 2^2]$ and we write out its eight standard tableaux and their associated lattice permutations.

$$\begin{array}{ccc} & & 2\\ & 1 & 3\\ 4 & & \end{array} \quad \begin{array}{ccc} & & 1\\ & 2 & 3\\ 4 & & \end{array} \quad \begin{array}{ccc} & & 1\\ & 2 & 4\\ 3 & & \end{array} \longrightarrow a_1a_1a_2a_3,\ a_1a_2a_1a_3,\ a_1a_2a_3a_1 \quad : \quad [2, 1^2]$$

$$\begin{array}{ccc} & & 2\\ & 1 & 4\\ 3 & & \end{array} \quad \begin{array}{ccc} & & 3\\ & 1 & 4\\ 2 & & \end{array} \qquad \longrightarrow a_1a_1a_2a_2,\ a_1a_2a_1a_2 \quad : \quad [2^2]$$

$$\begin{array}{ccc} & & 3\\ & 2 & 4\\ 1 & & \end{array} \quad \begin{array}{ccc} & & 2\\ & 3 & 4\\ 1 & & \end{array} \quad \begin{array}{ccc} & & 1\\ & 3 & 4\\ 2 & & \end{array} \longrightarrow a_1a_1a_1a_2,\ a_1a_1a_2a_1,\ a_1a_2a_1a_1 \quad : \quad [3, 1]$$

so that

2.561 $$[3^2, 1]-[2, 1] = [2, 1^2]+[2^2]+[3, 1].$$

By 2.52 we also have

2.562 $$[3^2, 1]-[2, 1] = \begin{vmatrix} [1] & [3] & [5]\\ 1 & [2] & [4]\\ 0 & 0 & [1] \end{vmatrix}^{\cdot}$$

$$= [2]\cdot[1]\cdot[1]-[3]\cdot[1]$$

which is readily seen to coincide with 2.561 by using Example 2.44 and the reduction [3] . [1] = [3, 1] + [4]. But we can also write

$$[3^2, 1] = \begin{vmatrix} [0] & [3] & [4] \\ [-1] & [2] & [3] \\ [-4] & [-1] & [0] \end{vmatrix}^{\cdot} + [3, 1^2]$$

$$= \begin{vmatrix} [3, 1^2] & [3] & [4] \\ [2, 1^2] & [2] & [3] \\ 0 & 0 & 1 \end{vmatrix}^{\cdot} = \begin{vmatrix} [3, 1^2] & [3] \\ [2, 1^2] & [2] \end{vmatrix}^{\cdot},$$

where the Frobenius symbol of $[3^2, 1]$ is

$$\begin{pmatrix} 2 & 1 \\ 2 & 0 \end{pmatrix}.$$

CHAPTER THREE

$\mathfrak{S}_n$ AND THE FULL LINEAR GROUP *GL*(*d*)

Introduction. Much of the subject-matter of this chapter goes back to Schur who was the first to recognize the fundamental duality between the representations of $\mathfrak{S}_n$ and $GL(d)$. This theory was beautifully developed by Weyl in his *Classical Groups*; treatments of it may also be found in Littlewood's *Theory of Group Characters* and in Murnaghan's *Theory of Group Representations.* It is not our purpose here (§ 3.2) to give a complete account of the subject, but to draw attention to the implications of these developments of Young's ideas. The duality between $\mathfrak{S}_n$ and $GL(d)$ underlies the whole theory of projective invariants as Young realized, but his approach to the subject was inhibited by his restricting his attentions to $\mathfrak{S}_n$.

We begin by extending the notions of *inducing* and *restricting* as they are pertinent in this and subsequent chapters. Taking $\mathscr{G}=\mathfrak{S}_{m+n}$ in Frobenius' Reciprocity Theorem (11.54), *we shall usually assume that* $\mathscr{H}=\mathfrak{S}_m\times\mathfrak{S}_n$. The reason for this is, of course, that we know (11.58) the representation theory of $\mathscr{H}$ from that of $\mathfrak{S}_n$. If $[\mu]$ is an irreducible representation of $\mathfrak{S}_m$ and $[\nu]$ of $\mathfrak{S}_n$, we have called (11.59) the representation of $\mathfrak{S}_{m+n}$ induced by the irreducible representation $[\mu]\times[\nu]$ of $\mathscr{H}$ an *outer product* $[\mu]\cdot[\nu]$, and we derive its reduction in 3.31. The whole of Schur's theory is based on the *inner product* (11.55 and 3.21) and we give a method for obtaining the reduction of $[\mu]\times[\nu]$ in § 3.4. Though more complicated than the outer product, the reduction can be carried through systematically in any given case.

In obtaining the irreducible representations of $GL(d)$ it is possible to confine attention to symmetric or skew-symmetric tensors only. This amounts to using the fundamental formulae 2.26 or 2.28 as in 3.271. Schur's original procedure is now applicable to representations of $\mathfrak{S}_n$ and we consider the *symmetrized* outer and inner products $[\mu]\odot[\nu]$ and $[\mu]\otimes[\nu]$ in § 3.5 and § 3.6. The reductions in these cases are much more difficult and only partial answers are available.

As in § 11.5, we reserve the term *Kronecker product* to apply to the multiplication of individual matrices, *not* representations. E.g., if the set of matrices (M) constitutes an irreducible representation $[\mu]$ of $\mathfrak{S}_m$ and (N) the representations $[\nu]$ of $\mathfrak{S}_n$, then the set of Kronecker product matrices $(M\times N)$ constitutes the *direct product* representation $[\mu]\times[\nu]$ of the direct product $\mathfrak{S}_m\times\mathfrak{S}_n$.

§	*Nomenclature*	*Symmetric Group*	$GL(d)$
3.2		$[1]\cdot[1]\cdot\ldots\cdot[1] = \Sigma f^{\nu}[\nu]$ of $\mathfrak{S}_n$	$A\times A\times\ldots\times A = \Sigma f^{\nu}\langle\nu\rangle$ of rank n
3.3	Outer product	$[\mu]\cdot[\nu]$ of $\mathfrak{S}_{m+n}$ with character $= \frac{(m+n)!}{m!\,n!}\chi^{\mu}\chi^{\nu}$	$\langle\mu\rangle\times\langle\nu\rangle$ of rank $m+n$ character $= \{\mu\}\{\nu\}$
3.4	Inner product	$[\mu]\times[\nu]$ of $\mathfrak{S}_m$ with character $= \chi^{\mu}\chi^{\nu}$	$\langle\mu\rangle\cdot\langle\nu\rangle$ of rank m character $= \{\mu\}\cdot\{\nu\}$
3.5	Symmetrized outer product	$[\mu]\odot[\nu]$ of $\mathfrak{S}_{mn}$ $[\mu]\cdot[\mu]\cdot\ldots\cdot[\mu] = \Sigma f^{\nu}[\mu]\odot[\nu]$	$\langle\mu\rangle\otimes\langle\nu\rangle$ of rank mn $\langle\mu\rangle\times\langle\mu\rangle\times\ldots\times\langle\mu\rangle = \Sigma f^{\nu}\langle\mu\rangle\otimes\langle\nu\rangle$
3.6	Symmetrized inner product	$[\mu]\otimes[\nu]$ of $\mathfrak{S}_m$ $[\mu]\times[\mu]\times\ldots\times[\mu] = \Sigma f^{\nu}[\mu]\otimes[\nu]$	$\langle\mu\rangle\odot\langle\nu\rangle$ of rank m $\langle\mu\rangle\cdot\langle\mu\rangle\cdot\ldots\cdot\langle\mu\rangle = \Sigma f^{\nu}\langle\mu\rangle\odot\langle\nu\rangle$

In seeking for a notation which would bring out the underlying duality between $\mathfrak{S}_n$ and $GL(d)$ we have tried to conform as much as possible with that in current use. The table overleaf will serve as a means of easy reference and will help coordinate the somewhat complicated details of a beautiful section of modern mathematics.

3.1 Inducing and restricting. In the preceding chapter we introduced the notation

3.11 $$[\lambda_1]\cdot[\lambda_2]\cdot\ \ldots\ \cdot[\lambda_h]$$

to denote both the disjoint diagram made up of the rows of $[\lambda]$, and also the permutation representation of $\mathfrak{S}_n$ *induced* by the identity representation $[\lambda_1]\times[\lambda_2]\times\ \ldots\ \times[\lambda_h]$ of the subgroup $\mathfrak{S}_{\lambda_1}\times\mathfrak{S}_{\lambda_2}\times\ \ldots \times\mathfrak{S}_{\lambda_h}$. The degree of 3.11 was seen to be equal to the number

3.111 $$\frac{n!}{\lambda_1!\,\lambda_2!\ldots\lambda_h!}$$

of standard skew tableaux, and we obtained its reduction in 2.25.

In order to extend these ideas we prove the following generalization of Young's Fundamental Theorem 2.17.

3.12 *The outer product*

$$[\mu]\cdot[\nu] = [\nu]\cdot[\mu],$$

where $[\mu]$ *is any irreducible representation of* $\mathfrak{S}_m$ *and* $[\nu]$ *is any irreducible representation of* $\mathfrak{S}_n$, *denotes that representation of* $\mathfrak{S}_{m+n}$ *induced by the irreducible representation* $[\mu]\times[\nu]$ *of* $\mathfrak{S}_m\times\mathfrak{S}_n$; *the actual matrices of the representation are obtainable by applying* 2.17 *to the standard tableaux of* $[\mu]\,.\,[\nu]$, *setting* $\rho=0$ *if* $r, r+1$ *belong to disjoint constituents.*

Proof. First, let us divide the $m+n$ symbols into two sets of m and n symbols each in

$$\frac{(m+n)!}{m!\,n!}$$

different ways. If $m=n$ we must distinguish between the two sets. From each such set of $m(n)$ symbols we form $f^\mu(f^\nu)$ standard tableau so that the number of standard *skew* tableaux is

3.121 $$f^{\mu\cdot\nu} = \frac{(m+n)!}{m!\,n!}f^\mu f^\nu.$$

If we now construct the matrices of the representation according to 2.17 we encounter no difficulty so long as $r, r+1$ belong to the same constituent $[\mu]$ or $[\nu]$. If $r, r+1$ belong to different constituents, we could choose (α) and (β) in an infinite number of ways so that

$$[\alpha]-[\beta] = [\mu]\cdot[\nu]$$

and the axial distance $\frac{1}{\rho}$ calculated with reference to $[\alpha]$ could be arbitrarily large. Thus it is natural to set $\rho=0$ in 2.17 (iii) in this case. Since the resulting matrices are just those which could have been constructed according to § 11.5 we have obtained the representation of $\mathfrak{S}_{m+n}$ *induced* by the irreducible representation $[\mu]\times[\nu]$ of the direct product $\mathfrak{S}_m\times\mathfrak{S}_n$. We shall call this representation $[\mu].[\nu]$ an *outer product* as in 11.59 and determine its irreducible components in § 3.33.

We can also extend the formula 2.37 to apply to outer products, since we may write

$$f^{\mu.\nu}=\frac{(m+n)!}{m!\,n!}f^{\mu}f^{\nu}$$

$$=\frac{(m+n)!}{m!\,n!}\cdot\frac{m!}{H^{\mu}}\cdot\frac{n!}{H^{\nu}},$$

so that

3.13 $$f^{\mu.\nu}=\frac{(m+n)!}{H^{\mu.\nu}}$$

if we set $H^{\mu.\nu}=H^{\mu}.H^{\nu}$. This result will be significant in Chapter V.

The process of *restricting* an irreducible representation $[\lambda]$ of $\mathfrak{S}_n$ to a representation of a subgroup of the form

3.14 $$\mathfrak{S}_{n_1}\times\mathfrak{S}_{n_2}\times\ldots\times\mathfrak{S}_{n_s}$$

where $n_1+n_2+\ldots+n_s=n$, is of equal importance. In § 2.5 we defined the skew representation $[\alpha]-[\beta]$, which we shall denote here by $[\alpha-\beta]$ since no ambiguity will arise. Consider now a sequence of Young diagrams

3.15 $$[\lambda]\supset[\lambda']\supset[\lambda'']\ldots\supset[\lambda^{s-1}]$$

containing $n, n', \ldots, n^{s-1}$ nodes, respectively, which we may represent symbolically as in the accompanying Figure.

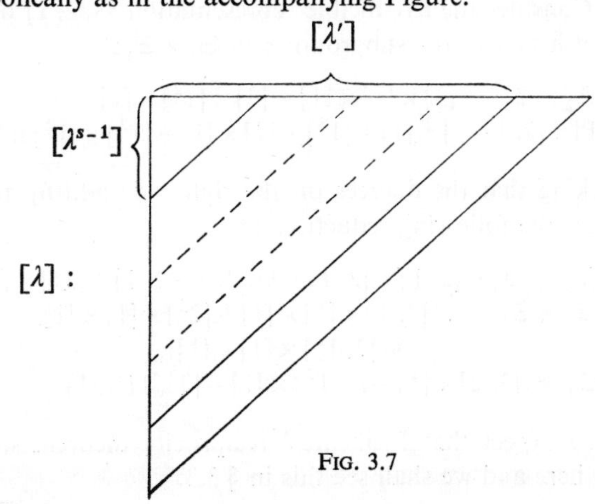

FIG. 3.7

If we set $n-n'=n_s$, $n'-n''=n_{s-1}$, ... $n^{s-1}=n_1$, then the skew diagrams

3.16 $$[\lambda^{s-1}], [\lambda^{s-2}-\lambda^{s-1}], \ldots [\lambda'-\lambda''], [\lambda-\lambda']$$

yield representations of $\mathfrak{S}_{n_1}, \mathfrak{S}_{n_2}, \ldots \mathfrak{S}_{ns}$, which are, except for the first, in general reducible. The standardness of a tableau $[\lambda]$ along with 3.15 implies that the first n_1 symbols 1, 2, ... n_1 are associated with $\mathfrak{S}_{n_1}$, the next n_2 with $\mathfrak{S}_{n_2}$ and so on. Conversely, such an association of the symbols taken in conjunction with the standardness of each skew tableau 3.16 implies the standardness of $[\lambda]$. Thus, if we construct the transpositions according to 2.17 which yield the matrices of the subgroups 3.14 we see that we actually have a direct *product*

3.17 $$[\lambda^{s-1}]\times \ldots \times[\lambda-\lambda'],$$

and allowing all possible choices for the sequence of s diagrams 3.15, we have the following

3.18 THEOREM. *If the irreducible representation* $[\lambda]$ *of* $\mathfrak{S}_n$ *be restricted to the subgroup* 3.14 *the resulting representation is a sum of direct products*:

$$\sum[\lambda^{s-1}]\times \ldots \times[\lambda-\lambda'],$$

each term of which is in general reducible, and the summation is taken over all possible sequences of s diagrams 3.16.

In applying the inducing and restricting processes it is convenient to use the symbolism introduced in § 11.5. Since these ideas are of such importance in all that follows we give the following example of their use.

3.19 *Example.* Consider the irreducible representation [3, 2, 1] of $\mathfrak{S}_6$ and let us restrict it first to the subgroup $\mathfrak{S}_3\times\mathfrak{S}_2\times\mathfrak{S}_1$:

$$\begin{aligned}[3,2,1]\downarrow\mathfrak{S}_3\times\mathfrak{S}_2\times\mathfrak{S}_1 = {} & [3]\times[2]\times[1]+[3]\times[1^2]\times[1] \\ & +3[2,1]\times[2,1-1]\times[1]+[1^3]\times[2]\times[1]+[1^3]\times[1^2]\times[1].\end{aligned}$$

It is worth checking that the degrees on the right side add up to 16. Similarly, we have the following reductions:

$$\begin{aligned}[3,2,1]\downarrow\mathfrak{S}_3\times\mathfrak{S}_3 &= [3]\times[2,1]+[2,1]\times[3,2,1-2,1]+[1^3]\times[2,1],\\ [3,2,1]\downarrow\mathfrak{S}_4\times\mathfrak{S}_1\times\mathfrak{S}_1 &= 2\{[3,1]\times[1]\times[1]+[2^2]\times[1]\times[1] \\ &\qquad +[2,1^2]\times[1]\times[1]\},\\ [3,2,1]\downarrow\mathfrak{S}_5\times\mathfrak{S}_1 &= [3,2]\times[1]+[3,1^2]\times[1]+[2^2,1]\times[1].\end{aligned}$$

It is natural to expect that Frobenius' reciprocity theorem should find application here and we shall see this in § 3.3.

3.2 The irreducible representation of $GL(d)$. Consider a non-singular $d \times d$ matrix A with elements from a field F which we shall take to be the field of complex numbers. The totality of all such matrices form a continuous group $GL(d)$. Weyl proves that every representation, irreducible over the given field, is a tensor representation of rank $n=1, 2, \ldots$ which appears as an irreducible component of the direct product.

$$\Pi_n(A) = A \times A \times \ldots \times A \qquad (n \text{ factors}).$$

In order to study the reduction in question we consider the commuting algebra of $\Pi_n(A)$ which has as basis the permutation matrices which interchange the n sets of variables $x_i, y_j, \ldots z_k$ associated with the n identical factors of $\Pi_n(A)$. Such matrices yield a representation ρ of $\mathfrak{S}_n$ and Schur's Lemma tells us that an irreducible representation $\langle\lambda\rangle$ of $GL(d)$ appears in $\Pi_n(A)$ with a *multiplicity* equal to the degree of the irreducible representation $[\lambda]$ of $\mathfrak{S}_n$. The *degree* of $\langle\lambda\rangle$ is equal to the multiplicity with which $[\lambda]$ appears in ρ (cf. § 3.2 in the Table in the Introduction to this Chapter).

3.21 *Example.* So that these ideas may be quite clear, let us consider the case $n=2$ in detail, in which the transformations of $\Pi_2(A)$ operate on the d^2 variables

3.211 $$x_1y_1, x_2y_2, \ldots x_dy_d;\ x_1y_2, x_2y_1, \ldots, x_{d-1}y_d, x_dy_{d-1}.$$

The matrix which interchanges the x_i and y_i will have the form

$$M = \begin{bmatrix} I_d & 0 & 0 & \ldots & \\ 0 & 0 & 1 & & \\ 0 & 1 & 0 & & \\ & & & \cdot & \\ & & & & \cdot \\ & & & & & \cdot \end{bmatrix},$$

where $\Pi_2(A)M = M\Pi_2(A)$. Since there exists (11.492) a transformation T such that

$$TMT^{-1} = \begin{pmatrix} I_{d+m} & 0 \\ 0 & -I_m \end{pmatrix}$$

where $m=\frac{1}{2}d(d-1)$, we may write

$$T\Pi_2(A)\,T^{-1}\,.\,TMT^{-1} = TMT^{-1}\,.\,T\Pi_2(A)\,T^{-1}$$

and conclude from 11.341 that $\Pi_2(A)$ splits into two irreducible representations $\langle 2\rangle$ and $\langle 1^2\rangle$ corresponding to the two representations $[2]$ and $[1^2]$ of $\mathfrak{S}_2$. The variables of $\langle 2\rangle$ are the components of the *symmetric tensor*

3.212 $$x_1y_1, x_2y_2, \ldots x_dy_d;\ \tfrac{1}{2}(x_1y_2+x_2y_1), \ldots \tfrac{1}{2}(x_{d-1}y_d+x_dy_{d-1}),$$

while those of $\langle 1^2 \rangle$ are the components of the *skew-symmetric tensor*

3.213 $$\tfrac{1}{2}(x_1y_2 - x_2y_1), \ldots \tfrac{1}{2}(x_{d-1}y_d - x_dy_{d-1}).$$

The dimension of $\langle 2 \rangle$ is clearly $d+m=\frac{1}{2}d(d+1)$ while that of $\langle 1^2 \rangle$ is $m=\frac{1}{2}d(d-1)$.

If we set $x_i=y_i$ in 3.212 we obtain the $\frac{1}{2}d(d+1)$ monomials

$$x_1^2, x_2^2, \ldots x_d^2; \quad x_1x_2, \ldots x_{d-1}x_d,$$

which undergo the linear transformations $(A)_2$ of $\langle 2 \rangle$. In general, equating $x_i=y_i= \ldots =z_i$ in the space of symmetric tensors of rank n we obtain the set of monomials

$$x_1^{n_1}\, x_2^{n_2} \ldots x_n^{n_n} \qquad \left(\textstyle\sum n_i = n\right)$$

which undergo the linear transformation $(A)_n$ of $\langle n \rangle$, which corresponds to the identity representation of $\mathfrak{S}_n$.

Now, we ask, what is the character of $\langle n \rangle$? If we take A in triangular form with characteristic roots $\alpha_1, \alpha_2, \ldots, \alpha_d$ down the diagonal, then it is easy to see that the sum of the diagonal elements of $(A)_n$ is

3.22 $$p_n = \Sigma\, \alpha_1^{n_1}\, \alpha_2^{n_2} \ldots \alpha_n^{n_n} \qquad \left(\textstyle\sum n_i = n\right)$$

where $\alpha_1^{n_1}\, \alpha_2^{n_2} \ldots \alpha_n^{n_n}$ represents *the complete symmetrized sum of all such terms taken over the characteristic roots of A*. We shall assume for convenience that $d>n$. In the contrary case those monomials involving more than d distinct α's will not appear.

If we take the direct product

3.23 $$\langle \lambda_1 \rangle \times \langle \lambda_2 \rangle \times \ldots \times \langle \lambda_h \rangle \qquad \lambda_1+\lambda_2+ \ldots +\lambda_h = n$$

of h such representations, the resulting representation of $GL(d)$ will have character

3.231 $$p_{\lambda_1}\, p_{\lambda_2} \ldots p_{\lambda_h} = \Sigma\, c_{\lambda\mu}\, \alpha_1^{\mu_1}\, \alpha_2^{\mu_2} \ldots$$

We shall call 3.23 an *inner product*, since the same element A of $GL(d)$ is involved in each factor. We determine the $c_{\lambda\mu}$ in the following theorem.

3.24 *The coefficient* $c_{\lambda\mu}$ *of* $\alpha_1^{\mu_1}\, \alpha_2^{\mu_2} \ldots$ *in the expansion of* $p_{\lambda_1}\, p_{\lambda_2} \ldots p_{\lambda_h}$ *is the multiplicity of the identity representation*

$$[\mu_1] \times [\mu_2] \times \ldots$$

of the subgroup $\mathfrak{S}_{\mu_1} \times \mathfrak{S}_{\mu_2} \times \ldots$ *in* $[\lambda_1] \cdot [\lambda_2] \cdot \ldots$ *when* $\mathfrak{S}_n$ *is restricted to* $\mathfrak{S}_{\mu_1} \times \mathfrak{S}_{\mu_2} \times \ldots$

Proof. Clearly $c_{\lambda\mu}$ is the number of ways of making up the product $\alpha_1^{\mu_1}\alpha_2^{\mu_2}\ldots$ by taking factors from the different p_{λ_i}. But this is just the number of ways of removing first μ_1 nodes then μ_2 nodes etc. from the skew diagram

3.241 $$[\lambda_1]\cdot[\lambda_2]\cdot\ldots[\lambda_h].$$

Each such set of μ_i nodes constitutes a skew diagram yielding a permutation representation of $\mathfrak{S}_{\mu_i}$, and every such representation contains the identity representation $[\mu_i]$ once and once only. Thus the coefficient $c_{\lambda\mu}$ is equal to the multiplicity of the identity representation $[\mu_1]\times[\mu_2]\times\ldots$ of $\mathfrak{S}_{\mu_1}\times\mathfrak{S}_{\mu_2}\times\ldots$ in 3.241 when $\mathfrak{S}_n$ is restricted to this subgroup.

In the previous chapter we considered the application of Young's raising operator R_{ik} to the skew diagram 3.241, but the same operator is applicable to 3.23 to yield

3.25 $$\langle\lambda\rangle = \Pi(1-R_{ik})\langle\lambda_1\rangle\times\langle\lambda_2\rangle\times\ldots$$
$$= |\langle\lambda_i-i+j\rangle|^{\times} = |\langle 1^{\lambda'_i-i+j}\rangle|^{\times}.$$

Multiplication $\cdot$ in 2.34 is to be replaced by $\times$. The character of $\langle\lambda\rangle$ is given by the *Schur function*

3.26 $$\{\lambda\} = \Pi(1-R_{ik})\,p_{\lambda_1}p_{\lambda_2}\ldots = \sum_{\mu}(\Pi(1-R_{ik})c_{\lambda\mu})\,\alpha_1^{\mu_1}\alpha_2^{\mu_2}\ldots$$
$$= |p_{\lambda_i-i+j}| = \sum_{\mu}\gamma_{\lambda\mu}\,\alpha_1^{\mu_1}\alpha_2^{\mu_2}\ldots,$$

where i refers to the row and j to the column in the determinants, and

$$\gamma_{\lambda\mu} = \Pi(1-R_{ik})c_{\lambda\mu}.$$

We have omitted any reference in this discussion to the characters q_e of the $\langle 1^e\rangle$ which could play a role exactly analagous to the p's, as indicated by the determinantal expression on the right of 3.25. The following result will clarify the significance of the integers $\gamma_{\lambda\mu}$.

3.27 *The coefficient $\gamma_{\lambda\mu}$ of $\alpha_1^{\mu_1}\alpha_2^{\mu_2}\ldots$ in $\{\lambda\}$ is the multiplicity of $[\lambda]$ in the permutation representation $[\mu_1]\cdot[\mu_2]\cdot\ldots$ of $\mathfrak{S}_n$.*

Proof. In the preceding theorem we saw that $c_{\lambda\mu}$ is the multiplicity of $[\mu_1]\times[\mu_2]\times\ldots$ in $[\lambda_1]\cdot[\lambda_2]\cdot\ldots$ when $\mathfrak{S}_n$ is restricted to $\mathfrak{S}_{\mu_1}\times\mathfrak{S}_{\mu_2}\times\ldots$. According to 2.26, $\gamma_{\lambda\mu}$ is the multiplicity of $[\mu_1]\times[\mu_2]\ldots$ in $[\lambda]$ when $\mathfrak{S}_n$ is restricted to $\mathfrak{S}_{\mu_1}\times\mathfrak{S}_{\mu_2}\times\ldots$. But by Frobenius' reciprocity theorem this multiplicity is equal to the multiplicity of $[\lambda]$ in the induced representation $[\mu_1]\cdot[\mu_2]\cdot\ldots$ of $\mathfrak{S}_n$, proving our statement.

We note that $\gamma_{\lambda\mu}=0$ if $[\mu]$ *precedes* $[\lambda]$ in dictionary order (§ 2.1), while $\gamma_{\lambda\lambda}=1$. Effectively, we have reduced the matrix $(c_{\lambda\mu})$ to triangular form $(\gamma_{\lambda\mu})$ by means of the operator $\Pi(1-R_{ik})$, obtaining thereby the explicit expression for $\{\lambda\}$ in terms of the characteristic roots of A.

The degree $\delta^{\lambda}(d)$ of $\langle\lambda\rangle$ is given by

3.281
$$\delta^{\lambda}(d) = \frac{\prod_{i<k} (l_i-l_k)}{(d-1)!\,(d-2)!\ldots 2!\,1!},$$

where we are assuming that $d>n$, $\lambda_{h+t}=0$ $(t=1, 2, \ldots, d-h)$ and

$$l_i = d+\lambda_i-i, \qquad i = 1, 2, \ldots, d.$$

As in the proof of 2.37 no factor in the numerator of 3.281 represents a hook length $\boldsymbol{h}_{ij}$ of $[\lambda]$. Thus if these missing factors are supplied in numerator and denominator we have

$$\delta^{\lambda}(d) = \prod_{i=1}^{d} (l_i!\,/\,(d-i)!)\,/\,\boldsymbol{H}^{\lambda}$$
$$= \prod_{i,\,j} (d+j-i)\,/\,\boldsymbol{H}^{\lambda}.$$

Setting $x=d$ in 2.16 and

$$\boldsymbol{G}^{\lambda}(d) = \prod_{i,\,j} (d+j-i),$$

we have the compact formula

3.282
$$\delta^{\lambda}(d) = \boldsymbol{G}^{\lambda}(d)\,/\,\boldsymbol{H}^{\lambda},$$

with one factor in the numerator and denominator associated with each node of $[\lambda]$. In particular we have

$$\delta^{2}(d) = \tfrac{1}{2}d(d+1), \quad \delta^{1^2}(d) = \tfrac{1}{2}d(d-1),$$

for the symmetric and skew symmetric tensors of rank 2.

We conclude this brief account by illustrating the foregoing theory in the following

3.29 *Example.* Let $n=4<d$, so that we have (using a single term to denote a complete symmetrized sum):

$$
\begin{aligned}
p_4 &= \alpha_1^4+\alpha_1^3\,\alpha_2+\alpha_1^2\,\alpha_2^2+\alpha_1^2\,\alpha_2\,\alpha_3+\alpha_1\,\alpha_2\,\alpha_3\,\alpha_4,\\
p_3p_1 &= \alpha_1^4+2\alpha_1^3\,\alpha_2+2\alpha_1^2\,\alpha_2^2+3\alpha_1^2\,\alpha_2\,\alpha_3+4\alpha_1\,\alpha_2\,\alpha_3\,\alpha_4,\\
p_2^2 &= \alpha_1^4+2\alpha_1^3\,\alpha_2+3\alpha_1^2\,\alpha_2^2+4\alpha_1^2\,\alpha_2\,\alpha_3+6\alpha_1\,\alpha_2\,\alpha_3\,\alpha_4,\\
p_2p_1^2 &= \alpha_1^4+3\alpha_1^3\,\alpha_2+4\alpha_1^2\,\alpha_2^2+7\alpha_1^2\,\alpha_2\,\alpha_3+12\alpha_1\,\alpha_2\,\alpha_3\,\alpha_4,\\
p_1^4 &= \alpha_1^4+4\alpha_1^3\,\alpha_2+6\alpha_1^3\,\alpha_2^3+12\alpha_1^3\,\alpha_2\,\alpha_3+24\alpha_1\,\alpha_2\,\alpha_3\,\alpha_4.
\end{aligned}
$$

Operating, we obtain:

$$\begin{aligned}
\{4\} &= p_4 &&= \alpha_1^4+\alpha_1^3\alpha_2+\alpha_1^2\alpha_2^2+\alpha_1^2\alpha_2\alpha_3+\alpha_1\alpha_2\alpha_3\alpha_4\\
\{3, 1\} &= p_3p_1-p_4 &&= \alpha_1^3\alpha_2+\alpha_1^2\alpha_2^2+2\alpha_1^2\alpha_2\alpha_3+3\alpha_1\alpha_2\alpha_3\alpha_4\\
\{2^2\} &= p_2^2-p_3p_1 &&= \alpha_1^2\alpha_2^2+\alpha_1^2\alpha_2\alpha_3+2\alpha_1\alpha_2\alpha_3\alpha_4\\
\{2, 1^2\} &= p_2p_1^2-p_2^2-p_3p_1+p_4 &&= \alpha_1^2\alpha_2\alpha_3+3\alpha_1\alpha_2\alpha_3\alpha_4\\
\{1^4\} &= p_1^4-3p_2p_1^2+p_2^2+2p_3p_1-p_4 &&= \alpha_1\alpha_2\alpha_3\alpha_4
\end{aligned}$$

which are particular cases of the reduction 3.26. In order to illustrate 3.25 we write

$$\langle 2, 1^2\rangle = \begin{vmatrix} \langle 2\rangle & \langle 3\rangle & \langle 4\rangle \\ 1 & \langle 1\rangle & \langle 2\rangle \\ 0 & 1 & \langle 1\rangle \end{vmatrix}^{\times} .$$

The diagonal term may be expanded as follows:

$$\langle 2\rangle\times\langle 1\rangle\times\langle 1\rangle = \langle 2, 1^2\rangle+\langle 2^2\rangle+2\langle 3, 1\rangle+\langle 4\rangle$$

with character

$$p_2p_1^2 = \{2, 1^2\}+\{2^2\}+2\{3, 1\}+\{4\},$$

as may be readily verified from the above tables.

3.3 The outer product $[\mu]\cdot[\nu]$. We now utilize the duality which we have seen to hold between $\mathfrak{S}_n$ and $GL(d)$ to obtain a clue to the reduction of the *outer product* $[\mu]\cdot[\nu]$ defined in § 3.1. To this end we write:

$$\begin{aligned}
\{2\}\,\{1^2\} &= (\alpha_1^2+\alpha_1\alpha_2)(\alpha_1\alpha_2)\\
&= \alpha_1^3\alpha_2+\alpha_1^2\alpha_2^2+3\alpha_1^2\alpha_2\alpha_3+6\alpha_1\alpha_2\alpha_3\alpha_4\\
&= \{3, 1\}+\{2, 1^2\}.
\end{aligned}$$

One or two further examples of this kind would make the following theorem plausible and its method of proof natural.

3.31 Reduction Theorem for Outer Products. *Each diagram constructed according to* 3.311, 3.312 *below defines an irreducible component of* $[\mu]\cdot[\nu]$ *and all such components are obtainable in this way.*

3.311 *To the tableau* $[\mu]$ *add the symbols of the first row of* $[\nu]$. *These may be added to one row or divided into any number of sets, preserving their order, the first set being added to one row of* $[\mu]$, *the second to a subsequent row, the third to a row subsequent to this and so on. After the additions no row of the compound tableau may contain more symbols than a preceding row, and no two added symbols may appear in the same column.*

Next add the second row of $[\nu]$, *according to the same rules, followed by the remaining rows in succession until all the symbols of* $[\nu]$ *have been used.*

3.312 *These additions must be such that each symbol from* $[\nu]$ *shall appear in a later row of the compound tableau than that occupied by the symbol immediately above it in* $[\nu]$.

Proof. From the commutativity of $\cdot$ multiplication we conclude that the order of writing the factors on the left side of 2.25 is unimportant. However, any rearrangement will affect the operator on the right, but this can be taken care of by allowing $i>j$ and multiplying through by a constant factor R. With this observation in mind, the rows of the two Young diagrams $[\mu]$ and $[\nu]$ may be rearranged to form a new diagram $[\lambda]=R[\mu;\nu]$ where

$$[\lambda_1]\cdot[\lambda_2]\cdot\ldots[\lambda_h] = ([\mu_1]\cdot[\mu_2]\cdot\ldots[\mu_u])\cdot([\nu_1]\cdot[\nu_2]\cdot\ldots[\nu_v])$$

and $h=u+v$. If we apply 2.25 to each side of this equation we obtain:

3.32
$$\begin{aligned}\Pi(1-R_{ik})^{-1}[\lambda] &= \Pi(1-R_{ik})^{-1}R[\mu;\nu]\\ &= \Pi(1-M_{ik})^{-1}[\mu]\cdot\Pi(1-N_{ik})^{-1}[\nu]\\ &= [\mu]\cdot[\nu]+\Sigma[\bar{\mu}]\cdot[\bar{\nu}],\end{aligned}$$

where M_{ik} operates on $[\mu]$ and N_{ik} on $[\nu]$ and $[\bar{\mu}]\cdot[\bar{\nu}]$ precedes $[\mu]\cdot[\nu]$ in a double dictionary ordering.

In systematizing the application of the raising operator in § 2.2 we assumed that all the symbols in the ith row of $[\lambda]$ were replaced by a_i. Of course the effect of this was to emphasize the *diagram* and nullify the effect of the arrangement of the symbols in any given row; 3.311 is just the application of this familiar raising operator to the diagram $[\mu;\nu]$.

To proceed with the proof of 3.31 we note that the theorem reduces to 2.25 in the case $[m]\cdot[n]$ since 3.312 is then of no effect. Let us assume 3.31 to be true for every $[\bar{\mu}]\cdot[\bar{\nu}]$ and prove it for $[\mu]\cdot[\nu]$.

Certainly, all the necessary irreducible components will appear on the left of 3.32 and it is only necessary to discard those which do not belong to $[\mu]\cdot[\nu]$. We observe first that no irreducible component of any $[\bar{\mu}]\cdot[\bar{\nu}]$ for $[\bar{\mu}]\neq[\mu]$ can satisfy 3.311. In the second place, the effect of the operator N_{ij} is to raise a symbol from the jth row to the *end* of the ith row of $[\nu]$ to yield $[\bar{\nu}]$. So far as the application of 3.31 to yield the components of $[\mu]\cdot[\bar{\nu}]$ is concerned, such a letter is indistinguishable from any other in the ith row of $[\bar{\nu}]$ and can thus be placed first, which contradicts 3.312. Thus all the irreducible components appearing on the left of 3.32 which do *not* satisfy the construction of 3.31 can be recognized as belonging to $\Sigma[\bar{\mu}]\cdot[\bar{\nu}]$ and those which remain and do satisfy 3.31 must yield the irreducible components of $[\mu]\cdot[\nu]$, as required.

3.33 *Example.* Let us apply the Reduction Theorem 3.31 to obtain the irreducible components of $[3, 2]\cdot[2, 1]$. It is most convenient to add the symbols of

$$[2,1]\ :\ \begin{array}{l} a_{11}a_{12} \\ a_{21} \end{array}$$

to $[3, 2]$, obtaining from the first row

$$\begin{array}{l} \cdot\,\cdot\,\cdot\; a_{11}a_{12}, \\ \cdot\,\cdot \end{array}\quad \begin{array}{l} \cdot\,\cdot\,\cdot\; a_{11}, \\ \cdot\,\cdot\; a_{12} \end{array}\quad \begin{array}{l} \cdot\,\cdot\,\cdot\; a_{11}, \\ \cdot\,\cdot \\ a_{12} \end{array}\quad \begin{array}{l} \cdot\,\cdot\,\cdot \\ \cdot\,\cdot\; a_{11} \\ a_{12} \end{array}\quad \begin{array}{l} \cdot\,\cdot\,\cdot \\ \cdot\,\cdot \\ a_{11}a_{12} \end{array}$$

To these compound tableaux we add a_{21} in all possible ways subject to 3.312:

$$\begin{array}{l} \cdot\,\cdot\,\cdot\; a_{11}a_{12}, \\ \cdot\,\cdot\; a_{21} \end{array}\quad \begin{array}{l} \cdot\,\cdot\,\cdot\; a_{11}a_{12}; \\ \cdot\,\cdot \\ a_{21} \end{array}\quad \begin{array}{l} \cdot\,\cdot\,\cdot\; a_{11}, \\ \cdot\,\cdot\; a_{12}a_{21} \end{array}\quad \begin{array}{l} \cdot\,\cdot\,\cdot\; a_{11}; \\ \cdot\,\cdot\; a_{12} \\ a_{21} \end{array}$$

$$\begin{array}{l} \cdot\,\cdot\,\cdot\; a_{11}, \\ \cdot\,\cdot\; a_{21} \\ a_{12} \end{array}\quad \begin{array}{l} \cdot\,\cdot\,\cdot\; a_{11}, \\ \cdot\,\cdot \\ a_{12}a_{21} \end{array}\quad \begin{array}{l} \cdot\,\cdot\,\cdot\; a_{11}; \\ \cdot\,\cdot \\ a_{12} \\ a_{21} \end{array}\quad \begin{array}{l} \cdot\,\cdot\,\cdot\,, \\ \cdot\,\cdot\; a_{11} \\ a_{12}a_{21} \end{array}$$

$$\begin{array}{l} \cdot\,\cdot\,\cdot\,; \\ \cdot\,\cdot\; a_{11} \\ a_{12} \\ a_{21} \end{array}\quad \begin{array}{l} \cdot\,\cdot\,\cdot\,, \\ \cdot\,\cdot \\ a_{11}a_{12} \\ a_{21} \end{array}$$

so that the required reduction is given by

$$\begin{aligned}[3, 2]\cdot[2, 1] = {} & [5, 3]+[5, 2, 1]+[4^2]+2[4, 3, 1]+[4, 2^2] \\ & +[4, 2, 1^2]+[3^2, 2]+[3^2, 1^2]+[3, 2^2, 1].\end{aligned}$$

The degrees can readily be checked using 2.37 and 3.13. If we replace brackets [ ] by $\langle\ \rangle$ we have the reduction of the representation $\langle 3, 2\rangle\times\langle 2, 1\rangle$ of $GL(d)$ with character $\{3, 2\}\{2, 1\}$, obtained by replacing brackets [ ] by { }.

Let us return now to the ideas of Theorem 3.18. If $[\lambda]$ is any irreducible representation of $\mathfrak{S}_{m+n}$ then we may suppose that

3.34 $$[\lambda]\downarrow\mathfrak{S}_m\times\mathfrak{S}_n = \sum_{\mu,\nu} m_{\mu\nu\lambda}\,[\mu]\times[\nu]$$

where $[\mu]$ is an *irreducible* representation of $\mathfrak{S}_m$ and $[\nu]$ of $\mathfrak{S}_n$. By Frobenius' reciprocity theorem we have

3.35
$$[\mu]\cdot[\nu] = \sum_{\lambda} m_{\mu\nu\lambda}\,[\lambda],$$

and the $m_{\mu\nu\lambda}$ can now be calculated by means of 3.31. On the other hand, it is easy to see that

3.36
$$[\lambda]-[\mu] = \sum_{\nu} m_{\mu\nu\lambda}\,[\nu].$$

The determination of those $m_{\mu\nu\lambda}>0$ in 3.36 corresponds to the application of the method of lattice permutations as in Example 2.56.

3.4 The inner product $[\alpha]\times[\beta]$. If we construct the Kronecker product of the two matrices representing the same element Q of $\mathfrak{S}_n$ in $[\alpha]$ and $[\beta]$, for all Q, we obtain a representation

3.41
$$[\alpha]\times[\beta] = [\beta]\times[\alpha]$$

with character $\chi^{\alpha}\chi^{\beta}$ which we have called (11.55) the *inner product.* We shall denote the corresponding representation of $GL(d)$ by $\langle\alpha\rangle\cdot\langle\beta\rangle$. Such an interchanging of the roles of $\cdot$ and $\times$ between the inner and outer product draws attention to the underlying duality of this whole theory.

Though its description is simple, the reduction of the inner product $[\alpha]\times[\beta]$ is unexpectedly complicated. Once more we have recourse to 2.26, writing:

3.42
$$[\alpha]\times[\beta] = \Pi(1-R_{ik})\,(I\mathscr{H}\uparrow\mathfrak{S}_n)\times[\beta]$$

where $\mathscr{H}=\mathfrak{S}_{\alpha_1}\times\mathfrak{S}_{\alpha_2}\times\ldots\times\mathfrak{S}_{\alpha_h}$ and R_{ij} operates on the subscripts α which appear in $\mathscr{H}$. Substituting from 11.57 we obtain the reduction

3.43
$$[\alpha]\times[\beta] = \Pi(1-R_{ik})\,([\beta]\downarrow\mathscr{H})\uparrow\mathfrak{S}_n.$$

The terms which appear on the right side of 3.43 are now outer products which can be evaluated by 3.31.

It is worth remarking that, if $[\alpha']$ is the *conjugate* of $[\alpha]$ obtained by interchanging rows and columns, we have

3.44
$$[\alpha']\times[\beta] = [\alpha]\times[\beta'],\quad [\alpha']\times[\beta'] = [\alpha]\times[\beta].$$

We illustrate the application of 3.43 in the following

3.45 *Example.* In Example 3.19 we obtained the restriction of the representation $[\beta]=[3, 2, 1]$ of $\mathfrak{S}_6$ to certain subgroups $\mathscr{H}$. If we replace the × by · in each term on the right we obtain the corresponding induced representations or outer products which we must further reduce by applying 3.31. Thus we have:

$$\begin{aligned}([3,2,1]\downarrow \mathfrak{S}_3\times\mathfrak{S}_2\times\mathfrak{S}_1)\uparrow\mathfrak{S}_6 \\ &= [3]\cdot[2]\cdot[1]+[3]\cdot[1^2]\cdot[1]+3[2,1]\cdot[2,1-1]\cdot[1] \\ &\quad +[1^3]\cdot[2]\cdot[1]+[1^3]\cdot[1^2]\cdot[1] \\ &= [6]+6[5,1]+9[4,2]+10[4,1^2]+7[3^2]+13[3,2,1] \\ &\quad +10[3,1^3]+7[2^3]+9[2^2,1^2]+6[2,1^4]+[1^6],\end{aligned}$$

and similarly we obtain

$$\begin{aligned}([3,2,1]\downarrow \mathfrak{S}_3\times\mathfrak{S}_3)\uparrow\mathfrak{S}_6 \\ &= 2[5,1]+3[4,2]+3[4,1^2]+2[3^2]+5[3,2,1]+3[3,1^3] \\ &\quad +2[2^3]+3[2^2,1^2]+2[2,1^4], \\ ([3,2,1]\downarrow \mathfrak{S}_4\times\mathfrak{S}_1\times\mathfrak{S}_1)\uparrow\mathfrak{S}_6 \\ &= 2[5,1]+4[4,2]+4[4,1^2]+4[3^2]+6[3,2,1]+4[3,1^3] \\ &\quad +4[2^3]+4[2^2,1^2]+2[2,1^4], \\ ([3,2,1]\downarrow \mathfrak{S}_5\times\mathfrak{S}_1)\uparrow\mathfrak{S}_6 \\ &= [4,2]+[4,1^2]+[3^2]+3[3,2,1]+[3,1^3]+[2^3]+[2^2,1^2].\end{aligned}$$

From 3.43, we must add and subtract according to 2.26:

$$[3,2,1] = [3]\cdot[2]\cdot[1]-[3]\cdot[3]-[4]\cdot[1]\cdot[1]+[5]\cdot[1],$$

so that we have finally

$$\begin{aligned}[3,2,1]\times[3,2,1] \\ &= [6]+2[5,1]+3[4,2]+4[4,1^2]+2[3^2]+5[3,2,1] \\ &\quad +4[3,1^3]+2[2^3]+3[2^2,1^2]+2[2,1]+[1^6].\end{aligned}$$

Changing brackets [ ] into $\langle\ \rangle$ or $\{\ \}$ and × into · , we have the reduction of $\langle 3,2,1\rangle\cdot\langle 3,2,1\rangle$ with character the inner product of Schur functions $\{3,2,1\}\cdot\{3,2,1\}$.

If we set $\mathscr{G}=\mathfrak{S}_{m+n}$ and $\mathscr{H}=\mathfrak{S}_m\times\mathfrak{S}_n$ with irreducible representation $\alpha=[\rho]\times[\sigma]$, then 11.56 becomes

3.46 $$(\alpha\mathscr{H}\uparrow\mathfrak{S}_{m+n})\times[\lambda] = ([\lambda]\downarrow\mathscr{H}\times\alpha\mathscr{H})\uparrow\mathfrak{S}_{m+n},$$

which, when combined with 3.34 yields:

3.47 $$([\rho]\,.\,[\sigma])\times[\lambda] = \sum_{\mu,\nu} m_{\mu\gamma\lambda}\,([\rho]\times[\mu])\,.\,([\sigma]\times[\nu]).$$

This interesting equation shows the relation between outer and inner products and can be used to facilitate their reduction.

3.5 Symmetrized outer products $[\mu] \odot [\nu]$. In the preceding sections we have developed methods for the reduction of outer and inner products into their irreducible components. The question now arises as to the effect on such a reduction of identifying two or more of the factors. The situation is quite analogous to that considered in § 3.2 where it was necessary to work through the commuting algebra to obtain the reduction of $\Pi_n(A)$.

Let us consider the formula given in the row § 3.5 in the Table of the Introduction:

3.51 $$[\mu] \cdot [\mu] \cdot \ldots (n \text{ factors}) = \sum f^\nu [\mu] \odot [\nu].$$

The representation of $\mathfrak{S}_{mn}$ on the left is that induced by the irreducible representation $[\mu] \times [\mu] \times \ldots$ (n factors) of the subgroup $\mathscr{H} = \mathfrak{S}_m \times \mathfrak{S}_m \times \ldots$ (n factors) with degree

$$\frac{(mn)!}{(m!)^n} (f^\mu)^n,$$

by 3.121. In order to see how this reduction arises we must study the commuting algebra which has as basis the $n!$ permutations (S) which interchange the n sets of f^μ variables in the representation $[\mu] \times [\mu] \times \ldots$ (n factors) of $\mathscr{H}$. (See Example 3.515 below.) The degree of the irreducible representation $[\nu]$ of $\mathfrak{S}_n$ is f^ν so it follows, as before, from Schur's Lemma (11.34) that the multiplicity of $[\mu] \odot [\nu]$ is f^ν. Since $\Sigma(f^\nu)^2 = n!$, the degree of $[\mu] \odot [\nu]$ must be

3.511 $$\frac{(mn)!}{(m!)^n n!} (f^\mu)^n f^\nu.$$

Since the order of the *normalizer* $\mathscr{N}(\mathscr{H})$ of $\mathscr{H}$ in $\mathfrak{S}_{mn}$ is $(m!)^n n!$, 3.511 suggests the existence of a representation $(\mu; \nu)$ of $\mathscr{N}(\mathscr{H})$ of degree $(f^\mu)^n f^\nu$, such that:

3.512 *The symmetrized outer product* $[\mu] \odot [\nu]$ *is that representation of* $\mathfrak{S}_{mn}$ *induced by the representation* $(\mu; \nu)$ *of* $\mathscr{N}(\mathscr{H})$, *where* $\mathscr{H} = \mathfrak{S}_m \times \mathfrak{S}_m \times \ldots$ (n factors).

Proof. We may write

3.513 $$\mathscr{N}(\mathscr{H}) = \mathscr{H} + \mathscr{H} S_2 + \ldots + \mathscr{H} S_{n!},$$

where S_i is a regular substitution which permutes the n ordered sets of m symbols amongst themselves. Thus we may represent any element of $\mathscr{N}(\mathscr{H})$ as a matrix product $AB = BA$ where

$$A = (S) \times (S)', \quad B = \{[\mu] \times [\mu] \times \ldots (n \text{ factors})\} \times (I)',$$

and $(S)^\nu$ represents S in $[\nu]$. Such a representation is of the required degree and is also irreducible, though not all irreducible representations of $\mathcal{N}(\mathcal{H})$ are of this form. A study of the characters (which we shall omit) shows that

3.514 $$\chi(A) \text{ in } [\alpha] \odot [\beta] = \frac{(mn)!}{(m!)^n n! n_A} \sum_S \chi^\beta(S)\, n_A^{\mathcal{H}S} \chi(A)$$

where n_A is the number of conjugates of any element A of S_{mn}, of which $n_A^{\mathcal{H}S}$ lie in $\mathcal{H}S$ and $\chi(A)$ is the character of A in $(\mu;\nu)$. Thus $[\mu] \odot [\nu]$ is actually that representation of $\mathfrak{S}_{mn}$ induced by the representation $(\mu;\nu)$ of $\mathcal{N}(\mathcal{H})$, as claimed in 3.512.

Since character tables are available up to $n=16$, many reductions of $[\mu] \odot [\nu]$ are thus open to direct calculation. The only difficulty lies in constructing the representation $(\mu;\nu)$ which we illustrate in the following

3.515 *Example.* If we take $m=3$, $n=2$ with $[\mu]=[2,1]$, $f^\mu=2$, we have

$$\mathcal{H} = \{1+(12)+(13)+(23)+(123)+(132)\} \times \{1+(45)+(46)+(56) +(456)+(465)\}$$

so that

$$\mathcal{N}(\mathcal{H}) = \mathcal{H} + \mathcal{H}(14)(25)(36), \quad S = (14)(25)(36).$$

If we denote the variables of $[2,1]\times[2,1]$ by the 'products' of the standard Young tableaux:

$$\begin{pmatrix}12\\3\end{pmatrix}\begin{pmatrix}45\\6\end{pmatrix}, \quad \begin{pmatrix}13\\2\end{pmatrix}\begin{pmatrix}45\\6\end{pmatrix}, \quad \begin{pmatrix}12\\3\end{pmatrix}\begin{pmatrix}46\\5\end{pmatrix}, \quad \begin{pmatrix}13\\2\end{pmatrix}\begin{pmatrix}46\\5\end{pmatrix},$$

the matrix (S) becomes

$$(S) = \begin{bmatrix} 1 & 0 & 0 & 0 \\ 0 & 0 & 1 & 0 \\ 0 & 1 & 0 & 0 \\ 0 & 0 & 0 & 1 \end{bmatrix}$$

Also

$$(S)^{[2]} = (1), \qquad (S)^{[1^2]} = (-1),$$

yielding the representations $(2,1;2)$ and $(2,1;1^2)$ of $\mathcal{N}(\mathcal{H})$, both of degree $2^2\cdot 1=4$.

Dualizing 3.51 we have the corresponding reduction theorem for $GL(d)$

3.516 $$\langle\mu\rangle \times \langle\mu\rangle \times \ldots \times \langle\mu\rangle = \sum f^\nu \langle\mu\rangle \otimes \langle\nu\rangle$$

with characters the products of Schur functions:

3.517 $$\{\mu\}\{\mu\}\ldots\{\mu\} = \sum f^\nu \{\mu\} \otimes \{\nu\}.$$

Much effort has been put into devising a reasonably simple method for obtaining the reduction of $[\mu] \odot [\nu]$ (and so also of $\{\mu\} \otimes \{\nu\}$). If we denote the multiplicity of an irreducible representation $[\lambda]$ of $\mathfrak{S}_{mn}$ in $[\mu] \odot [\nu]$ by $([\mu] \odot [\nu])_\lambda$ then it is not difficult to see that

3.52 $$([\mu] \odot [\nu])_\lambda = ([\mu'] \odot [\nu])_{\lambda'} \qquad m \text{ even,}$$
$$= ([\mu'] \odot [\nu'])_{\lambda'} \qquad m \text{ odd,}$$

but to calculate these multiplicities explicitly with any generality seems exceedingly difficult. The following result is fundamental and follows immediately from 3.512 by examining the characters on both sides of the equation:

3.53 $$([\mu] \odot [\nu_1]) \cdot ([\mu] \odot [\nu_2]) = [\mu] \odot ([\nu_1] \cdot [\nu_2]).$$

The outer product in the bracket on the right side indicates the applicability of the raising operator, and from 2.26 and 2.28 we have

3.531 $$[\mu] \odot [\nu] = |\, [\mu] \odot [\nu_i - i + j] \,|^{\cdot} = |\, [\mu] \odot [1^{\nu_i' - i + j}] \,|^{\cdot}$$

as in 2.34. It is interesting that any $[\mu] \odot [\nu]$ is thus expressible in terms of those $[\mu] \odot [n]$ which are significant in the application of these ideas to the Theory of Invariants. However, to proceed further we must know the reduction of the $[\mu] \odot [n]$ in the general case.

An alternative approach is to adopt a step-by-step method using the following special case of 3.53:

3.54 $$([\mu] \odot [\bar{\nu}]) \cdot [\mu] = [\mu] \odot ([\bar{\nu}] \cdot [1]).$$

Let us assume that we know the multiplicity $\bar{\rho}_{il}$ in

3.541 $$[\mu] \odot [\bar{\nu}^l] = \sum \bar{\rho}_{il}[\bar{\lambda}^i]$$

so that knowing the σ_{ji} in

3.542 $$[\bar{\lambda}^i] \cdot [\mu] = \sum \sigma_{ji}[\lambda^j]$$

by 3.31, we have for the left side of 3.54

3.543 $$[\mu] \odot [\bar{\nu}^l] \cdot [\mu] = \sum_{i,j} \sigma_{ji}\, \bar{\rho}_{il}[\lambda^j].$$

We are trying to determine the ρ_{jk} in

3.544 $$[\mu] \odot [\nu^k] = \sum \rho_{jk}[\lambda^j].$$

To this end we use the relation

3.545 $$[\bar{\nu}^l] \cdot [1] = \sum \varepsilon_{kl}[\nu^k],$$

in which $\varepsilon_{kl}=1$ or 0 according as $[\nu^k]$ of $\mathfrak{S}_{n+1}$ can or cannot be obtained from $[\bar{\nu}^l]$ of $\mathfrak{S}_n$ by adding a single node. Thus we have for the right side of 3.54

3.547 $$[\mu]\odot([\bar{\nu}^l]\cdot[1]) = \sum_{j,k} \rho_{jk}\,\varepsilon_{kl}[\lambda^j].$$

Combining this with 3.543, we write the resulting relation in the form

3.548 $$\boldsymbol{R}\,\boldsymbol{E} = \boldsymbol{S}\,\bar{\boldsymbol{R}},$$

setting $\bar{\boldsymbol{R}}=(\bar{\rho}_{il})$, $\boldsymbol{S}=(\sigma_{ji})$, $\boldsymbol{E}=(\varepsilon_{kl})$ and $\boldsymbol{R}=(\rho_{jk})$. While this is a necessary condition on the ρ_{jk} it is not in general sufficient to determine them.

In order to obtain a further condition we consider the character (§ 4.6) of an $m(n+1)$-cycle on both sides of the equation

3.549 $$[\lambda^j]\,\mathfrak{S}_{m(n+1)}\downarrow\mathcal{N}(\mathcal{H}) = \sum \rho_{jk}(\mu\cdot\nu^k),$$

which is equivalent to 3.544 by 3.512 for $n+1$ and Frobenius' reciprocity theorem. We omit the proof of the following result which uses ideas to be developed in Chapter IV.

3.55 *If* $[\lambda^j]$ *has no* $(n+1)$-*core*:

$$\sum_k \rho_{jk}\,\tau_k = \sigma_j,$$

where $\sigma_j=\pm 1$, 0 *is defined in* 4.63, *and* $\tau_k=\pm 1$ *or* 0 *according as* $[\nu^k]$ *is or is not an* $(n+1)$-*hook of even or odd leg length. If* $[\lambda^j]$ *has an* $(n+1)$-*core*

$$\sum \rho_{jk}\tau_k = 0.$$

Various other procedures for obtaining the reduction of $[\mu]\odot[\nu]$ or equivalently of $\langle\mu\rangle\otimes\langle\nu\rangle$ or $\{\mu\}\otimes\{\nu\}$ have been developed and many tables of these reductions have been given, but we shall content ourselves here with an application of the method outlined above in a simple case.

3.56 *Example.* It is not difficult to show that $[2]\odot[2]=[4]+[2^2]$ and $[2]\odot[1^2]=[3,1]$. Passing to the next stage, let us assume the reductions:

3.561
$$\begin{aligned} [2]\odot[3] &= [6]+[4,2]+[2^3] && \text{of degree 15,}\\ [2]\odot[2,1] &= [5,1]+[4,2]+[3,2,1] && \text{of degree 30,}\\ [2]\odot[1^3] &= [4,1^2]+[3^2] && \text{of degree 15,}\end{aligned}$$

and determine $[2]\odot[4]$, $[2]\odot[3,1]$ etc. It is easy to verify that the matrix equation 3.548 becomes

$$
\bar{R}\begin{bmatrix} 1 & 0 & 0 \\ 1 & 1 & 0 \\ 0 & 1 & 0 \\ 0 & 1 & 1 \\ 0 & 0 & 1 \end{bmatrix} = \begin{matrix} \\ \\ \\ \\ \\ j_1 \\ \\ j_2 \\ \\ \\ \\ \\ \\ \\ \\ \\ \end{matrix}\begin{bmatrix} 1 & 0 & 0 & 0 & 0 & 0 & 0 \\ 1 & 1 & 0 & 0 & 0 & 0 & 0 \\ 1 & 1 & 1 & 0 & 0 & 0 & 0 \\ 0 & 1 & 0 & 1 & 0 & 0 & 0 \\ 0 & 1 & 1 & 0 & 1 & 0 & 0 \\ 0 & 1 & 1 & 1 & 0 & 1 & 0 \\ 0 & 0 & 0 & 1 & 0 & 0 & 0 \\ 0 & 0 & 1 & 0 & 0 & 0 & 0 \\ 0 & 0 & 1 & 1 & 1 & 1 & 0 \\ 0 & 0 & 1 & 0 & 0 & 1 & 1 \\ 0 & 0 & 0 & 1 & 0 & 1 & 0 \\ 0 & 0 & 0 & 0 & 0 & 1 & 0 \\ 0 & 0 & 0 & 0 & 0 & 1 & 0 \\ 0 & 0 & 0 & 0 & 0 & 1 & 1 \\ 0 & 0 & 0 & 0 & 1 & 0 & 0 \\ 0 & 0 & 0 & 0 & 0 & 0 & 1 \end{bmatrix} \begin{bmatrix} 1 & 0 & 0 \\ 0 & 1 & 0 \\ 1 & 1 & 0 \\ 0 & 0 & 1 \\ 0 & 0 & 1 \\ 0 & 1 & 0 \\ 1 & 0 & 0 \end{bmatrix}, \tag{3.562}
$$

where the rows of $\bar{R}$ correspond to the representation of $\mathfrak{S}_6$ appearing on the right of 3.561, arranged in dictionary order, while the rows of **S** are the significant representations of $\mathfrak{S}_8$ also arranged in dictionary order; the columns of E and $\bar{R}$ are associated with [3], [2, 1], [1^3] respectively.

Consider first the case $j_1 = [5, 2, 1]$ for which 3.562 yields:

$$
\begin{aligned}
&\rho_{j_1,[4]} + \rho_{j_1,[3,1]} && = 1, \\
&\qquad \rho_{j_1,[3,1]} + \rho_{j_1,[2^2]} + \rho_{j_1,[2,1^2]} && = 3, \\
&\qquad\qquad \rho_{j_1,[2,1^2]} + \rho_{j_1,[1^4]} && = 1,
\end{aligned} \tag{3.563}
$$

Since ρ is a non-negative integer, these equations have the unique solution

$$
\rho_{j_1,[3,1]} = \rho_{j_1,[2^2]} = \rho_{j_1,[2,1^2]} = 1, \quad \rho_{j_1,[4]} = \rho_{j_1,[1^4]} = 0.
$$

Actually, [5, 2, 1] is a 4-core and since $\tau_{[3,1]} = -1$, $\tau_{[2^2]} = 0$, $\tau_{[2,1^2]} = 1$, 3.55 is satisfied automatically.

In the case of $j_2 = [4^2]$ we have:

$$
\begin{aligned}
&\rho_{j_2,[4]} + \rho_{j_2,[3,1]} && = 1, \\
&\qquad \rho_{j_2,[3,1]} + \rho_{j_2,[2^2]} + \rho_{j_2,[2,1^2]} && = 1, \\
&\qquad\qquad \rho_{j_2,[2,1^2]} + \rho_{j_2,[1^4]} && = 0,
\end{aligned} \tag{3.564}
$$

and these equations have the two possible solutions

(i) $\rho_{j_2,[4]} = \rho_{j_2,[2^2]} = 1$, all other ρ's zero;
(ii) $\rho_{j_2,[3,1]} = 1$, all other ρ's zero.

Since two successive 4-hooks of leg length zero can be removed from $[4^2]$, we conclude that

$$\sum_k \rho_{jk}\,\tau_k = 1.$$

In case (i) $\tau_{[4]} = 1$, $\tau_{[2^2]} = 0$ while in case (ii) $\tau_{[3,1]} = -1$. Thus case (i) is the correct solution.

Applying the conditions 3.548 and 3.55 for all j we obtain the decompositions:

$$\begin{aligned}
&[2] \odot [4] &&= [8]+[6,2]+[4^2]+[4,2^2]+[2^4] &&\text{of degree } 105\\
&[2] \odot [3,1] &&= [7,1]+[6,2]+[5,3]+[5,2,1]+[4,3,1] &&\\
& &&\quad +[4,2^2]+[3,2^2,1] &&\text{of degree } 315\\
3.565\quad &[2] \odot [2^2] &&= [6,2]+[5,2,1]+[4^2]+[4,2^2]+[3^2,1^2] &&\\
& && &&\text{of degree } 210\\
&[2] \odot [2,1^2] &&= [6,1^2]+[5,3]+[5,2,1]+[4,3,1] &&\\
& &&\quad +[4,2,1^2]+[3^2,2] &&\text{of degree } 315\\
&[2] \odot [1^4] &&= [5,1^3]+[4,3,1] &&\text{of degree } 105.
\end{aligned}$$

Using 3.52 we may read off the corresponding reductions of $[1^2] \odot [4]$, $[1^2] \odot [3,1]$, etc.

3.6 Symmetrized inner products $[\mu] \otimes [\nu]$. Corresponding to 3.51, we have the following reduction of the product of n identical factors:

3.61 $$[\mu]\times[\mu]\times \ldots \times[\mu] = \sum f^\nu\, [\mu] \otimes [\nu].$$

We shall call $[\mu] \otimes [\nu]$ the *symmetrized inner product* of symmetry type $[\nu]$. There is a very close analogy here with the reduction of $\Pi_n(A)$ in § 3.2. In fact if we limit the matrices A to those of the irreducible representation $[\mu]$ of $\mathfrak{S}_m$ we have immediately the degree $\delta^\nu(f^\mu)$ of $[\mu] \otimes [\nu]$, according to 3.283.

Corresponding to 3.53 we have the equation

3.62 $$([\mu] \otimes [\nu_1])\times([\mu] \otimes [\nu_2]) = [\mu] \otimes ([\nu_1]\cdot[\nu_2]),$$

so that again we may write:

3.63 $$[\mu] \otimes [\nu] = |\,[\mu] \otimes [\nu_i - i + j]\,|^\times = |\,[\mu] \otimes [1^{\nu_i' - i + j}]\,|^\times.$$

In our previous applications of the operator we saw no particular advantage in using 2.28 rather than 2.26. But if we must actually calculate the characters of $[\mu] \otimes [\nu]$ we would wish to have them expressed as simply as possible in terms of the roots $\alpha_1, \alpha_2, \ldots$ of the matrices of $[\mu]$. Thus, the Schur functions $\{1^n\}$ are preferable to

$\{n\}$ as example 3.29 shows, so that 2.28 is to be preferred to 2.26. Of course, as in § 3.2, $f^\mu \geqq n$ if every representation $[\mu] \otimes [\nu]$ is to be defined.

3.64 *Example.* In Example 3.45 we obtained the reduction of $[3, 2, 1] \times [3, 2, 1]$. Let us now determine the distribution of its irreducible components according to

$$[3, 2, 1] \times [3, 2, 1] = [3, 2, 1] \otimes [2] + [3, 2, 1] \otimes [1^2].$$

Since $\{1^2\} = \alpha_1 \alpha_2$, we must determine the characteristic roots of each class of conjugate elements and add all combinations of these, taken two at a time. The degree of $[3, 2, 1] \otimes [1^2]$ is 120 by 3.282, and we carry this process through in the case of a cycle Q_3. From a table of characters $\chi(Q_3)$ in $[3, 2, 1]$ is -2 so that the characteristic roots must be,

$$(1+\varepsilon+\varepsilon^2) \text{ four times}, (\varepsilon+\varepsilon^2) \text{ twice}, \qquad \varepsilon^3 = 1.$$

Taking products of these, two at a time, we obtain

$$(1+\varepsilon+\varepsilon^2) \text{ thirty-nine times}, 1 \text{ three times},$$

so that the required character is 3. The results of such computations are given in the following table:

c	1^6	$1^4 2$	$1^3 3$	$1^2 4$	$1^2 2^2$	123	15	6	24	2^3	3^2
g_c	1	15	40	90	45	120	144	120	90	15	40
χ	120	-8	3	0	-8	1	0	1	0	-8	3

and the required multiplicities are obtainable from 11.371:

$$[3, 2, 1] \otimes [1^2] = 3[4, 1^2] + [3^2] + 2[3, 2, 1] + 3[3, 1^3] + 2[2^2, 1^2] + [2, 1^4] \qquad \text{of degree } 120.$$

From Example 3.45:

$$[3, 2, 1] \otimes [2] = [6] + 2[5, 1] + 3[4, 2] + [4, 1^2] + [3^2] + 3[3, 2, 1] + [3, 1^3] + 2[2^3] + [2^2, 1^2] + [2, 1^4] + [1^6].$$

Of course such a brutal attack on the problem requires the use of character tables (which are available for $n \leqq 16$), but the amount of work involved would be prohibitive for large values of f^μ. However, certain general theorems can be proved in special cases, e.g.

3.65 $$[\mu] \otimes [1^n] = [1^m] \qquad n = f^\mu,$$

3.66 $$[m-1, 1] \otimes [1^k] = [m-k, 1^k] \qquad 0 < k < m.$$

The proofs of 3.65 and 3.66 follow immediately from the form of the Schur function $\{1^k\}=\alpha_1\alpha_2,\ldots,\alpha_k$. Using 3.63, it is possible to deduce the reduction of any $[m-1, 1]\otimes[\nu]$, and these have been tabulated by Murnaghan for $n\leqq 6$.

3.67 *Example.* It follows from 3.65 that $[2, 1]\otimes[1^2]=[1^3]$ so that $[2, 1]\otimes[2]=[3]+[2, 1]$. More generally:

$$\begin{aligned}[m-1, 1]\otimes[1^2] &= [m-2, 1^2],\\ [m-1, 1]\otimes[2] &= [m]+[m-1, 1]+[m-2, 2],\end{aligned}$$

and similarly:

$$\begin{aligned}[m-1, 1]\otimes[1^3] &= [m-3, 1^3],\\ [m-1, 1]\otimes[2, 1] &= [m-1, 1]+[m-2, 2]+[m-2, 1^2]+[m-3, 2, 1],\\ [m-1, 1]\otimes[3] &= [m]+2[m-1, 1]+[m-2, 2]+[m-2, 1^2]+[m-3, 3].\end{aligned}$$

We illustrate the application of 3.63 by writing

$$\begin{aligned}[m-1, 1]\otimes[2, 1] &= \begin{vmatrix}[m-1, 1]\otimes[1^2] & 1\\ [m-1, 1]\otimes[1^3] & [m-1, 1]\otimes[1]\end{vmatrix}^{\times}\\ &= [m-2, 1^2]\times[m-1, 1]-[m-3, 1^3],\end{aligned}$$

and we have seen how to calculate $[m-2, 1^2]\times[m-1, 1]$ in § 3.4.

Corresponding to the inner symmetrized products of $\mathfrak{S}_n$ we have the reduction

3.68 $$\langle\mu\rangle\cdot\langle\mu\rangle\cdot\ldots\cdot\langle\mu\rangle = \sum f^{\nu}\langle\mu\rangle\odot\langle\nu\rangle$$

of $GL(d)$, with characters the corresponding products $\{\mu\}\odot\{\nu\}$ of Schur functions. To obtain the theory it is only necessary to replace brackets [ ] by ⟨ ⟩ or { } and multiplication × by · in the results of this section.

CHAPTER FOUR

THE CHARACTERS OF $\mathfrak{S}_n$ AND THE CONTENT OF [λ]

Introduction. The relation 2.37 expressing the degree f^λ of $[\lambda]$ in terms of all the hook lengths $\boldsymbol{h}_{ij}$ gives perhaps the clearest indication of the importance of the hook graph $\boldsymbol{H}[\lambda]$ in the ordinary representation theory of $\mathfrak{S}_n$. In this chapter we shall study the fundamental relationship which exists between *hooks* and *characters* in §§ 4.1, 4.2 and 4.5.

In § 2.5 we defined the skew diagram $[\alpha]-[\beta]$; if this is a skew q-hook H we say that H is *removable* from $[\alpha]$ to yield $[\beta]$. If at most b skew q-hooks are removable in succession from $[\alpha]$,

$$n = a+bq,$$

and we call b the *weight* of $[\alpha]$. Also, we call the residue containing a nodes, which remains after these b skew q-hooks have been removed, the *q-core* of $[\alpha]$.

To illustrate these definitions, consider the case of [4, 3, 2, 1] with $n=10$, $q=3$, $b=3$, $a=1$. We indicate two possible ways of removing the three 3-hooks, which may be right or skew.

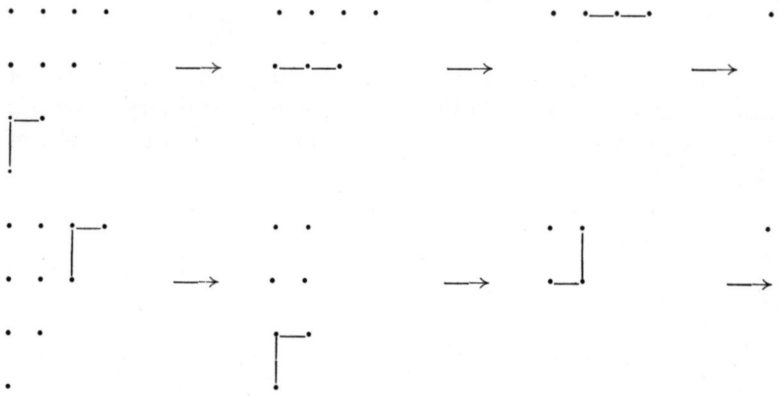

The total number of ways is 6 as given by the *degree* of

$$[4, 3, 2, 1]_3 = [1]_3^0 \cdot [1]_3^1 \cdot [1]_3^2,$$

according to 4.55.

In § 4.3 we introduce the notion of the *content* $G^\lambda(x)$. By reducing the coefficients of this polynomial modulo q we obtain the *q-content* $G_q^\lambda(x)$ and the *q-graph* $G_q[\lambda]$ by means of which we attach a definite residue r to each node of $[\lambda]$.

Using these ideas, we define in § 4.4 the *q-quotient*

$$[\lambda]_q = [\lambda]_q^0 \cdot [\lambda]_q^1 \cdot \ldots \cdot [\lambda]_q^{q-1}$$

which describes the q-hook structure of $[\lambda]$. This q-quotient has significance for the character theory of $\mathfrak{S}_n$, but more important, it provides the clue to the modular representation theory to be developed in subsequent chapters.

Our conclusions in § 4.3 are independent of the value assigned to the variable x in $g_{ij}(x) = x+j-i$. One can make this invariance explicit by thinking of the Young diagram as being superimposed upon a lattice $G(x) = (g_{ij}(x))$, and free to move over it. Only one operator T is necessary to describe the horizontal and vertical translations involved. In terms of this operator we can modify the partition generating function to yield, according to 4.63, not only the *number* of diagrams $[\lambda]$ for each n, but their actual *content* $G^\lambda(x)$.

It is important to observe that in this chapter q need *not* be prime.

4.1 Character of a cycle. The expression of an irreducible representation in terms of permutation representations according to 2.26 enables us to calculate the characters of $\mathfrak{S}_n$ in a natural manner.

4.11 LEMMA. *The character χ of a cycle Q_n of length n in the irreducible representation $[\lambda]$ of $\mathfrak{S}_n$ is given by*

$$\chi^\lambda(Q_n) = \begin{cases} (-1)^l & \text{if } [\lambda] = [n-l, 1^l], \\ 0 & \text{otherwise.} \end{cases}$$

Proof. By 2.17, the character of any element Q of $\mathfrak{S}_n$ in the representation $[\lambda_1] \cdot [\lambda_2] \cdot \ldots \cdot [\lambda_h]$ is equal to the number of standard skew diagrams in which all the symbols of every cycle of Q appear in the same row. Since this can never happen for a cycle Q_n of length n unless all the symbols lie in *one* row, we conclude that the character of Q_n is zero in $[\lambda_1] \cdot [\lambda_2] \ldots [\lambda_h]$ except when $\lambda_1 = n$, $\lambda_2 = \ldots = \lambda_h = 0$.

For $[n]$ to appear in 2.26 it is necessary and sufficient that $\lambda_1 = n-l$, $\lambda_2 = \lambda_3 = \ldots = \lambda_{l+1} = 1$ since no raising operator R_{ij} appears in the expansion to a power higher than 1. If this condition is satisfied, $[n]$ will be the last term in the expansion and will be associated with the operator

$$(-1)^l R_{12} R_{13} \ldots R_{1,\, l+1},$$

proving the lemma.

We must now consider the character of Q_n in a skew representation $[\alpha]-[\beta]$ of $\mathfrak{S}_n$. While it would be possible to carry through the operator approach, the dependence on the determinant is cumbersome and unnecessary. It will be sufficient if we obtain the multiplicity of hook-representations $[n-l, 1^l]$ in $[\alpha]-[\beta]$ since the character of Q_n vanishes for all other irreducible representations. We shall prove that:

4.12 *If the skew representation* $[\alpha]-[\beta]$ *of* $\mathfrak{S}_n$:

(i) *contains interior nodes of* $[\alpha]$, *no hook components of* $[\alpha]-[\beta]$ *exist;*

(ii) *is a single skew hook of leg length* l *then* $[n-l, 1^l]$ *appears once as a component of* $[\alpha]-[\beta]$ *and no other hook components exist;*

(iii) *consists of several disjoint skew hooks, then the number of hook components* $[n-l, 1^l]$ *of* $[\alpha]-[\beta]$, *for which* l *is even is equal to the number for which* l *is odd.*

Proof of case (*i*). If $[\alpha]-[\beta]$ contains an interior node of $[\alpha]$ it must contain the configuration where the interior node is ringed. A little

consideration will show that no four elements of $[n-l, 1^l]$ can be arranged in this pattern without violating 3.312.

Proof of case (*ii*). If $[\alpha]-[\beta]$ is itself a skew hook, then only the equivalent right hook can be built into $[\alpha]-[\beta]$ to satisfy 3.36, since the number of horizontal and vertical steps is just accounted for.

Proof of case (*iii*). This case is a little more complicated and we begin by assuming that $[\alpha]-[\beta]$ consists of just two disjoint skew hooks whose equivalent right hooks are $[n_1-l_1, 1^{l_1}]$ and $[n_2-l_2, 1^{l_2}]$ where $n_1+n_2=n$. To find the irreducible components of $[\alpha]-[\beta]$ we must build on the irreducible components of the skew-hook representation of $\mathfrak{S}_{n_1}$ with those of the skew-hook representation of $\mathfrak{S}_{n_2}$ in all possible ways according to 3.35. But it is not difficult to see that a hook representation of $\mathfrak{S}_n$ can arise only by building on $[n_1-l_1, 1^{l_1}]$ with $[n_2-l_2, 1^{l_2}]$, or vice versa, to obtain

4.13 $$[n-l, 1^l] \text{ and } [n-l-1, 1^{l+1}]$$

where $l_1+l_2=l$. Repeating the above argument yields 2^{m-1} hook representations when $[\alpha]-[\beta]$ contains m disjoint hook-constituents and these are, by pairs, of even and odd leg length by 4.13, proving case (iii).

4.14 *Examples.* The following three examples illustrate the three cases (i), (ii), (iii) considered above.

(i) $[4^2, 3, 2, 1]-[2^3, 1^2] = [3, 2, 1]+[2^3]+[2^2, 1^2]$,
(ii) $[4^2, 3, 2, 1]-[3, 2, 1^3] = [3, 1^3]+2[3, 2, 1]+[3^2]+[2^3]+[2^2, 1^2]$,
(iii) $[4^2, 3, 2, 1]-[3^2, 2] = [4, 2]+[4, 1^2]+[3^2]+3[3, 2, 1]+2[3, 1^3] +[2^3]+2[2^2, 1^2]+[2, 1^4]$.

If we combine 4.11 and 4.12 we have the following important generalization of 4.11:

4.15 *The character of a cycle Q_n of length n in the skew representation $[\alpha]-[\beta]$ of $\mathfrak{S}_n$ is given by*

$$\chi^{\alpha-\beta}(Q_n) = \begin{cases} (-1)^l \text{ if } [\alpha]-[\beta] \text{ is a skew hook of leg length } l, \\ 0 \text{ otherwise.} \end{cases}$$

Proof. Only case (iii) of 4.12 needs comment and it is obvious that the sum of $(-1)^l$ over all hook representations which arise vanishes, by 4.13.

If instead of considering the character of a cycle Q_n we look for information concerning the degree of $[\alpha]-[\beta]$ we have the following analogous result:

4.16 *The degree $f^{\alpha-\beta}$ of the skew representation $[\alpha]-[\beta]$ of $\mathfrak{S}_p$, where p is a prime, satisfies the congruence*

$$f^{\alpha-\beta} \equiv \begin{cases} (-1)^l \text{ if } [\alpha]-[\beta] \text{ is a skew hook of leg length } l, \\ 0 \text{ otherwise.} \end{cases} \pmod p$$

Proof. By 2.37, f^γ is divisible by p unless $[\gamma]=[p-l, 1^l]$, in which case

$$f^\gamma = \frac{p!}{H^\gamma} = \frac{(p-1)(p-2)\dots(p-l)}{1 \quad 2 \quad \dots \quad l} \equiv (-1)^l \pmod{p}.$$

By 4.12, $[\alpha]-[\beta]$ contains a single p-hook $[p-l, 1^l]$ as an irreducible component if and only if $[\alpha]-[\beta]$ is a skew p-hook of leg length l; cases (i) and (iii) of 4.12 yield zero.

4.2 Characters of $\mathfrak{S}_n$. We are now in a position to calculate the character of any element Q of $\mathfrak{S}_n$ in $[\lambda]$ by applying 4.15 to each cycle in succession. Let us suppose that

$$Q = Q' \, Q_m$$

where it is no restriction to assume that Q_m is a cycle of length m on the last m symbols. If we consider the matrices $(r, r+1)$ constructed according to 2.17 then it is clear that the standard diagrams can be divided into sets according as the first n-m symbols constitute a diagram $[\mu]$ contained in $[\lambda]$, for all possible $[\mu]$. The last m symbols form the possible standard skew diagrams $[\lambda]-[\mu]$, for each such $[\mu]$. Moreover the character of Q can be written:

4.21 $$\chi^{\lambda}(Q) = \sum_{\mu} \chi^{\mu}(Q') \cdot \chi^{\lambda-\mu}(Q_m).$$

This formula 4.21 was first proved by Murnaghan but it was Nakayama's observation of the significance of the hook representations which led to many of these developments. Taking $Q=I$, $m=1$, each successive application of 4.21 yields a hook [1], so that $\chi^{\lambda}(I)=f^{\lambda}$ as in § 2.1. For a general Q, it is only when $[\lambda]-[\mu]$ is a skew-hook that we obtain a contribution to the right side of 4.21, in virtue of 4.15. Thus, by successive applications of 4.21 *the character* $\chi^{\lambda}(Q)$ *is expressible in terms of the hook-structure of* $[\lambda]$. We shall illustrate the application of 4.21 by calculating the tables of characters 4.22, 4.23 and 4.24 of $\mathfrak{S}_2$, $\mathfrak{S}_3$ and $\mathfrak{S}_4$. We recall that the number of elements in a class C_i is

$$g_i = n!\Big/\left(\prod_{t=1}^{\infty} t^{\alpha_t} \prod_{t=1}^{\infty} \alpha_t!\right),$$

assuming that such an element has α_1 cycles of length 1, α_2 cycles of length 2, etc., with

$$1\alpha_1+2\alpha_2+3\alpha_3+\ldots = n.$$

In the case of $\mathfrak{S}_2$ there are only two irreducible representations [2] and $[1^2]$ which are two hooks of *parity* $+1$ and -1.

4.22

C_i	(1^2)	(2)
g_i	1	1
$[2]$	1	1
$[1^2]$	1	-1

For $n=3$ there are three irreducible representations [3], [2, 1] and $[1^3]$ and 4.11 yields immediately the last column of the character table corresponding to the class (3). To calculate the character of the class (2)(1) in [2, 1] we have from 4.21

$$\chi^{2,1}(2)(1) = \chi^2(2) \cdot 1 + \chi^{1^2}(2) \cdot 1 = 0.$$

The characters of (2)(1) in [3] and $[1^3]$ can be similarly found.

4.23

C_i	$(1)^3$	(2)(1)	(3)
g_i	1	3	2
[3]	1	1	1
[2, 1]	2	0	−1
$[1^3]$	1	−1	1

For $n=4$ we proceed as before, utilizing the results obtained for $n=3$. The characters of the class (4) are given by 4.11. Calculating the characters of (3)(1) in [3, 1], $[2^2]$ and $[2, 1^2]$, we have from 4.21

$$\begin{aligned}
\chi^{3,1}(3)(1) &= \chi^{3}(3)\,.\,1+\chi^{2,1}(3)\,.\,1 &&= 0\,,\\
\chi^{2^2}(3)(1) &= \chi^{2,1}(3)\,.\,1 &&= -1\,,\\
\chi^{2,1^2}(3)(1) &= \chi^{2,1}(3)\,.\,1+\chi^{1^3}(3)\,.\,1 &&= 0\,.
\end{aligned}$$

Proceeding similarly, we have

$$\begin{aligned}
\chi^{3,1}(2)(2) &= \chi^{2}(2)\,.\,(\chi(2)\text{ in }[3,1]-[2])\\
&\quad+\chi^{1^2}(2)\,.\,(\chi(2)\text{ in }[3,1]-[1^2]) = -1\,,\\
\chi^{2^2}(2)(2) &= \chi^{2}(2)\,.\,(\chi(2)\text{ in }[2^2]-[2])\\
&\quad+\chi^{1^2}(2)\,.\,(\chi(2)\text{ in }[2^2]-[1^2]) = 2\,,\\
\chi^{2,1^2}(2)(2) &= \chi^{2}(2)\,.\,(\chi(2)\text{ in }[2,1^2]-[2])\\
&\quad+\chi^{1^2}(2)\,.\,(\chi(2)\text{ in }[2,1^2]-[1^2]) = -1\,.
\end{aligned}$$

It is unnecessary to write out the reductions yielding $\chi^\lambda(2)(1)^2$.

4.24

C_i	(1^4)	$(2, 1^2)$	(2^2)	(3, 1)	(4)
g_i	1	6	3	8	6
[4]	1	1	1	1	1
[3, 1]	3	1	−1	0	−1
$[2^2]$	2	0	2	−1	0
$[2, 1^2]$	3	−1	−1	0	1
$[1^4]$	1	−1	1	1	−1

Such tables have been calculated up to $n=16$. The step-by-step procedure envisioned above is straightforward except in so far as the number of possible choices for a given q-hook increases. Indeed, it soon becomes apparent that a knowledge of the q-hook structure of $[\lambda]$ would be highly desirable. We shall return to this problem in § 4.5.

4.3 The content of $[\lambda]$. Though apparently remote from the theory we have been developing, the ideas which we shall introduce now are of the utmost importance. Indeed they seem to form a sort of geometrical background which, when taken in conjunction with the hook graph, provides a basis for the study of the modular representation theory.

In § 2.1 we introduced the quantity $g_{ij}(x)=x+j-i$ in terms of which Young's matrix representations of $\mathfrak{S}_n$ were expressed. We now remove all restrictions on the suffixes i, j in 2.16, defining a matrix $\mathbf{G}(x)$ with (i, j)-element

4.31 $$g_{ij}(x) = x+j-i = x_{j-i} \qquad (i, j = -\infty, \ldots -1, 0, 1, \ldots \infty)$$

and associate the (i, j)-element of $[\lambda]$ with $g_{ij}(x)$. This amounts to superimposing $[\lambda]$ upon $\mathbf{G}(x)$ in a natural manner, and leads to the following (cf. 3.282)

4.32 *Definition.* If ρ_t elements x_t, such that $j-i=t$, are associated with the tth diagonal of $[\lambda]$, we define the *content* $\mathbf{G}^\lambda(x)$ of $[\lambda]$ to be

4.321 $$\mathbf{G}^\lambda(x) = \prod_{t=1-h}^{\lambda_1-1} x_t^{\rho_t},$$

and the content of the skew diagram $[\lambda]-[\mu]$ to be $\mathbf{G}^\lambda(x)/\mathbf{G}^\mu(x)$.

We can enumerate the positions in the tth diagonal of $[\lambda]$ as follows:

$$\begin{array}{lr} (1, t+1), \quad \ldots, (\rho_t, t+\rho_t), & t \geqq 0, \\ (-t+1, 1), \ldots, (-t+\rho_t, \rho_t), & t < 0, \end{array}$$

and it is clear that $\mathbf{G}^\lambda(x)$ is completely determined when the ρ_t are given. Thus:

4.33 *Two Young diagrams* $[\lambda]$ *and* $[\mu]$ *are identical if and only if they have the same content.*

To answer the converse question as to the necessary and sufficient condition on the ρ's for 4.321 to be the content of a diagram $[\lambda]$, we utilize Frobenius' notation 2.54 in order to shift the emphasis from the rows to the diagonals.

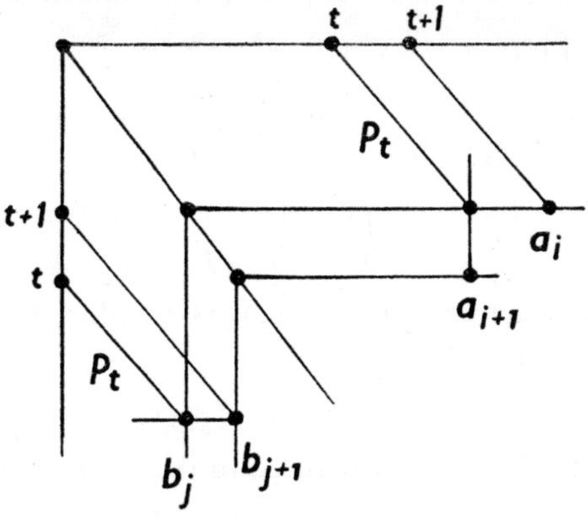

Consider first the case $t \geqq 0$. If $a_{i+1} < t \leqq a_i$ $(i = 1, 2, \ldots, s)$, then

$$\rho_t = i.$$

Similarly, if $t \leqq 0$ and $b_{j+1} < -t \leqq b_j$ $(j = 1, 2, \ldots, s)$, then

$$\rho_t = j.$$

Thus we have

4.34
$$\rho_t - \rho_{t+1} = \begin{cases} 1 \text{ if } t = a_i, \\ -1 \text{ if } t+1 = -b_{i+1}, \\ 0 \text{ otherwise.} \end{cases}$$

This establishes the 'only if' part of the following theorem:

4.35 *There exists a partition* (λ) *of n whose Young diagram* [λ] *has content*

$$\prod x_t^{\rho_t},$$

if and only if

$$r_t = \rho_t - \rho_{t+1} = \begin{cases} 0, \quad 1 \text{ for } t \geqq 0, \\ 0, \ -1 \text{ for } t \leqq 0, \end{cases}$$

and
$$\Sigma\, r_t = 0.$$

To establish the 'if' part we denote by s the number of positive r_t and define a_i and b_i by 4.34. Then the diagram [λ] whose Frobenius' symbol is 2.54 has content

$$\prod x_t^{\rho_t}.$$

Besides proving the theorem, we have obtained a construction for [λ], being given its content $G^{\lambda}(x)$.

4.36 *Example.* The monomial in the x_t (polynomial in x)

$$\prod x_t^{\rho_t} = x_{-4}x_{-3}^2x_{-2}^2x_{-1}^3x_0^3x_1^3x_2^2x_3^2x_4x_5x_6$$

satisfies the condition of 4.35, and is in fact the content of the Young diagram [7, 5, 4, 3, 2] with Frobenius' symbol

$$\begin{pmatrix} 6, & 3, & 1 \\ 4, & 3, & 1 \end{pmatrix}.$$

4.4 The q-hook structure of $[\lambda]$. Let us now reduce the element $g_{ij}(x)$ of $\boldsymbol{G}(x)$ modulo q, to yield

$$g_{ij}(x) = x+j-i = x_{j-i} \equiv x_r = x+r \qquad (\text{mod } q).$$

The content $\boldsymbol{G}^\lambda(x)$ is similarly reduced to the *q-content* $\boldsymbol{G}_q^\lambda(x)$, where

$$\boldsymbol{G}^\lambda(x) \equiv \boldsymbol{G}_q^\lambda(x) \qquad (\text{mod } q).$$

If $[\lambda]$ is a q-hook then $\boldsymbol{G}_q^\lambda(x)$ will contain a factor x_r associated with each of q successive diagonals of $[\lambda]$, so that the q-content of every q-hook is the same. This remark applies also to every skew q-hook. More generally,

4.41 *The q-content of any skew mq-hook is $(x_0x_1 \ldots x_{q-1})^m$.*

It is important in what follows to emphasize the residue r in x_r, and to this end we now set $x=0$, writing $g_{ij}(0)=g_{ij}$.

4.42. *Definitions.* We shall call the (i, j) node of $[\lambda]$ an *r-node* if and only if

$$g_{ij} = j-i \equiv r \geqq 0 \qquad (\text{mod } q).$$

If in place of the (i, j) node of $[\lambda]$ we write r, we have an array which we shall call the *q-graph* $\boldsymbol{G}_q[\lambda]$ of $[\lambda]$.

The following lemma establishes the fundamental connection between $\boldsymbol{G}_q[\lambda]$ and the hook graph $\boldsymbol{H}[\lambda]$.

4.43 *If the i-th row of $[\lambda]$ ends in an s-node and the j-th column in a t-node then*

$$\boldsymbol{h}_{ij} \equiv s-t+1 \qquad (\text{mod } q).$$

Proof. It is not difficult to see that

$$\lambda_i - i \equiv s \ (\text{mod } q), \quad j-\lambda'_j \equiv t \ (\text{mod } q)$$

so that the required congruence is an immediate consequence of 2.35.

In order to study the q-hook structure of $[\lambda]$ let us define a hook of length $\boldsymbol{h}_{ij}=mq$ whose *head node* (i, λ_i) in $[\lambda]$ is of residue class r, to be a *(q, r) hook.* No ambiguity will arise if we call (i, j) a *(q, r) node.* From 4.43 we have:

4.44 *The necessary and sufficient condition that* (i, j) *be the corner node of a* (q, r) *hook is that*

$$\lambda_i - i \equiv r \equiv j - \lambda'_j - 1 \pmod{q}.$$

The foot node of such a hook is (λ'_j, j) and that part of the rim lying between such head and foot nodes is a skew-hook, also of length mq, *equivalent* to the right hook with (i, j) as corner node. Whenever we think of 'removing' a hook, as in the Introduction and § 4.5, it will be this skew hook that we have in mind.

Consider now the hook graph $\boldsymbol{H}[\lambda]$, and let us denote the subset of all (q, r) nodes in $\boldsymbol{H}[\lambda]$ by the symbol

$$[\lambda]_q^r \qquad (r = 0, 1, \ldots, q-1).$$

Corresponding to each (q, r) node of $[\lambda]_q^r$ we have a uniquely defined head node H_a in $[\lambda]$, all (q, r) nodes in the same *row* of $\boldsymbol{H}[\lambda]$ having the same head node H_a. Let us arrange these head nodes of (q, r) hooks of $[\lambda]$ in the order

$$H_1, H_2, \ldots, H_u$$

where H_a is *higher* than H_{a+1} in $[\lambda]$. Similarly we may arrange the *foot-nodes* of (q, r) hooks of $[\lambda]$ in the order

$$F_1, F_2, \ldots, F_v$$

where F_v is to the *left* of F_{v+1} in $[\lambda]$. From the condition $\lambda_1 \geqq \lambda_2 \geqq \ldots \geqq \lambda_h$, we conclude that the (q, r) nodes of $[\lambda]$ are arranged in u rows and v columns, and from 4.44 we conclude that $[\lambda]_q^r$ *is a right Young diagram.*

If we let the (q, r) hook with head node H_a and foot node F_b in $[\lambda]$ be of length $m_{ab}q$, then we must show that (m_{ab}) is the hook graph of $[\lambda]_q^r$. Now, the necessary and sufficient condition that an r-node be an H_i is that it have no $(r+1)$-node to the right of it. Similarly, the necessary and sufficient condition that an $(r+1)$-node be an F_j is that it have no r-node below it. Since the order of the residue classes along the rim of $[\lambda]$ is fixed we conclude that:

4.45 *If c head nodes* H_i *and d foot nodes* F_j *lie between* H_a *and* F_b *on the rim of* $[\lambda]$ *then* $m_{ab} = c + d + 1$.

But since each head node H_a defines a row and each foot node F_b defines a column of $[\lambda]_q^r$ we conclude that m_{ab} is the required hook length, by 2.35. Thus we have proved the important

4.46 THEOREM. *If we delete all elements in the hook graph $\boldsymbol{H}[\lambda]$ not divisible by q, then the remaining elements*

$$h_{ij} = h_{ij}^{(r)}q \qquad (r = 0, 1, \ldots, q-1)$$

can be divided into disjoint sets whose (q, r) nodes constitute the right diagrams

$$[\lambda]_q^r \qquad (r = 0, 1, \ldots, q-1),$$

with hook graphs $(h_{ij}^{(r)})$.

We shall call the skew diagram

4.47 $$[\lambda]_q = [\lambda]_q^0 \cdot [\lambda]_q^1 \cdot \ldots [\lambda]_q^{q-1}$$

the *q-quotient* of $[\lambda]$, and the disjoint right diagrams $[\lambda]_q^i$ the disjoint *constituents* of $[\lambda]_q$.

By setting $x=0$ in our definition of the q-graph $G_q[\lambda]$ we introduce an arbitrary element into the association of q-residues with the nodes of $[\lambda]$. Taking x to be any fixed integer $\neq 0$ would rearrange the residue classes in $[\lambda]_q$ but would make no significant change in the application of these ideas (cf. § 4.6).

4.48 *Example.* Let us construct the hook-graph and the 3-graph of $[9, 6, 5, 4, 3, 2, 1]$, superposing them in order to bring out the connection established above.

$$\begin{array}{ccccccccc}
\textcircled{15_0} & 13_1 & 11_2 & \textcircled{9_0} & 7_1 & 5_2 & \textcircled{3_0} & 2_1 & 1_2 \\
& & & & & & \nwarrow F_1 & & \nwarrow H_1 \\
11_2 & \textcircled{9_0} & 7_1 & 5_2 & \textcircled{3_0} & 1_1 & & & \\
\textcircled{9_1} & 7_2 & 5_0 & \textcircled{3_1} & 1_2 & & & & \\
& & & & \nwarrow H_2 & & & & \\
7_0 & 5_1 & \textcircled{3_2} & 1_0 & & & & & \\
& & & \nwarrow F_2 & & & & & \\
5_2 & \textcircled{3_0} & 1_1 & & & & & & \\
\textcircled{3_1} & 1_2 & & & & & & & \\
& \nwarrow H_3 & & & & & & & \\
1_0 & & & & & & & & \\
\nwarrow F_3 & & & & & & & &
\end{array}$$

After removing q-hooks as explained in the Introduction we have q-core $[\phi]$, and

$$[9, 6, 5, 4, 3, 2, 1]_3 = [1]_3^0 \cdot [2, 1]_3^1 \cdot [3, 2, 1]_3^2.$$

The $H_1, H_2, H_3; F_1, F_2, F_3$ in the figure correspond to the constituent $[3, 2, 1]_3^2$ and their arrangement illustrates the proof of 4.45.

4.5 Character of a product of *mq* cycles. Let us now assume that the number of q-hooks removable from $[\lambda]$ is b, i.e. that $[\lambda]_q$ contains b nodes, so that

4.51 $$n = a+bq.$$

If we wish to calculate the character of an element AB of $\mathfrak{S}_n$, where A is any substitution of $\mathfrak{S}_a$ and B is a product of b cycles of length q, we can proceed as in § 4.2 with b repetitions of 4.21:

4.52 $$\chi^{\lambda}(AB) = \sum \chi^{\mu}(A) \cdot \chi^{(q)}(Q_1) \cdot \chi^{(q)}(Q_2) \ldots \chi^{(q)}(Q_b),$$

where μ is an irreducible representation of $\mathfrak{S}_a$, and $Q_1, Q_2, \ldots, Q_b$ are b cycles of length q. In view of 4.15 we need only consider those terms on the right in which the (q)'s are skew-hook representations of $\mathfrak{S}_q$. If we denote by l_i the leg length of the skew-hook representation of Q_i, then:

4.53 *The expression*

$$\sigma = \chi^{(q)}(Q_1)\, \chi^{(q)}(Q_2) \ldots \chi^{(q)}(Q_b) = (-1)^{\Sigma l_i},$$

as well as the q-core $[\tilde{\lambda}]$, *is independent of the order of removing the b q-hooks from* $[\lambda]$.

Proof. Let us fix our attention on the removal of two successive skew q-hooks $(q)_1$ and $(q)_2$ from $[\lambda]$. If these are disjoint the order of their removal is immaterial and

4.54

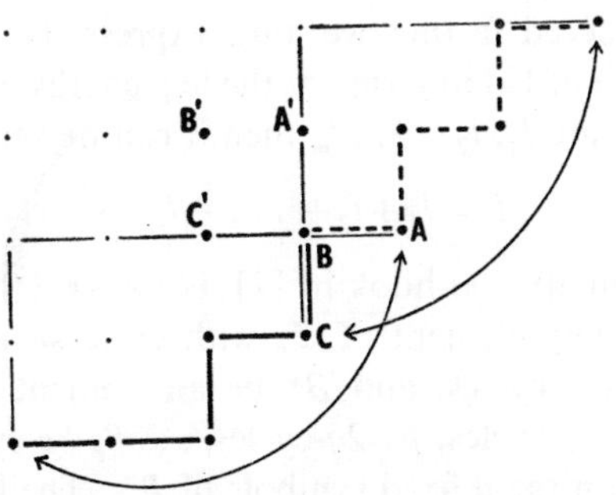

σ is unaffected. On the other hand if they overlap as do, for instance, the (i, j) and (s, t) hooks for

$$i < s, \quad j > t,$$

then the order is important. It is easy to see, however, that the order of removal only affects the overlapping part. To fix ideas let us suppose that the nodes ABC are common to $(q)_1$ and $(q)_2$. Let $A'B'C'$ be the neighbouring nodes to ABC along their respective diagonals. (Note that they have the same content!) If ABC are removed in say $(q)_1$ then $A'B'C'$ will replace them in $(q)_2$ with new leg length $l'_2 = l_2 + 1$. On the other hand if ABC are removed first along with $(q)_2$, $A'B'C'$ will replace them in $(q)_1$ with new leg length $l'_1 = l_1 - 1$. Thus

$$l_1 + l'_2 = l_2 + l'_1 + 2,$$

so that σ remains the same and the same nodes are removed from $[\lambda]$ in either case. Successive application of the argument proves the theorem.

Returning now to 4.52, if $b = b_0 + b_1 + \ldots + b_{q-1}$ where $[\lambda]_q^r$ contains b_r nodes and is a representation of $\mathfrak{S}_{b_r}$ of degree $f^{(r)}$, then the number of different ways of removing the b q-hooks is equal to f_q^λ where

4.55
$$f_q^\lambda = \frac{b!}{b_0!\, b_1! \ldots b_{q-1}!} f^{(0)} f^{(1)} \ldots f^{(q-1)}$$

and f_q^λ is the degree of the skew representation $[\lambda]_q$ of $\mathfrak{S}_b$, by 4.47. Since the q-core $[\tilde{\lambda}]$ of $[\lambda]$ is uniquely determined and every term in the summation in 4.52 is the same, by 4.53, we have the

4.56 THEOREM. *If A is any permutation of $\mathfrak{S}_a$ and B is the product of b cycles of length q on the remaining $n-a=bq$ symbols, then*

$$\chi^\lambda(AB) = \sigma \,.\, f_q^\lambda \cdot \chi^{\tilde{\lambda}}(A).$$

If B contains more than b q-cycles $\chi^\lambda(AB) = 0$.

In order to proceed farther we must express the leg length l of an mq-hook $(mq\text{-}l, 1^l)$ of $[\lambda]$ in terms of the leg lengths of its m component q-hooks. If these are $l_1, l_2, \ldots, l_m$ then it can be verified that

4.57
$$l = l_1 + l_2 + \ldots + l_m + s$$

where the representative m-hook in $[\lambda]_q$ is $[m-s, 1^s]$.

Now let B' be any element of $\mathfrak{S}_b$ with cycle structure β_1 1-cycles, β_2 2-cycles, ... β_b b-cycles, and B^* be an element of $\mathfrak{S}_n$ $(n = a + bq)$ with a 1-cycles, β_1 q-cycles, β_2 $2q$-cycles, ... β_b bq-cycles and let A be any permutation on the a fixed symbols of B^*. The following theorem generalizes 4.56 and gives the further information seen to be desirable in § 4.2 for the calculation of characters:

4.58
$$\chi^\lambda(AB^*) = \sigma \,.\, (\chi(B') \text{ in } [\lambda]_q) \cdot \chi^{\tilde{\lambda}}(A).$$

Proof. As before, we are only interested in those terms in the expansion

$$\chi^{\lambda}(AB^*) = \sum \chi^{\tilde{\lambda}}(A) \,.\, \chi(q) \ldots \chi(2q) \ldots \chi(bq)$$

which arise from a sequence of $\beta_1+\beta_2+\ldots+\beta_b$ skew hook representations. Consider one such term and apply 4.57 to each of its skew constituents. Adding over the l's we obtain σ and over the s's we obtain $\chi(B')$ in $[\lambda]_q$, as in 4.21.

As in 4.56, if $\Sigma\beta_i > b$ then

4.581 $$\chi^{\lambda}(AB^*) = 0.$$

4.59 *Example.* Taking $[\lambda] = [5, 4, 2^2, 1]$ it is readily verified that

$$\sigma = 1, \quad [5, 4, 2^2, 1]_2 = [1^2]_2^0 \,.\, [2]_2^1, \quad [\tilde{\lambda}]_2 = [3, 2, 1].$$

The calculation

$$\chi(1^3, 3, 2^4) = 1 \,.\, 6 \,.\, (-2) = -12$$

illustrates 4.56, while the calculation

$$\chi(1^3, 3, 4^2) = 1 \,.\, (-2) \,.\, (-2) = 4$$

illustrates 4.58. In accordance with 4.581,

$$\chi(1, 3, 2^5) = 0.$$

4.6 The translation operator T. In § 4.3 we thought of the Young diagram $[\lambda]$ as a pattern of nodes superposed upon the matrix $\mathbf{G}(x)$. Each element $g_{ij}(x) = x+j-1$ 'covered' by the node (i, j) was called the *content* x_{j-i} of that node, and we defined the content $\mathbf{G}^{\lambda}(x)$ of $[\lambda]$ by 4.321.

It is natural to consider the effect on $\mathbf{G}^{\lambda}(x)$ of translating the diagram $[\lambda]$ over the matrix $\mathbf{G}(x)$. To this end we define an operator $\boldsymbol{T}$ such that

$$xT = T(x+1) = x+1, \text{ since } 1T = 1,$$

so that

4.61 $$\begin{aligned} x_{j-i}T &= x_{(j+1)-i} = x_{j-(i-1)}, \\ x_{j-i}T^{-1} &= x_{(j-1)-i} = x_{j-(i+1)}. \end{aligned}$$

If we apply the operator to $\mathbf{G}^{\lambda}(x)$, it follows from 4.41 that $\mathbf{G}^{\lambda}(x)T^n$ is the content of the set of nodes of $\mathbf{G}(x)$ covered by $[\lambda]$ when $[\lambda]$ is translated n units to the *right* or n units *upwards*, while $\mathbf{G}^{\lambda}(x)T^{-n}$ is the content of the set covered by $[\lambda]$ when $[\lambda]$ is translated n units to the *left* or n units *downwards*.

The study of the symmetric group begins, in a sense, with the study of the partition generating function

4.62 $$\mathscr{P}(x) = (1-x)^{-1}(1-x^2)^{-1}(1-x^3)^{-1}\dots = 1+p_1x+p_2x^2+\dots$$

in which the coefficient p_n of x^n is the number of partitions of n. Using the notion of content and the operator T we have:

4.63 $$(1-T^{-1}x_0)^{-1}(1-T^{-1}x_0x_1)^{-1}(1-T^{-1}x_0x_1x_2)^{-1}\dots = 1+\sum_{n=1}^{\infty}\sum_{\lambda} \boldsymbol{G}^{\lambda}(x).$$

Proof. It is sufficient to remark that

$$(x_0\,x_1\dots x_{\lambda_i-1})T^{1-i} = x_{1-i}\,x_{2-i}\dots x_{\lambda_i-i},$$

which is equivalent to calculating the content of the ith row of $[\lambda]$ by first calculating it in the first row and then translating this row downward to the ith position. Doing this in succession for each row of $[\lambda]$ we have

$$\boldsymbol{G}^{\lambda}(x) = (T^{-1}x_0x_1\dots x_{\lambda_h-1})(T^{-1}x_0x_1\dots x_{\lambda_{h-1}-1})\dots (T^{-1}x_0x_1\dots x_{\lambda_1-1}).$$

If α_j of the λ_i are equal to $j(j=1, 2, \dots, n)$, we have

$$\boldsymbol{G}^{\lambda}(x) = (T^{-1}x_0)^{\alpha_1}(T^{-1}x_0x_1)^{\alpha_2}\dots(T^{-1}x_0x_1\dots x_{n-1})^{\alpha_n}$$

which identifies $\boldsymbol{G}^{\lambda}(x)$ with a unique term on the left of 4.63. Conversely, each term on the left is the content of some Young diagram, proving the result.

There is another application of the operator T which is of interest. In 4.34 we established the connection between the content $\boldsymbol{G}^{\lambda}(x)$ and the Frobenius' symbol. It remains to relate $\boldsymbol{G}^{\lambda}(x)$ to $[\lambda]$ itself in an explicit manner via the first column hook length $\boldsymbol{h}_{i1}=\boldsymbol{h}_i$. The truth of the following lemma is obvious

4.64 *If* $[\lambda]=[\lambda_1, \lambda_2, \dots, \lambda_h]$ *then*

$$x_{\lambda_i-i}T^h = x_{\lambda_i+h-i} = x_{\boldsymbol{h}_i}, \quad x_{1-h}T^h = x_{1-h+h} = x_1.$$

Let L be the first column or set of left end nodes of the rows of $[\lambda]$ and let R be the set of right end nodes of the rows of $[\lambda]$. Then it amounts to the same thing to shift $[\lambda]$ to the left under the operation T^{-1} and add R on the right or to add L on the left of $[\lambda]$. We may write these equivalent operations in terms of the content as follows:

4.65 $$\boldsymbol{G}^{L}(x)\,T^{-1}\,.\,\boldsymbol{G}^{\lambda}(x) = \boldsymbol{G}^{\lambda}(x)\,T^{-1}\,.\,\boldsymbol{G}^{R}(x)$$

Now let us shift this 'bordered' $[\lambda]$ h places to the right by operating with T^h. First we note that

$$G^L(x)T^{-1+h} = x_0 x_1 \ldots x_{h-1}.$$

Next let

4.66 $$\theta = G^R(x)T^h = \prod_{i=1}^{h} x_{\boldsymbol{h}_i}$$

by 4.64. Thus 4.65 becomes

$$G^\lambda(x)T^h(x_0x_1 \ldots x_{h-1}) = G^\lambda(x)T^{-1+h}\,\theta.$$

Since

$$T^h(x_0x_1 \ldots x_{h-1}) = (Tx_0)^h,$$

this can be written

$$G^\lambda(x)(Tx_0)^h = G^\lambda(x)T^{-1+h}\,\theta,$$

so that

4.67 $$\theta = \frac{G^\lambda(x)}{G^\lambda(x)T^{-1}}\,(Tx_0)^h.$$

We can go one step further, since from 4.35

$$\frac{G^\lambda(x)}{G^\lambda(x)T^{-1}} = \prod_{t=-h}^{\lambda_1-1} x_t^{r_t},$$

so that

4.68 $$\theta = \prod_{t=-h}^{\lambda_1-1} x_t^{r_t}\,(Tx_0)^h.$$

In view of 4.34, this provides a direct analytical connection between the Frobenius' symbols a_i, b_i and the λ_i, which can now be obtained by 4.67 from any given monomial satisfying the conditions of 4.35.

4.69 *Example.* Suppose

$$G^\lambda(x) = x_{-4}x_{-3}^2x_{-2}^2x_{-1}^3x_0^3x_1^3x_2^2x_3^2x_4x_5x_6$$

as in Example 4.36, so that $h=5$. Thus

$$\frac{G^\lambda(x)}{G^\lambda(x)T^{-1}} = x_{-5}^{-1}\,x_{-4}^{-1}\,x_{-2}^{-1}\,x_1\,x_3\,x_6,$$

and
$$\begin{aligned}\theta &= (x_{-5}^{-1}\,x_{-4}^{-1}\,x_{-2}^{-1}\,x_1\,x_3\,x_6)\,(Tx_0)^5\\ &= x_0^{-1}\,x_1^{-1}\,x_3^{-1}\,x_6\,x_8\,x_{11}\,x_0\,x_1\,x_2\,x_3\,x_4\\ &= x_2\,x_4\,x_6\,x_8\,x_{11}.\end{aligned}$$

Thus $(\boldsymbol{h}_1, \boldsymbol{h}_2, \boldsymbol{h}_3, \boldsymbol{h}_4, \boldsymbol{h}_5) = (11, 8, 6, 4, 2)$ by 4.66, so that

$$(\lambda_1, \lambda_2, \lambda_3, \lambda_4, \lambda_5) = (7, 5, 4, 3, 2).$$

$a' = (32^2 1^3)$
$b' = (32^2)$
$a = (631)$
$b = (431)$
$\lambda = (a|b)$
$= (75432)$

CHAPTER FIVE

THE p-BLOCK STRUCTURE OF $\mathfrak{S}_n$

Introduction. Having defined the q-quotient $[\lambda]_q$ of a Young diagram $[\lambda]$, we prove in § 5.1 the complementary theorem that $[\lambda]$ is uniquely determined by $[\lambda]_q$ and the q-core $[\tilde{\lambda}]$. If we take $q=p$, a prime, we can derive the equality 5.22:

$$e(f^{\lambda}) = e(n!)-e((n-a)!)+e(f_p^{\lambda}),$$

which makes explicit for $\mathfrak{S}_n$ the unknown ε in 12.54(iii). Similarly, the curious congruence 5.28 which depends on Wilson's Theorem, is valid only for $q=p$.

In 1940-1 Nakayama noticed the significance of a *p-hook* in the reduction formula 4.21 due to Murnaghan and derived the equivalent of 5.27, which, along with 12.58, enabled him to conclude that a *p-core* $[\tilde{\lambda}]$, from which no p-hook is removable, is modularly irreducible and constitutes a block by itself. Moreover, he conjectured that in general two ordinary representations of $\mathfrak{S}_n$ belong to the same p-block if and only if they have the same p-core. This conjecture was proved by Brauer and the present author in 1947.

Since then Nakayama and Osima have given a more direct proof of the necessity of the conjecture, which we utilize in § 5.3. The proof of sufficiency, however, is more difficult and seems to require the older ideas. We shall not reproduce Brauer's argument in every detail but we shall try to make it plausible, referring the reader to the paper in question. Lately Osima (12) and Farahat and Higman have given alternative proofs. The difficulty and delicacy of all these arguments would suggest that we are at the heart of the matter and should stimulate the search for some generalization of Young's ideas, in terms of which the notion of a p-block of $\mathfrak{S}_n$ becomes almost trivial. Finally, by replacing the *defect* δ by the *weight* b according to 5.351, we achieve a further simplification of ideas.

In view of the important role played by the hook-graph H $[\lambda]$ in these developments it is not surprising that the Fundamental Theorem can be phrased (§ 5.4) in terms of the q-content, *even when q is not prime.*

5.1 Construction of $[\lambda]$ when $[\lambda]_q$ and the q-core $[\tilde{\lambda}]$ are given. In order to establish the defining property of a q-core we first make the following

Definition. A residue class of integers x_i congruent to r (mod q) will be called *complete* if and only if the members of the class can be arranged in order $x_0, x_1, \ldots, x_t$, where

$$x_i = r + iq \qquad (0 \leqq i \leqq t).$$

5.11 THEOREM. *If the first column hook lengths* $\boldsymbol{h}_1, \boldsymbol{h}_2, \ldots, \boldsymbol{h}_h$ *of* $[\lambda]$ *are divided into residue classes* (mod q), *then* $[\lambda]$ *is a q-core if and only if*

(i) *the* 0*-class is empty;*
(ii) *each r-class is empty or complete for* $0 < r < q$.

Proof. If we set $j=1$ in 4.43, $\lambda_1' = h \equiv 1-t$ (mod q), so that

5.12 $$s \equiv \boldsymbol{h}_i - h \qquad (\text{mod } q).$$

Thus, separating the $\boldsymbol{h}_i$'s into residue classes picks out all those rows of $[\lambda]$ whose end nodes belong to the same residue class. The condition (i) is obviously necessary and implies that no row of $[\lambda]$ can end in $s \equiv -h$ (mod q). To require, as in (ii), that a class of $\boldsymbol{h}_i$'s be complete implies that an s-node lies below each $s+1$-node on the rim of $[\lambda]$, and conversely. Thus, for $[\lambda]$ to be a q-core, condition (ii) is certainly necessary. On the other hand, taken along with (i) it is also sufficient, as we wished to prove.

We shall refer to a set of $\boldsymbol{h}_i$'s satisfying 5.11 (i) and (ii) as a *core set.* Starting from the foot of the first column, we can readily reconstruct a q-core $[\lambda]$ from its core set.

Now let us consider the effect on $\boldsymbol{H}[\lambda]$ of removing an mq-hook to yield $[\mu]$. From the representation point of view it is natural to remove the skew hook $[\lambda]-[\mu]$, but here we shall proceed according to the following steps:

(1) Delete from $\boldsymbol{H}[\lambda]$ all the hook numbers in the (i, j) right hook.

(2) Diminish by mq each of the integers $\boldsymbol{h}_{sj}$ $(s<i)$ standing above $\boldsymbol{h}_{ij}$ and move the reduced jth column of $\boldsymbol{H}[\lambda]$ past the $\lambda_i - j$ columns of the hook arm to form the λ_ith column of $\boldsymbol{H}[\mu]$.

(3) Diminish by mq each of the integers $\boldsymbol{h}_{it}$ $(t>j)$ standing to the left of $\boldsymbol{h}_{ij}$ and move the reduced ith row of $\boldsymbol{H}[\lambda]$ past the $\lambda_j' - i$ rows of the hook leg to form the λ_j'th row of $\boldsymbol{H}[\mu]$.

The effect of these operations on the $\boldsymbol{h}_{ij}$ which are divisible by q is to transform $[\lambda]_q$ into $[\mu]_q$ in a well defined manner so that:

5.13 *If* $[\lambda]-[\mu]$ *is a skew mq-hook, then* $[\lambda]_q - [\mu]_q$ *is a skew m-hook and there is a* 1-1 *correspondence between the mq-hooks of* $[\lambda]$ *and the m-hooks of* $[\lambda]_q$.

We turn now to the problem of constructing $[\lambda]$ when the core $[\tilde{\lambda}]$

and the q-quotient $[\lambda]_q$ are given, reversing the steps (1), (2) and (3) above. In general the depth h of $[\lambda]$ will be greater than the depth $\tilde{h}$ of $[\tilde{\lambda}]$, so we adopt the convenient trick of adding vacuous rows, thus *extending* the cores set $\tilde{\Gamma}(\tilde{z}_i)$ for $i=1, 2, \ldots, h$, to the *basic set*

$$\Gamma : z_1 = \tilde{z}_1+e, z_2 = \tilde{z}_2+e, \ldots z_{\tilde{h}} = \tilde{z}_{\tilde{h}}+e, z_{\tilde{h}+1} = e-1, \ldots$$
$$\ldots z_{h-1} = 1, z_h = 0.$$

Again we may divide Γ into residue classes, the zero class now appearing for $e>0$. We take the q-quotient $[\lambda]_q$ as in 4.46, setting

$$[\lambda]_q^r = [\lambda_1^r, \lambda_2^r, \ldots, \lambda_{t_r}^r] \quad (r = 0, 1, \ldots, q-1),$$

and add the quantities

5.14 $$\lambda_t^r \cdot q \qquad (t = 1, 2, \ldots, t_r),$$

in order to the t_r *largest* members in the appropriate residue class of Γ. We determine this class r by requiring that

5.15 $$r \equiv z_i - h \pmod{q},$$

as in 5.12.

The only problem which remains is to determine the necessary extension e. Clearly, *e must be large enough to yield at least t_r members in the r-th residue class.* If e is unnecessarily large, the last one or more z_i of Γ will remain unchanged. The resulting diagram $[\lambda]$ is unaffected, however, by increasing e above its minimum value. Thus:

5.16 *The Young diagram $[\lambda]$ is uniquely determined when its q-core $[\tilde{\lambda}]$ and its q-quotient $[\lambda]_q$ are given.*

The following example will serve to make the construction clear.

5.17 *Example.* Assume that $q=3$, $[\tilde{\lambda}]=[2, 1^2]$ and that

$$[\lambda]_3^0 = [2, 1], \ [\lambda]_3^1 = [1^2], \ [\lambda]_3^2 = [1].$$
$$\tilde{\Gamma} : \tilde{z}_1 = 4, \ \tilde{z}_2 = 2, \ \tilde{z}_3 = 1.$$

We choose $e=7$, so that the basic set becomes:

$$\Gamma : z_1 = 11, \ z_2 = 9, \ z_3 = 8, \ z_4 = 6, \ z_5 = 5, \ z_6 = 4,$$
$$z_7 = 3, \ z_8 = 2, \ z_9 = 1, \ z_{10} = 0.$$

Here $z_6=4$, $z_9=1$ belong to the 0-class by 5.15, so to these we must add $3.\lambda_1^0=6$ and $3.\lambda_2^0=3$ respectively; $z_1=11$, $z_3=8$, $z_5=5$, $z_8=2$ belong to the 1-class, so we must add $3.\lambda_1^1=3$ to 11 and $3.\lambda_2^1=3$ to 8;

similarly $z_2=9$, $z_4=6$, $z_7=3$, $z_{10}=0$ belong to the 0 class and we must add $3.\lambda_1^2=3$ to 9. Rearranging, we obtain the set

$$14,\ 12,\ 11,\ 10,\ 6,\ 5,\ 4,\ 3,\ 2,\ 0.$$

These are not the first column hook lengths since $z_{10}=0$ remains unchanged; while $z_9=1$ is changed into 4. Thus it would have been sufficient to take $e=6$, so that we obtain the first column hook lengths:

$$\begin{aligned} h_1 = 13,\ h_2 = 11,\ h_3 = 10,\ h_4 = 9,\ h_5 = 5,\\ h_6 = 4,\ h_7 = 3,\ h_8 = 2,\ h_9 = 1 \end{aligned}$$

of $[5, 4^3, 1^5]$.

We can now give an answer to the important question, how many diagrams exist with a given q-core $[\tilde{\lambda}]$ containing a nodes and having b removable q-hooks so that $n=a+bq$?

5.18 *If $p(m)$ is the number of partitions of m, then the number $l(b)$ of Young diagrams having q-core $[\tilde{\lambda}]$ and b removable q-hooks is given by*

$$l(b) = \sum_{b_0, b_1, \ldots, b_{q-1}} p(b_0)\, p(b_1) \ldots p(b_{q-1})$$

$$\sum_0^{q-1} b_i = b, \qquad (0 \leqq b_i \leqq b).$$

for any $[\tilde{\lambda}]$. This enumeration is valid for all values of q.

Proof. It is only necessary to remark that the expression

$$p(b_0)\, p(b_1) \ldots p(b_{q-1})$$

enumerates all possible skew diagrams $[\lambda]_q$ associated with a given partition of b, and so, by 5.16, the number of diagrams $[\lambda]$ with q-core $[\tilde{\lambda}]$ associated with such a partition. Summing over all partitions of b yields the number $l(b)$ in question.

5.2 The hook graph $H[\lambda]$. In § 12.5 we saw that the power of a prime p dividing the degree f^λ of $[\lambda]$ is intimately related to the block structure of the decomposition matrix D. *We now assume that* $q=p$, and prove the following explicit form of 12.54(iii):

5.21 $$e(f^\lambda) = e(n!) - e(n-a)! + e(f_p^\lambda),$$

where $e(m)$ is the exponent of the maximum power of p which divides m, f_p^λ is the degree of $[\lambda]_p$, and a is the number of nodes in the p-core of $[\lambda]$.

Proof. By 2.37

5.22 $$e(f^\lambda) = e(n!) - e(H^\lambda),$$

but by 4.46, those h_{ij} which are divisible by p may be written

5.23
$$h_{ij} = h_{ij}^{(r)} \cdot p,$$

where (h_{ij}^r) is the hook graph of the constituent $[\lambda]_p^r$ of $[\lambda]_p$. As in 3.13,

5.24
$$f_p^\lambda = b! \,/\, H_p^\lambda,$$

so that

$$e(f_p^\lambda) = e(b!) - e(H_p^\lambda),$$

where $H_p^\lambda = \Pi h_{ij}^r$ for all i, j and all r. Finally, by 5.23

$$\begin{aligned} e(H^\lambda) &= b + e(H_p^\lambda) \\ &= [b + e(b!)] - e(f_p^\lambda) \\ &= e(n-a)! - e(f_p^\lambda), \end{aligned}$$

since $n-a=bp$ and $e[(bp)!]=b+e(b!)$. Thus

$$e(f^\lambda) = e(n!) - e(n-a)! + e(f^\lambda{}_p)$$

by 5.22, proving the theorem.

We conclude from 12.58 and 5.21 that:

5.25 *Every p-core* $[\tilde{\lambda}]$ *containing n nodes yields a modularly irreducible representation of* $\mathfrak{S}_n$ *which constitutes a block by itself and an indecomposable component of the regular representation of* $\mathfrak{S}_n$.

There is another approach to the equation 5.22 which is worth developing. Clearly, only the factors of H^λ divisible by p affect $e(H^\lambda)$, i.e. the terms making up $[\lambda]_p$. But we may treat each disjoint constituent of $[\lambda]_p$ in the same manner, constructing $[\lambda]_{p^2}$ whose nodes represent the p^2-hooks removable from $[\lambda]$. Continuing thus, we obtain $[\lambda]_{p^3}$, $[\lambda]_{p^4}$, etc., and have the sequence of diagrams

5.26
$$[\lambda],\ [\lambda]_p,\ [\lambda]_{p^2},\ \ldots\ [\lambda]_{p^r}.$$

We denote the number of nodes in the respective p-cores by

$$a,\ a_1,\ a_2,\ \ldots,\ a_r.$$

Let us think of removing the a_r p^r-hooks from $[\lambda]$ which correspond to the p-core

$$[\lambda]_{p^r}.$$

The effect on $[\lambda]_{p^{r-1}}$ will be to remove all its p-hooks leaving nothing but the core. We then remove the corresponding a_{r-1} p^{r-1}-hooks from $[\lambda]$. The successive removal of hooks corresponding to the cores of the diagrams 5.26 leads to the *p-series*:

$$p^r, \ldots (a_r \text{ times});\; p^{r-1}, \ldots (a_{r-1} \text{ times});\; \ldots p, \ldots (a_1 \text{ times}).$$

The removal of all such hooks reduces $[\lambda]$ to its p-core $[\tilde{\lambda}]$, so that

$$n = a + a_1 p + a_2 p^2 + \ldots + a_n p^r.$$

By applying 5.21 in succession to the diagrams in 5.26 we can write 5.22 in the form

5.27 $$e(f^\lambda) = e(n!) - [a_1 e(p!) + a_2 e(p^2!) + \ldots + a_r e(p^r!)].$$

In 5.13 we saw the effect on $\boldsymbol{H}[\lambda]$ of removing a p-hook. If this process be repeated b times we have reduced $[\lambda]$ to its p-core $[\tilde{\lambda}]$ and we ask the question—What is the relationship between $\boldsymbol{H}[\lambda]$, $\boldsymbol{H}[\lambda]_p$ and $\boldsymbol{H}[\tilde{\lambda}]$? In order to answer this question we prove first the following

5.28 LEMMA. *In the diagram* $[p-k, \lambda_2, \lambda_3, \ldots, \lambda_{k+1}]$

$$\Pi \boldsymbol{h} \equiv -(-1)^k \quad (\text{mod } p),$$

where $\Pi \boldsymbol{h} = \boldsymbol{h}_{12}\boldsymbol{h}_{13} \ldots \boldsymbol{h}_{1,\,p-k}\, \boldsymbol{h}_{21}\, \boldsymbol{h}_{31} \ldots \boldsymbol{h}_{k+1,\,1}$ (omitting $\boldsymbol{h}_{11}$).

Proof. In the simple case of $[p-k, 1^k]$ we have, as in 4.16,

$$\begin{aligned} \Pi \boldsymbol{h} &= 1\; 2 \ldots (p-k-1)\; k\; (k-1) \ldots 2\; 1 \\ &\equiv 1\; 2 \ldots (p-k-1)\,(p-k)\,(p-k+1) \ldots (p-2)\,(p-1) \\ &\qquad (-1)^k \quad (\text{mod } p) \\ &= (p-1)!\,(-1)^k \\ &\equiv -(-1)^k \quad (\text{mod } p) \end{aligned}$$

by Wilson's Theorem.

If we assume the result in the general case, and set $x = k-i+j$, $\boldsymbol{h}_{i1} = x$, $\boldsymbol{h}_{1j} = p-(x+1)$, then adding a node in the (i,j)-position changes $\boldsymbol{h}_{i1}$ into $x+1$ and $\boldsymbol{h}_{1j}$ into $p-x$, leaving every other $\boldsymbol{h}_{k1}$, $\boldsymbol{h}_{1n}$ unaltered. Thus $\Pi \boldsymbol{h}$ remains unaltered modulo p, proving the lemma.

We are now in a position to prove the following interesting result involving the expression σ of 4.53.

5.29 THEOREM. $$\frac{\boldsymbol{H}^\lambda}{p^b \boldsymbol{H}_p^\lambda} \equiv (-1)^b\, \sigma\, \boldsymbol{H}^{\tilde{\lambda}} \quad (\text{mod } p).$$

Proof. As we saw in 4.45

$$\boldsymbol{h}_{ij} = \boldsymbol{h}_{ij}^r \cdot p,$$

so that the product of all those elements of $\boldsymbol{H}[\lambda]$ divisible by p is given by $p^b \boldsymbol{H}_p^\lambda$.

If we apply the steps (1), (2), (3) in § 5.1 to remove each of the b p-hooks in succession from $[\lambda]$ we are deleting b sets of products of $\boldsymbol{h}$'s each of which is congruent by the lemma to $-(-1)^k$. Thus we conclude that

$$\frac{\boldsymbol{H}^{\lambda}}{p^b \boldsymbol{H}_p^{\tilde{\lambda}}} \equiv \prod (-(-1)^k)\, \boldsymbol{H}^{\tilde{\lambda}} \pmod p \qquad b \text{ factors}$$
$$= (-1)^b\, \sigma\, \boldsymbol{H}^{\tilde{\lambda}}$$

by 4.53, since the subtractions of p from the remaining $\boldsymbol{h}_{ij}$ lead to the $\tilde{\boldsymbol{h}}$'s of $\boldsymbol{H}[\tilde{\lambda}]$.

5.3 The blocks of $\mathfrak{S}_n$. According to the 12.51, two ordinary representations $[\lambda]$, $[\mu]$ of $\mathfrak{S}_n$ belong to the same p-block if and only if

$$\gamma_i^{\lambda} \equiv \gamma_i^{\mu} \pmod p$$

for all classes C_i of $\mathfrak{S}_n$. We may take p rather than $\wp$, since all representations of $\mathfrak{S}_n$ are rational by 2.17. We recall the definition 11.41:

5.31 $$\gamma_i^{\lambda} = g_i \chi_i^{\lambda} / f^{\lambda}.$$

In 1940-1 Nakayama conjectured that *two representations* $[\lambda]$ *and* $[\mu]$ *of* $\mathfrak{S}_n$ *belong to the same p-block if and only if they have the same p-core* $[\tilde{\lambda}]$. The proof which we give here of this important result proceeds in two, not independent, stages. Throughout we shall assume that $n = a + bp$, where $[\lambda]$ is of weight b with p-core $[\tilde{\lambda}]$ containing a nodes. A will denote an element of $\mathfrak{S}_a$, assumed to be expressed on the symbols $1, 2, \ldots, a$, and B will denote a product of b cycles, each of length p, on the remaining bp symbols taken in succession. We prove first that

5.32 $$\gamma^{\lambda}(AB) \equiv (-1)^b\, \gamma^{\tilde{\lambda}}(A) \pmod p.$$

Proof. From 2.37, 4.56 and 5.31 we have

(5.321) $$\gamma^{\lambda}(AB) = g(AB)\,(\sigma f_p^{\lambda} \chi^{\tilde{\lambda}}(A))\, \boldsymbol{H}^{\lambda} / n!$$

Let us begin by showing that the number $g(AB)$ of conjugates of AB in $\mathfrak{S}_n$ is given by

5.322 $$g(AB) = \frac{g_A\, n!}{a!\, b!\, p^b}$$

where g_A is the number of conjugates of A in $\mathfrak{S}_a$. Consider the $b!$ elements of $\mathfrak{S}_b^*$ which permute the b p-cycles of B. Clearly each element of $\mathfrak{S}_b^*$ commutes with B as will each element of the Abelian group $\mathscr{P}$ of order p^b generated by all these b p-cycles taken separately. Moreover each element of $\mathscr{P}$ commutes with each element of $\mathfrak{S}_b^*$. Thus the normalizer of B in $\mathfrak{S}_n$ is the direct product

$$\mathfrak{S}_a \times \mathfrak{S}_b^* \times \mathscr{P}$$

of order $a!\,b!\,p^b$, so that $g\,(AB)$ has the required form.

Thus 5.321 becomes

5.323
$$\gamma^{\lambda}(AB) = \frac{g_A}{a!\,b!\,p^b} \cdot \sigma f_p^{\lambda} \chi^{\bar{\lambda}}(A) \cdot H^{\lambda},$$
$$= \sigma\, \gamma^{\bar{\lambda}}(A)\, H^{\lambda} \,/\, (p^b\, H_p^{\lambda}\, H^{\bar{\lambda}})$$

since $\gamma^{\bar{\lambda}}(A) = g_A\, \chi^{\bar{\lambda}}(A)\, H^{\bar{\lambda}} \,/\, a!$. Thus, finally, by 5.29

5.324
$$\gamma^{\lambda}(AB) \equiv (-1)^b\, \gamma^{\bar{\lambda}}(A) \qquad \text{(mod } p)$$

as desired. *If AB has more than b p-cycles one must be part of A so that both sides of* 5.32 *vanish.*

Consider now the effect of replacing B by the identity element in $\mathfrak{S}_n$. In the first place we must use 4.16 instead of 4.15 to derive the congruence

$$\chi^{\lambda}(A) \equiv \sigma \,.\, f_p^{\lambda} \,.\, \chi^{\bar{\lambda}}(A) \qquad \text{(mod } p).$$

Then, by an argument similar to that used above

$$g(A) = \frac{g_A\, n!}{a!\,(bp)!}.$$

It follows from Wilson's Theorem that

$$\frac{(bp)!}{b!\,p^b} \equiv (-1)^b \qquad \text{(mod } p),$$

so that after making the appropriate changes, the preceding conclusion remains valid if we delete the factor $(-1)^b$ in 5.32. Thus we have

5.33
$$\gamma^{\lambda}(A) \equiv \gamma^{\bar{\lambda}}(A) \qquad \text{(mod } p).$$

5.34 *The necessity of the Nakayama Conjecture.* If we assume that $[\lambda]$ and $[\mu]$ belong to the same block **B** of $\mathfrak{S}_n$ we have by 12.51:

5.341
$$\gamma^{\lambda}(AB) \equiv \gamma^{\mu}(AB) \qquad \text{(mod } p),$$

so that from 5.32

5.342
$$\gamma^{\bar{\lambda}}(A) \equiv \gamma^{\bar{\mu}}(A). \qquad \text{(mod } p).$$

Thus 5.342 identifies $[\bar{\lambda}]$ with $[\bar{\mu}]$, by 12.57 and 5.25.

5.35 *The sufficiency of the Nakayama Conjecture.* We must now show, conversely, that if $[\lambda]$ and $[\mu]$ have the same p-core then they must belong to the same p-block of $\mathfrak{S}_n$.

In 5.16 we showed that *every* irreducible representation $[\lambda]$ of $\mathfrak{S}_n$ is defined uniquely by a p-core $[\tilde{\lambda}]$ containing a nodes and a p-quotient $[\lambda]_p$ containing b nodes where $n=a+bp$. Moreover, the exact power of p dividing f^λ is given by 5.21, so that (cf. 12.54(iii)) *the highest power of p dividing g/f^λ is p^δ where*

5.351 $$\delta = e((bp)!) = b+e(b!).$$

But we have just seen that all irreducible representations $[\lambda]$ in a given block **B** have the same p-core $[\tilde{\lambda}]$. Thus the number of blocks is not less than the number of p-cores, and it remains to show that no two $[\lambda]$'s having the same p-core can belong to different blocks.

If we take A to be a p-regular element of $\mathfrak{S}_a$, defined as above, whose normalizer $\mathcal{N}$ in $\mathfrak{S}_a$ is of order prime to p, then the normalizer of A in $\mathfrak{S}_n$ is the direct product $\mathcal{H}=\mathcal{N}\times\mathfrak{S}_{n-a}$ and the defect group of the class containing A is a p-Sylow subgroup of $\mathcal{H}$ of order p^δ, where δ is given by 5.351.

We may summarize the important theorem 4.56 thus:

(i) If B' contains $b'>b$ p-cycles then $\chi^\lambda(A'B')=0$ for all A';

(ii) There exists a p-regular element A of $\mathfrak{S}_a$ such that $\chi^\lambda(AB)\neq 0$ if B contains exactly b p-cycles.

If we assume that the defect of the block containing $[\lambda]$ is $\delta'>\delta$, then it can be shown that there exists a p-regular element A' and a product B' of $b'>b$ p-cycles such that $\chi^\lambda(A'B')\neq 0$ contradicting (i). On the other hand, if $\delta'<\delta$, then $b'<b$ and $\chi^\lambda(AB)=0$ for all A, which contradicts (ii). Thus we conclude that *every diagram with p-core $[\tilde{\lambda}]$ yields a representation of $\mathfrak{S}_n$ of defect exactly $\delta=b+e(b!)$.*

We are now ready to complete the proof of the sufficiency of Nakayama's conjecture. If $[\lambda]$ and $[\mu]$ have the same p-core $[\tilde{\lambda}]$, it follows from 5.33 that

5.33 unproved

5.352 $$\gamma^\lambda(A) \equiv \gamma^\mu(A) \pmod{p}.$$

Since this relation holds for all p-regular elements A which belong to classes of defect δ we conclude from 12.57 that $[\lambda]$ and $[\mu]$ belong to the same block. Thus:

5.36 FUNDAMENTAL THEOREM. *The necessary and sufficient condition that two irreducible representations of $\mathfrak{S}_n$ should belong to the same p-block is that they should have the same p-core.*

In 12.5 we remarked that for $\mathscr{G}=\mathfrak{S}_n$ it would be more natural and significant to replace the notion of the *defect* δ by that of the *weight* b for any block **B**. The relation between δ and b is given by 5.351. Note that b can take any integral value for a p-core, but this is not true of δ.

5.4 The primeness of q. As we saw in § 5.1 the notions of the q-core $[\lambda]$ and the q-quotient $[\lambda]_q$ are valid for all q, as are also the important theorems 5.16 and 5.18 according to which the number of diagrams $[\lambda]$ of given q-core and weight may be enumerated.

In § 5.2 and § 5.3 we found it necessary to insist that $q=p$, a prime. The significance of this restriction will become clearer in the following chapter where we shall establish explicitly the correspondence between the p-regular classes of $\mathfrak{S}_n$ and the indecomposables of the regular representation, i.e. the columns of the decomposition matrix D.

Let us return for a moment to 5.11, and by adding zero rows to $[\lambda]$ arrange that $h\equiv 0(q)$. With this understood, 5.12 takes the form

5.41 $$h_i \equiv r \qquad (\text{mod } q),$$

where r is the q-residue class of the node at the end of ith row of $[\lambda]$ and $h_i=\lambda_i+h-i$ is the corresponding first column hook length.

Consider now two representations $[\lambda]$ and $[\bar{\lambda}]$ of $\mathfrak{S}_n$ each having the same q-content as defined in § 4.4. If we start from the null graph and add nodes, then in the two sequences

$$h_1, h_2, \ldots, h_h$$
$$\bar{h}_1, \bar{h}_2, \ldots, \bar{h}_h$$

there must be the same number of terms congruent to each residue r, by 5.41. If $[\lambda]$ is a p-core then 5.11 requires that

$$h_1, h_2, \ldots, h_h$$

be a basic set Γ from which we could obtain the corresponding core set $\bar{\Gamma}$ by subtracting the appropriate integer, so that conditions (i) and (ii) of 5.11 are satisfied. Since all the h_i's must be different, any change could only increase n, so that

$$h_i = \bar{h}_i.$$

Thus we conclude that:

5.42 *Two q-cores are equal if and only if they have the same q-content.*

Taking 5.42 in conjunction with 4.41 and replacing *block* by *set* we may rephrase the Fundamental Theorem 5.36 as follows:

5.43 *The necessary and sufficient condition that two irreducible representations of* $\mathfrak{S}_n$ *belong to the same q-set is that they have the same q-content.*

If we denote a *q-set* of Young diagrams $[\lambda]$ with the same q-core $[\tilde{\lambda}]$ by Q and if $q=q_1q_2$, then it follows from 4.46 that

$$[\lambda]_q = \Big[[\lambda]_{q_1}\Big]_{q_2} = \Big[[\lambda]_{q_2}\Big]_{q_1}.$$

This implies that, for suitably chosen Q_1 and Q_2,

5.44 $$Q \subset Q_1 \cap Q_2.$$

Finally, we remark that taking residues in 4.63 leads to the congruence

5.45 $$(1-T^{-1}x_0)^{-1}(1-T^{-1}x_0x_1)^{-1}(1-T^{-1}x_0x_1x_2)^{-1}\dots$$
$$\equiv 1+\sum_{n=1}^{\infty}\sum_{\lambda} \mathbf{G}_q^{\lambda}(x) \pmod{q},$$

where $\mathbf{G}_q^{\lambda}(x)$ is the q-content of $[\lambda]$. Also, $\theta\equiv\theta_q \pmod{q}$.

CHAPTER SIX

THE DIMENSIONS OF A p-BLOCK

Introduction. As in the preceding chapter, we develop first those parts of the theory which do not depend on the primeness of q. In § 6.1 the processes of *r-inducing* and *r-restricting* are studied and in § 6.2 *complementation* with reference to a certain r-Boolean algebra is defined for each $[\lambda]$. In particular, corresponding to the enumeration of the $l(b)$ Young diagrams $[\lambda]$ of weight b with q-core $[\tilde{\lambda}]$ in § 5.1:

$$l(b) = \sum p(b_0)\, p(b_1) \ldots p(b_{q-1}) \qquad \left(\sum_{i=0}^{q-1} b_i = b,\, 0 \leqq b_i \leqq b\right),$$

we show in § 6.3 that the number of such diagrams which are *q-regular*, i.e. have no q rows of equal length, is given by

$$l'(b) = \sum p(b_1)\, p(b_2) \ldots p(b_{q-1}) \qquad \left(\sum_{i=1}^{q-1} b_i = b,\, 0 \leqq b_i \leqq b\right).$$

The similarity between these two expressions indicates that they have a common basis of ideas, though these ideas go much deeper in the case of $l'(b)$ than in the case of $l(b)$.

In order to equate the number of regular diagrams with the number of regular classes or modularly irreducible representations in a block *it is necessary to assume that* $q=p$. Sections 6.4 and 6.5 are devoted to proving that the D-matrix of a p-block of weight b has $l(b)$ rows and $l'(b)$ columns, irrespective of the p-core. Thus, for $q=p$:

$$k = \Sigma l(b), \quad k' = \Sigma l'(b),$$

where k is the number of classes of $\mathfrak{S}_n$, k' of which are regular.

6.1 r-inducing and r-restricting. The processes of inducing and restricting are intimately related via Frobenius' reciprocity theorem 11.54, and their expressions in terms of the representations theory of $\mathfrak{S}_n$ was developed in Chapter III. In order to see the significance of these processes in the modular theory of $\mathfrak{S}_n$, and of the corresponding Nakayama reciprocity formulae 12.61, 12.62, we must study them in the light of the *q-graph* $G_q[\lambda]$ defined in § 4.5.

In § 5.4 we saw that the representations $[\lambda]$ of $\mathfrak{S}_n$ could be separated into q-sets which were distinguished according to the q-core $[\tilde{\lambda}]$ or the

q-content G_q. Thus the process of adding a node in all possible ways to $[\lambda]$ would in general lead to new diagrams belonging to *different* q-sets of $\mathfrak{S}_{n+1}$. For example, denoting this inducing process by $\uparrow$, we would have for $q=3$:

$$[3, 2, 1] \uparrow [4, 2, 1]+[3^2, 1]+[3, 2^2]+[3, 2, 1^2],$$

where the added node is of residue class 0 in the case of [4, 2, 1] and $[3, 2, 1^2]$, of class 1 in the case of $[3^2, 1]$ and of class 2 in the case of $[3, 2^2]$, with cores [1], $[2, 1^2]$, [3, 1] respectively. If we write the residue class r above the $\uparrow$ we have a well defined process which we shall call *r-inducing*. For example,

$$[3, 2, 1] \overset{0}{\uparrow} [4, 2, 1]+[3, 2, 1^2],$$

r-restricting is defined in a similar manner; for example,

$$[4, 2, 1] \underset{0}{\downarrow} [3, 2, 1]+[4, 1^2].$$

The following theorem is an immediate consequence of 5.43:

6.11 *The necessary and sufficient condition that two diagrams $[\lambda']$ and $[\lambda'']$ obtained by adding (removing) a node to (from) a given diagram $[\lambda]$ should have the same p-core, is that the added (removed) nodes should have the same residue class.*

In order to study the effects of such addition or removal of an r-node we make the following

6.12 *Definitions.* We shall call†

(i) the number u of r-nodes which can be added to $[\lambda]$ the *r-defect* of $[\lambda]$;

(ii) the number v of r-nodes which can be removed from $[\lambda]$ the *r-affect* of $[\lambda]$.

We denote by $\tilde{u}$ and $\tilde{v}$ the *r-defect* and the *r-affect* of the core $[\tilde{\lambda}]$ of $[\lambda]$.

Recalling that the class of a hook is defined to be the class of its head node (§ 4.4) we have the following two simple results:

6.13 *Neither adding nor removing an mq-hook of class different from r or $r-1$ changes u, v, $\tilde{u}$ or $\tilde{v}$.*

Proof. Note that an mq-hook of class different from r or $r-1$ cannot begin or end in an r-node, and such a node must be internal to the corresponding skew hook taken along the rim of $[\lambda]$. Thus the addition

† Attention should be drawn to the quite different meaning of *defect* in 12.53 and 12.55.

or removal of such a hook does not affect u and v. The core remains the same, so $\tilde{u}$, $\tilde{v}$ remain unchanged.

6.14 *Neither adding nor removing an r-node changes the constituents of* $[\lambda]_q$ *of class different from* r *or* $r-1$, *but does modify both these constituents.*

Proof. Note that an r-node can be added at the end of a row of $[\lambda]$ whose final node is of class $r-1$, and, except in the first row, provided such an r-position is also at the foot of a column whose final node is of class $r+1$ and only in such places. But the $\boldsymbol{h} \equiv 0 \pmod q$ which yield the constituent of $[\lambda]_q$ of class $r-1$ lie in rows which end in $(r-1)$-nodes and consequently in columns which end in r-nodes, and those which yield the constituent of class r lie in rows which end in r-nodes and in columns which end in $(r+1)$-nodes. Thus the addition of an r-node modifies both these constituents, but will not affect any other constituent of $[\lambda]_q$. A similar argument applies to the removal of an r-node.

In order to study the change in the *weight* b of $[\lambda]$ let us consider first the effect of adding an r-node at an *r-position* P at the intersection of the ith row and jth column of $[\lambda]$, for which we assume $d>0$.

(i) Consider first those $\boldsymbol{h} \equiv 0 \pmod q$ which lie in the ith row and are so changed into $\boldsymbol{h} \equiv 1 \pmod q$. Clearly the number of $\boldsymbol{h}_{ik} \equiv 0 \pmod q$ in $\boldsymbol{H}[\lambda]$ for $k<j$ is equal to the number of foot-nodes of class r below P, which number we denote by $(r)_{FB}$. On the other hand the number of $\boldsymbol{h}_{lj} \equiv 0 \pmod q$ for $l<i$ which lie in the jth column is equal to the number of head-nodes of class r which lie *above* P, which we denote by $(r)_{HA}$. Thus, neglecting other changes, adding an r-node at P *decreases* the weight by

$$\bar{\Delta} = (r)_{FB} + (r)_{HA}.$$

Certainly all the v removable r-nodes of $[\lambda]$ contribute to $\bar{\Delta}$, but other r-nodes contribute as well as the following diagrams show.

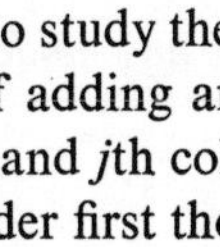

FIG. 6.1

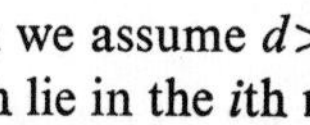

FIG. 6.2

If the arrangement illustrated in Fig. 6.1 appears ε_A times on the rim of λ *above* P and that in Fig. 6.2 appears ε_B times *below* P then

6.141 $$\bar{\Delta} = (r)_{FB} + (r)_{HA} = v + \varepsilon_A + \varepsilon_B.$$

(ii) Let us turn now to those $\boldsymbol{h} \equiv -1 \pmod q$ which are changed into $\boldsymbol{h} \equiv 0 \pmod q$. If we set $s = r-1$ in 4.43, it follows that the number of

$\boldsymbol{h}_{ik} \equiv -1 \pmod{q}$ for $k<j$ is equal to the number of foot-nodes of class $r+1$ *below* P; denote this number by $(r+1)_{FB}$. On the other hand, the number of $\boldsymbol{h}_{lj} \equiv -1 \pmod{q}$ for $l<i$ which lie in the jth column is similarly equal to the number of head-nodes of class $r-1$ lying *above* P, which we denote by $(r-1)_{HA}$. Thus, again neglecting other changes, adding an r-node at P *increases* the weight by

$$\Delta = (r+1)_{FB}+(r-1)_{HA}.$$

As before, Δ enumerates not only the $(r-1)$-nodes as in Fig. 6.1 and $(r+1)$-nodes as in Fig. 6.2 but also all those places where an r-node could be added, excluding P itself. Thus we have

6.142 $$\Delta = (r+1)_{FB}+(r-1)_{HA} = (u-1)+\varepsilon_A+\varepsilon_B.$$

Subtracting 6.141 from 6.142 we have the desired change in weight of $[\lambda]$. Removing an r-node interchanges the roles of u and v and also of Δ and $\bar{\Delta}$, so that we have:

6.15 *The change in weight of* $[\lambda]$ *arising by adding an r-node is given by*

$$u-v-1,$$

and by removing an r-node is given by

$$v-u-1,$$

where u and v are respectively the r-defect and r-affect of $[\lambda]$.

While 6.15 gives the *increment* in the weight of $[\lambda]$, it is important to realize that a corresponding change of $\tilde{u}-\tilde{v}-1$ must have taken place in the weight of the core $[\tilde{\lambda}]$, so that

6.16 $$u-v = \tilde{u}-\tilde{v}.$$

In particular, for a core either $\tilde{u}$ or $\tilde{v}$ vanishes, since otherwise a p-hook would be removable.

The following property of cores is important:

6.17 *If the r-defect (affect) of a q-core* $[\tilde{\lambda}]$ *is* $\tilde{u}(\tilde{v})$ *then the addition (removal) of* $\tilde{u}(\tilde{v})$ *r-nodes yields a q-core* $[\tilde{\lambda}_1]$. *For at least one value of r,* $\tilde{u}(\tilde{v})$ *must vanish.*

Proof. We need only consider the $\boldsymbol{h} \equiv -1 \pmod{q}$ which appears at the intersection of the rows and columns ending in the u r-positions. Adding an r-node at each position changes each such $\boldsymbol{h} \equiv -1 \pmod{q}$ into $\boldsymbol{h} \equiv +1 \pmod{q}$. No new $\boldsymbol{h} \equiv 0 \pmod{q}$ appear by 6.14, so $[\tilde{\lambda}_1]$ must be a p-core. A similar argument applies to the removal of $\tilde{v}$

r-nodes. Finally, $\tilde{u}(\tilde{v})$ must vanish for at least one r in consequence of 5.11, as can also be seen directly.

It follows from 6.17 that:

6.18 *Every q-core is obtainable by adding to the nul core* $[\phi]$ *first one node of class zero, ...* $\tilde{u}$ *nodes of class r, ... and so on, two successive values of r being necessarily distinct.*

That the sequence of such additions is not, in general, unique, we illustrate in the following

6.19 *Example.* Consider the case $q=4$; starting with the nul-core $[\phi]$ and adding $\tilde{u}$ nodes of class r, in succession, for

$$r = 0,\ 1,\ 3,\ 0,\ 2,\ 1,\ 3,$$
$$\tilde{u} = 1,\ 1,\ 1,\ 1,\ 2,\ 2,\ 2,$$

we obtain the 4-core [4, 3, 2, 1]. The successive additions of residues 1, 3 could be taken in the order 3, 1, and similarly 0, 2 in the order 2, 0, without changing the final result. Thus there are eight possible sequences of 4-cores leading from $[\phi]$ to [4, 3, 2, 1], according to 6.18. In 7.64 we shall see that, for $q=p$ this process leads to successive blocks of representations all of which have the same D-matrix.

6.2 The r-Boolean algebra associated with $[\lambda]$. Let us now examine the totality of diagrams obtainable from a given one by r-inducing and r-restricting in all possible ways. We attach the r-affect v as a label, writing

$$[\lambda] = [\lambda^v],$$

and say that the *dimension* of such a diagram is v and the *dimension* of the whole set is

$$u+v = d.$$

Such a set constitutes an *r-Boolean algebra* (rBA) in which $[\lambda^0]$ plays the role of the zero element and $[\lambda^d]$ that of the unit element. Clearly, an rBA is generated by any one of its elements. It remains to define the operations $\cup$, $\cap$.

If $[\lambda']$ and $[\lambda'']$ are any two elements of an rBA let us define

$$[\lambda'] \cup [\lambda'']$$

to be that diagram $[\lambda]$ of smallest dimension which contains both $[\lambda']$ and $[\lambda'']$. Similarly, let us define

$$[\lambda'] \cap [\lambda'']$$

to be that diagram $[\lambda]$ of largest dimension which is contained in both $[\lambda']$ and $[\lambda'']$. The existence and uniqueness of these diagrams follows immediately from our construction. Since r-nodes are added independently the number of elements in the rBA is 2^d, while the number of dimension v is

$$\binom{d}{v}.$$

If we denote the r-defect and r-affect of $[\lambda^i]$ by u_i and v_i respectively, the weight b_i of $[\lambda^i]$ can be obtained by successive applications of 6.15 so that

6.21 $$b_i = \sum_{j=0}^{i} (u_j - v_j - 1) = \sum_{j=d}^{i+1} (v_j - u_j - 1),$$

according as we induce from $[\lambda^0]$ upwards or restrict from $[\lambda^d]$ downwards. From our definition 6.12 it follows immediately that

$$u_i - v_i = (u_{i+1} - v_{i+1}) + 2,$$

so that second differences of b are constant. Thus:

6.22 *The weight b_i of a diagram $[\lambda^i]$ of dimension i in an* rBA *is given by the expression*

$$b_i = b_d + u_i(d - u_i) = b_d + u_i v_i.$$

In order to clarify these ideas we give the following illustration.

6.23 *Example.* $[\lambda^0] = [5, 4^3, 3]$, $[\lambda^4] = [6, 5, 4^3, 1]$, $q=2$, $r=1$.

v	0	1	2	3	4
u	4	3	2	1	0
$\tilde{v}$	0	0	0	2	4
$\tilde{u}$	4	2	0	0	0
b	7	10	11	10	7

The most important property of an rBA is that it determines a unique *complement*

$$[\lambda^*] = [\lambda^{d-i}],$$

of dimension $d-i$, of every element

$$[\lambda] = [\lambda^i],$$

of dimension i. We shall see the significance of this in the following section. From 6.17 we have the following expressions for the r-defect and r-affect of the core:

$$\tilde{u} = \tfrac{1}{2}\{u-v+|u-v|\},$$
$$\tilde{v} = \tfrac{1}{2}\{v-u+|u-v|\},$$

which imply that:

6.24 $$v = u^*, \qquad \tilde{v} = \tilde{u}^*.$$

Proof. The first relation is immediate, and using this we have

$$\tilde{v} = \tfrac{1}{2}\{v-u+|u-v|\}$$
$$= \tfrac{1}{2}\{u^*-v^*+|v^*-u^*|\} = \tilde{u}^*.$$

Combining 6.24 and 6.21 or directly from 6.22 we conclude that

6.25 $$b = b^*.$$

Corresponding to 6.13, we can prove that:

6.26 *The q-quotients of* $[\lambda]$ *and its complement* $[\lambda^*]$ *in an* rBA *are the same except for the interchange of the r and $(r-1)$-constituents.*

Proof. We distinguish three cases.

(i) If the ith row of $[\lambda]$ ends in a removable r-node and the jth column in an $(r+1)$-node above an r-position then $\boldsymbol{h}_{ij} \equiv 0 \pmod{q}$. Clearly, removing the r-node at the end of the ith row and adding an r-node at the foot of the jth column does not change the (i, j) hook length so that $\boldsymbol{h}^*_{ij} = \boldsymbol{h}_{ij} \equiv 0 \pmod{q}$. It does however change the residue class of the hook from r to $r-1$. Similarly, if the ith row ends in an r-position and the jth column in a removable r-node the length of the (i, j)-hook remains the same but its class is changed from $r-1$ to r.

(ii) If the ith row of $[\lambda]$ ends in a removable r-node and the jth column in an $(r+1)$-node below which no r-node can be added as in Fig. 6.3,

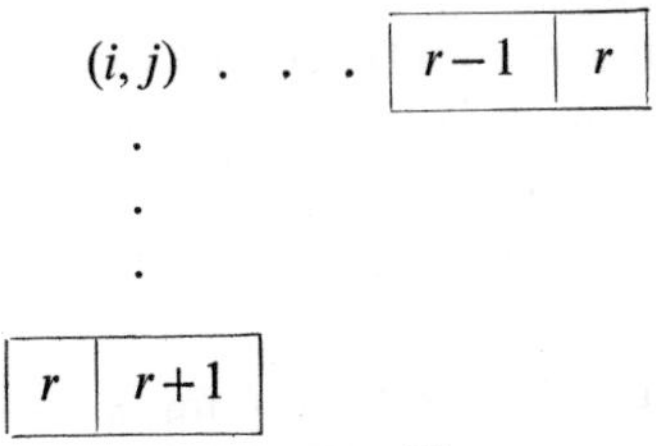

FIG. 6.3

then removing the r-node yields $\boldsymbol{h}^*_{i,\,j-1}=\boldsymbol{h}_{ij}\equiv 0 \pmod q$. Similarly, if the jth column ends in a removable r-node and no r-node can be added at the end of the ith row as in Fig. 6.4,

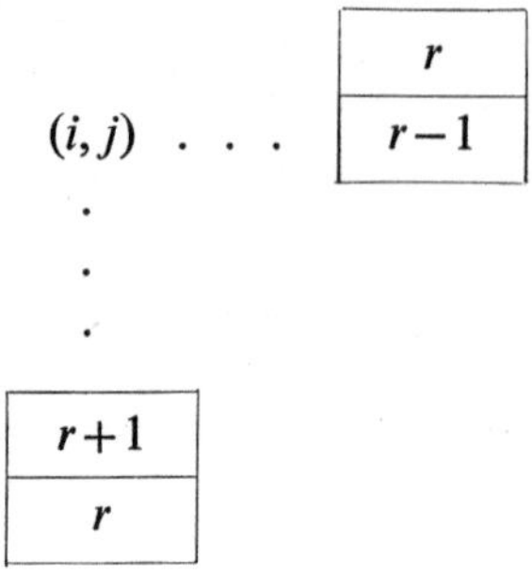

FIG. 6.4

then removing this r-node yields $\boldsymbol{h}^*_{i-1,\,j}=\boldsymbol{h}_{ij}\equiv 0 \pmod q$. Conversely, we may think of adding an r-node in the appropriate r-positions in Figs. 6.3 and 6.4 to yield similar conclusions.

(iii) In this third case we have to consider (i, j)-hooks such that no r-node can be added or removed from the end of the ith row or the jth column. The situation is as indicated in Fig. 6.5.

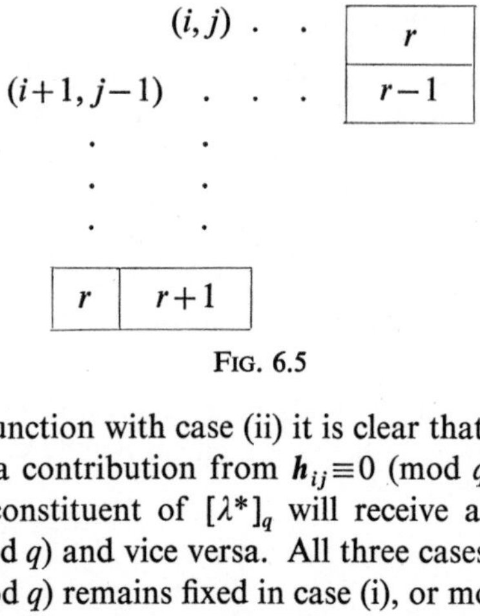

FIG. 6.5

Taken in conjunction with case (ii) it is clear that if the r-constituent of $[\lambda]_q$ receives a contribution from $\boldsymbol{h}_{ij}\equiv 0 \pmod q$ in case (iii), then also the (r−1)-constituent of $[\lambda^*]_q$ will receive a contribution from $\boldsymbol{h}_{i+1,\,j-1}\equiv 0 \pmod q$ and vice versa. All three cases are concordant, in that an $\boldsymbol{h}\equiv 0 \pmod q$ remains fixed in case (i), or moves one place in its row or column in case (ii), or diagonally in case (iii), so that the r and $r-1$ constituents of $[\lambda]_q$ and $[\lambda^*]_q$ are interchanged, the others remaining unaltered.

6.27 *Example.* If $[\lambda]=[7, 5, 4^3, 2^2, 1^2]$ for $q=3$, $r=1$, then $u=2$, $v=2$ so that

$$[\lambda]_3 = [3^3]_3^0 \cdot [1]_3^1 \cdot —,$$

We have $[\lambda^*] = [8, 6, 4^3, 2, 1^2]$ and

$$[\lambda^*]_3 = [1]_3^0 \cdot [3^3]_3^1 \cdot —.$$

Each of the changes described in cases (i), (ii), (iii) is illustrated.

6.3 q-regular and q-singular Young diagrams. Let us now make the following

6.31 *Definition.* A diagram $[\lambda]$ is said to be *q-regular* if no q of its rows are of equal length; otherwise $[\lambda]$ is *q-singular.*

As we saw in the preceding section, the process of complementation in an rBA consists of adding u r-nodes to $[\lambda]$ and removing the existing v r-nodes to obtain $[\lambda^*]$. Effectively we have increased v by $u-v$. This implies that $\tilde{v}=0$, and

$$u-v = \tilde{u}$$

by 6.17, and we have added $\tilde{u}$ r-nodes to the core $[\tilde{\lambda}]$ of $[\lambda]$ to obtain the core $[\tilde{\lambda}^*]$ of $[\lambda^*]$. Each diagram in a given q-set with q-core $[\tilde{\lambda}]$ is associated with such an rBA in which complementation can take place. Clearly all the complements $[\lambda^*]$ lie in a q-set of $\mathfrak{S}_{n+\tilde{u}}$ of the same weight b with q-core $[\tilde{\lambda}^*]$.

What is the effect of complementation on a p-regular diagram? To begin with, let us consider the 0-element $[\lambda^0]$ of an rBA for which $v=0$ and let us add an r-node in each of the possible $u=\tilde{u}$ r-positions. It is possible that the addition of any given r-node will lead to a singular diagram, i.e. one having q rows of equal length; if so, we shall call the corresponding r-position a *singular* position.

Corresponding to a given singular position P there exists a *regular* position P' at which an r-node can be added as indicated in Fig. 6.6, the resulting diagram being regular.

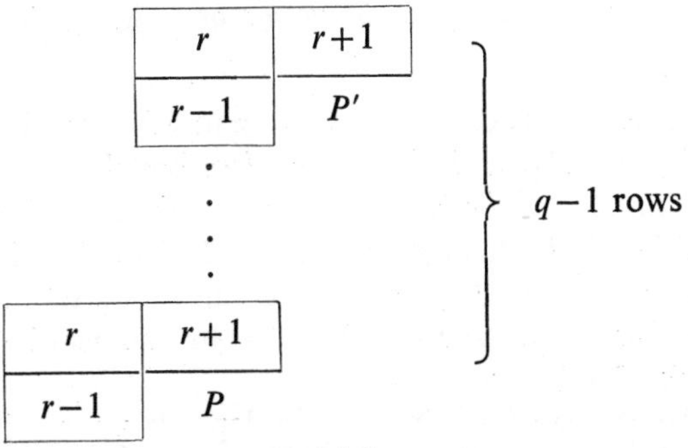

FIG. 6.6

Of course P' may itself be a singular position, but the sequence of singular positions must eventually yield a regular position, since adding an r-node in the first row of $[\lambda]$ cannot yield a singular diagram.

Adding all $\tilde{u}$ r-nodes to $[\lambda^0]$ yields its complement $[\lambda^d]$, and if $[\lambda^0]$ is regular then so also is $[\lambda^d]$, since all singular positions and their corresponding regular positions are filled. A similar argument shows that $[\lambda^d]$ is singular if $[\lambda^0]$ is singular, and conversely.

When we consider an arbitrary element of an rBA for which $0<v<u+v=d$ the situation is somewhat different, since if a regular position is occupied by an r-node, then in the complement the corresponding singular position will be occupied and the diagram will be singular. To overcome this difficulty we define a *modified complement.* This definition favours regular diagrams, but a similar one would favour singular diagrams.

6.32 *Definition.* If in a regular diagram $[\lambda]$, a singular r-position is vacant while its corresponding regular position is occupied by an r-node, then the *modified* complement of $[\lambda]$ in the appropriate rBA is that diagram obtained from $[\lambda^*]$ by raising all r-nodes which occupy singular positions to the corresponding regular positions.

Clearly, the modified complement of a modified complement is the original diagram. We may think of complementation in the ordinary sense as a special case of modified complementation, and so state the following theorem:

6.33 *The property that a diagram be regular is invariant under modified complementation in the appropriate* rBA.

But complementation or modified complementation amounts to adding $\tilde{u}$ r-nodes to the core, as we have seen, and every core can be obtained in this way by 6.19. Thus:

6.34 *The number of q-regular diagrams of weight b is independent of the core.*

Let us return to the construction given in § 5.1 for $[\lambda]$ when $[\lambda]_q$ and the core $[\tilde{\lambda}]$ are given. *If* $[\lambda]$ *is singular then there will be at least q successive integers in the basic set of first column hook lengths* Γ, and this condition is both necessary and sufficient for singularity. We propose to enumerate the regular diagrams in a q-set of weight b *with a suitably chosen core*, and then by 6.34 the enumeration will hold for every block of weight b.

Since the choice of a suitable core depends upon q in a somewhat subtle manner, we consider first the case $q=2$. Here there is only one type of core and by taking the number of rows to be g we have the corresponding core set to be

$$\tilde{\Gamma} : 2g-1, 2g-3, \ldots, 3, 1.$$

If we extend $\tilde{\Gamma}$ to Γ as in § 5.1 where e is *even* it will always be possible to obtain at least two consecutive terms provided $b \leqq g+1$, and the diagrams have non-vacuous $[\lambda]_q^r$, where $r \equiv -g \pmod 2$. If $b > g+1$ then the diagram defined by

$$[\lambda]_q^r = [b],$$

with $r \equiv -g \pmod 2$, will have no two consecutive $\boldsymbol{h}_i$ and so will be regular.

Moreover, if e is *odd* all the terms in the extended set Γ are even except some of those at the end so it will be necessary to add (from the top down) at least $g+2$ multiples of 2 to obtain a set of first column hook lengths, i.e. $b > g+1$.

By denying singularity we obtain regularity so we have proved the following theorem:

6.35 *For $q=2$, and $b \leqq g+1$ the necessary and sufficient condition that a diagram be regular is that in its 2-quotient the constituent $[\lambda]_q^r$ be vacuous for $r \equiv -g \pmod 2$.*

For $q > 2$ the situation is complicated by the fact that there are $q-1$ classes of terms in a core set and some of these may be vacuous. Thus to produce q consecutive first column hook lengths the weight b will be limited by the *shortest* residue class in the core set; we call the length g of this shortest class the *grade* of the core. If any class is vacuous, $g=0$, and $b=1$ is the only possible case yielding such an enumeration of regular diagrams.

Let us examine the situation more carefully. By 5.11 we have

$$\tilde{\Gamma} \ldots \underbrace{(gq-1) \ldots (gq-q+1)}_{q-1} \ldots \underbrace{(2q-1) \ldots (q+1)}_{q-1} \quad \underbrace{(q-1) \ldots 2, 1}_{q-1},$$

in which there are at most g sets of $q-1$ consecutive integers, and no $z_i \equiv 0 \pmod q$ appear. If we extend $\tilde{\Gamma}$ to Γ for $0 < e < q$

$$\Gamma \ldots \underbrace{(gq+e-1) \ldots (gq-q+e+1)}_{q-1} \ldots \underbrace{(2q+e-1) \ldots (q+e+1)}_{q-1}$$

$$\underbrace{(q+e-1) \ldots (e+1)}_{q-1} \quad e-1, \ldots 1, 0,$$

and we still have g sets of $q-1$ consecutive integers but now *no* integer $\equiv e \pmod q$ appears. If $e=mq$ there will be $g+m$ sets of $q-1$ consecutive integers along with m integers $\equiv 0 \pmod q$.

Now let us add the multiples of q determined by $[\lambda]_q$ to the extended set Γ. We have two cases to consider according as $[\lambda]_q^r$ is or is not vacuous for $n \equiv -\tilde{h} \pmod q$.

(*a*) *If* $[\lambda]_q^r$ *is vacuous* and $b \leqq q+1$, then it is sufficient to choose $0 \leqq e < q$ to obtain any required $[\lambda]$, and no such set will have q consecutive first column hook lengths so $[\lambda]$ must be *regular*. We have the extreme case when $[\lambda]_q^{r+1}=[1^{g+1}]$, for which we must take $e=q-1$.

(*b*) *If* $[\lambda]_q^r$ *is not vacuous* and $b \leqq g+1$, then we must set $e=mq$ when $m \leqq b$ is the number of rows of $[\lambda]_q^r$. Adding the appropriate multiple of q to the zero residue class yields at least q consecutive first column hook lengths in each case so that $[\lambda]$ must be *singular*.

Since the conditions are both necessary and sufficient for regularity and singularity if $b \leqq g+1$ we have the following generalization of 6.35:

6.36 *If* $b \leqq g+1$, *the necessary and sufficient condition that* $[\lambda]$ *be regular is that in* $[\lambda]_q$ *the constituent* $[\lambda]_q^r$ *be vacuous for* $r \equiv -\tilde{h} \pmod q$.

Combining 6.34 and 6.36 we have the important

6.37 THEOREM. *The number of q-regular representations of* $\mathfrak{S}_n$ *with q-core* $[\tilde{\lambda}]$ *and weight b is* $l'(b)$ *where*

$$l'(b)=\sum p(b_1)\,p(b_2)\ldots p(b_{q-1}) \qquad \left(\sum_1^{q-1} b_1=b,\ 0 \leqq b_i \leqq b\right).$$

But we can draw yet another conclusion from this analysis of Γ. Let us consider the question: how many r-nodes, for $r \equiv -\tilde{h} \pmod q$, can be removed from $[\lambda]$? Such an r-node must be the head node of some first column hook of length $\boldsymbol{h}_i$ and if it is removable *there can be no first column hook of length* $\boldsymbol{h}_i - 1$. For regular diagrams considered in (*a*) above there will be *no* head nodes of residue class e while in (*b*) where $e=mq$, those which do appear will not be removable, since adding a necessary multiple of q to the zero class always *fills* a gap in Γ. Thus:

6.38 *For* $b \leqq g+1$ *the diagrams with given q-core* $[\tilde{\lambda}]$ *are all zero elements* ($v=0$) *of their respective* rBA's *with* $r \equiv -\tilde{h}$ *(mod q), for which* $d=u=\tilde{u}$.

All has been proved except the last statement which follows from 6.17.

It is desirable to illustrate these conclusions in an example which will show the mechanism at work.

6.39 *Example.* $\mathfrak{S}_{15}$ with $q=3$ has a block with core $[\tilde{\lambda}]=[2^2, 1^2]$ for which $g=2$ and $b=3$, $\tilde{h}=4\equiv-2 \pmod 3$ so $r=2$, $u=\tilde{u}=2$. In the following table we list first the $l'(3)=10$ regular diagrams followed by the 12 singular ones. The first column hook lengths are left as they come after the appropriate additions have been made to Γ.

In order to see the effect of taking $e=q+1$, it is sufficient to observe that $[\lambda]_q$ must take the form $[1^4]$, —, —, with $b>g+1$ and the corresponding $[\lambda]$ has $v=1$.

$[\lambda]_3$	e	Γ	*First column hook lengths*	$[\lambda]$
—· [3]· —	0	5, 4, 2, 1	14, 4, 2, 1	$[11, 2, 1^2]$
3]· —· —	0	5, 4, 2, 1	5, 13, 2, 1	$[10, 3, 1^2]$
1]· [2]· —	0	5, 4, 2, 1	11, 7, 2, 1	$[8, 5, 1^2]$
—· [2, 1]· —	0	5, 4, 2, 1	11, 4, 5, 1	$[8, 3^2, 1]$
2]· [1]· —	0	5, 4, 2, 1	8, 10, 2, 1	$[7, 6, 1^2]$
1]· —· —	0	5, 4, 2, 1	5, 10, 2, 3	$[7, 3^2, 2]$
1]· $[1^2]$· —	0	5, 4, 2, 1	8, 7, 5, 1	$[5^2, 4, 1]$
$^2]$· [1]· —	0	5, 4, 2, 1	8, 7, 2, 4	$[5^2, 3, 2]$
—· $[1^3]$· —	1	6, 5, 3, 2, 0	9, 5, 6, 2, 3	$[5, 3^2, 2^2]$
$^3]$· —· —	2	7, 6, 4, 3, 1, 0	7, 9, 4, 6, 1, 3	$[4, 3^2, 2^2, 1]$
—· [2]· [1]	3	8, 7, 5, 4, 2, 1, 0	14, 7, 5, 4, 2, 1, 3	$[8, 2, 1^5]$
2]· —· [1]	3	8, 7, 5, 4, 2, 1, 0	8, 13, 5, 4, 2, 1, 3	$[7, 3, 1^5]$
1]· [1]· [1]	3	8, 7, 5, 4, 2, 1, 0	11, 10, 5, 4, 2, 1, 3	$[5^2, 1^5]$
—· $[1^2]$· [1]	3	8, 7, 5, 4, 2, 1, 0	11, 7, 8, 4, 2, 1, 3	$[5, 3^2, 1^4]$
—· [1]· [2]	3	8, 7, 5, 4, 2, 1, 0	11, 7, 5, 4, 2, 1, 6	$[5, 2^4, 1^2]$
—· [1]· $[1^2]$	6	11, 10, 8, 7, 5, 4, 3, 2, 1, 0	14, 10, 8, 7, 5, 4, 6, 2, 1, 3	$[5, 2, 1^2]$
$^2]$· —· [1]	3	8, 7, 5, 4, 2, 1, 0	8, 10, 5, 7, 2, 1, 3	$[4, 3^2, 2, 1^3]$
1]· —· [2]	3	8, 7, 5, 4, 2, 1, 0	8, 10, 5, 4, 2, 1, 6	$[4, 3, 2^3, 1^2]$
1]· —· $[1^2]$	6	11, 10, 8, 7, 5, 4, 3, 2, 1, 0	11, 13, 8, 7, 5, 4, 6, 2, 1, 3	$[4, 3, 1^8]$
—· —· [3]	3	8, 7, 5, 4, 2, 1, 0	8, 7, 5, 4, 2, 1, 9	$[3^3, 2^2, 1^2]$
—· —· [2, 1]	6	11, 10, 8, 7, 5, 4, 3, 2, 1, 0	11, 10, 8, 7, 5, 4, 9, 2, 1, 3	$[2^5, 1^5]$
—· —· $[1^3]$	9	14, 13, 11, 10, 8, 7, 6, 5, 4, 3, 2, 1, 0	14, 13, 11, 10, 8, 7, 9, 5, 4, 6, 2, 1, 3	$[2^2, 1^{11}]$

If we remove $\tilde{v}=2$ nodes of class zero from the regular diagrams above, there is no ambiguity in reaching the regular diagrams of weight 3 associated with the core $[2, 1^2]$ except in the case of $[4, 3^2, 2^2, 1]$ for which $v=3$. Modified complementation intervenes here and the regular diagram in question is $[4, 3, 2^2, 1^2]$ with 3-quotient $[3]\cdot - \cdot -$. All other regular diagrams of the block with core $[2, 1^2]$ have $[\lambda]_3^0$ vacuous, as we would expect. The explanation is, of course, that the grade of $[2, 1^2]$ is 1 instead of 2.

6.4 p-regular diagrams and p-regular classes of $\mathfrak{S}_n$. Let us consider the quotient of partition generating functions (4.62):

6.41 $$\frac{\mathscr{P}(x)}{\mathscr{P}(x^q)} = \frac{(1-x^q)(1-x^{2q})\ldots}{(1-x)(1-x^2)\ldots}$$

which can be simplified in two ways:

(i) By dividing $(1-x^m)$ in the denominator into $(1-x^{mq})$ in the numerator to yield the generating function for the number of partitions of n in which no summand appears q or more times.

(ii) By cancelling equal factors $(1-x^{mq})$ in numerator and denominator to yield the generating function for the number of partitions of n containing no summand of the form mq.

Since the generating function is the same in each case we have:

6.42 *The number of q-regular representations of $\mathfrak{S}_n$ is equal to the number of classes of substitutions no one of which contains a cycle of length a multiple of q.*

Certainly, the *order* of a substitution containing a cycle of length q is divisible by q. But if $q=q_1q_2$ when $(q_1q_2)=1$, there will be other substitutions of order divisible by q which do *not* possess a cycle of length a multiple of q. This situation cannot arise when $q=p$ so that, defining a p-regular class as in § 12.2 we conclude from 12.39 that

6.43 *The number of p-regular ordinary representations of $\mathfrak{S}_n$ is equal* (i) *to the number of p-regular classes of $\mathfrak{S}_n$ and so equal* (ii) *to the number of modularly irreducible representations of $\mathfrak{S}_n$, for any prime p.*

We must show that 6.43(ii) remains valid if we confine our attention to any one block **B**. If we assume the following Lemma we have an easy proof of this important result (cf. 6.34):

6.44 LEMMA. *The number $l'(b)$ of modularly irreducible representations of $\mathfrak{S}_n$ in the p-block* **B** *of weight b is independent of the p-core.*

From the expression in 5.18 for the number $l(b)$ of diagrams belonging to a given p-block of weight b it follows that we may write a generating function for $l(b)$ in the form

6.45 $$\mathscr{L}(x) = 1+l(1)x+l(2)x^2+\ldots = [\mathscr{P}(x)]^p.$$

If now $c(a)$ is the number of p-cores with a nodes, we may write

$$\mathscr{C}(x) = 1+c(1)\,x+c(2)\,x^2+\dots,$$

so that

6.46 $$\mathscr{C}(x)\mathscr{L}(x^p) = \mathscr{C}(x)[\mathscr{P}(x^p)]^p = \mathscr{P}(x),$$

where $n=a+bp$. On the other hand, if we set

$$\mathscr{L}'(x) = 1+l'(1)\,x+l'(2)\,x^2+\dots$$

and assume 6.44, we have

6.47 $$\mathscr{C}(x)\mathscr{L}'(x^p) = \mathscr{P}(x)\,/\,\mathscr{P}(x^p),$$

by 6.41 and 6.42 for $q=p$. Thus, combining 6.46 and 6.47 we have

$$\mathscr{L}'(x^p) = [\mathscr{P}(x^p)]^{p-1}$$

or

6.48 $$\mathscr{L}'(x) = [\mathscr{P}(x)]^{p-1}$$

which agrees with 6.37, as desired.

We can give an alternative approach to these ideas by defining integers

$$n_j = \lambda'_j-\lambda'_{j+1} \qquad (j = 1, 2, \dots, \lambda_1-1),$$
$$n_{\lambda_1} = \lambda'_{\lambda_1}.$$

Thus $[\lambda]$ is p-regular if and only if every $n_j<p$; also, $[\lambda]$ is p-singular if and only if at least one $n_j>p$. In the latter case we may set

6.49 $$n_j = n_j^{(1)}+n_j^{(2)}\,p, \qquad 0<n_j^{(1)}<p,$$

so that the $n_j^{(1)}$ define a p-regular diagram $[\lambda^{(1)}]$. It is easy to see that $[\lambda^{(1)}]$ is obtainable from the p-singular $[\tilde{\lambda}]$ by removing p-hooks $[1^p]$; thus $[\lambda]$ *and* $[\lambda^{(1)}]$ *have the same p-core* $[\tilde{\lambda}]$. Conversely, given a p-regular diagram $[\lambda^{(1)}]$ and *any* $[\lambda^{(2)}]$ the equations 6.49 define a unique p-singular diagram $[\lambda]$.

If we denote by $k(n)$ the number of classes of $\mathfrak{S}_n$ and assume 6.44, we may write 6.37 in the form

6.491 $$l'(b) = l(b)-\sum_{a=1}^{b} l'(b-a)\,k(a).$$

If the number of p-regular diagrams in a block of weight ω is denoted by $g(\omega)$ and if $[\lambda^{(2)}]$ contains a nodes, we have

6.492 $$g(b) = l(b)-\sum_{a=1}^{b} g(b-a)\,k(a).$$

Certainly, $g(1)=l'(1)$ for $\mathfrak{S}_p$ (cf. § 7.1) and assuming that $g(\omega)=l'(\omega)$ for $\omega<b$, it follows from 6.491 and 6.492 that $g(b)=l'(b)$.

6.5 The number of modular irreducible representations in a block.

Consider a substitution of P of $\mathfrak{S}_n$ such that

6.51 $$P = \pi_1 \pi_2 \ldots \pi_s,$$

where no two π's have a common symbol and each π_i is a cycle of length $c_i p (c_1 \geqq c_2 \geqq \ldots \geqq c_s)$. We set

$$c = \sum_i c_i \qquad (0 \leqq c < t),$$

where $n=n'+tp$ $(0\leqq n'<p)$, and call P an element of *type* $(c_1, c_2, \ldots, c_s)$ and *weight* c. Each partition of c yields a representative of a class of conjugates, and if we set

$$r = \sum p(c) \qquad (0\leqq c\leqq t),$$

we have a set of elements $P_1=I, P_2, \ldots, P_r$ such that every p-singular element of $\mathfrak{S}_n$ is conjugate to some VP_i where P_i is of weight c and V is a p-regular element of $\mathfrak{S}_{n-cp}$. If we denote the number of p-regular classes of $\mathfrak{S}_n$ by $k'(n)$ then

6.52 $$k = p(n) = \sum_{c=0}^{t} k'(n-cp)\, p(c).$$

Now let us suppose that the block $\mathbf{B}$ of $\mathfrak{S}_n$ includes $l(b)$ ordinary representations $[\lambda]$ of weight b with core $[\tilde{\lambda}]$, containing a nodes, so that $n=a+bp$. If we apply the reduction 4.21 to VP_i, s times if P_i is of the form 6.51, we obtain

6.53 $$\chi^{\lambda}(VP_i) = \begin{cases} \sum_{\mu} m_{\lambda,\mu}^{\ i} \chi^{\mu}_{(c)}(V), \quad [\mu] \subset \mathbf{B}_{(c)}, & c \leqq b, \\ 0, & c > b, \end{cases}$$

where the $m_{\lambda,\mu}^{\ i}$ are integers, and $\mathbf{B}_{(c)}$ is a block of $\mathfrak{S}_{n-cp}$ of weight $b-c$ with core $[\tilde{\lambda}]$. Such a block will have a decomposition matrix

$$(d^{(c)}_{\mu\nu})$$

where ν is a modularly irreducible representation of $\mathfrak{S}_{n-cp}$ with character $\phi^{\nu}_{(c)}$. Thus

6.54 $$\chi^{\mu}_{(c)}(V) = \sum_{\nu} d^{(c)}_{\mu\nu}\, \phi^{\nu}_{(c)}(V)$$

where, as before, V is a p-regular element of $\mathfrak{S}_{n-cp}$. Thus, combining 6.53 and 6.54 we have

6.55
$$\chi^{\lambda}(VP_i) = \begin{cases} \sum_{\nu} u^i_{\lambda\nu}\,\phi^{\nu}_{(c)}(V), \quad \nu \subset \mathbf{B}_{(c)}, & c \leqq b \\ 0, & c > b \end{cases}$$

where the $u^i_{\lambda\nu}$ are again integers and we set $u^i_{\lambda\nu}=0$, if $\nu \not\subset \mathbf{B}_{(c)}$.

Since we have agreed that $P_1=I$, for which $c=0$, it follows from 12.23 that

$$u^1_{\lambda\nu} = d_{\lambda\nu}.$$

If we set

$$U^i = (u^i_{\lambda\nu}), \quad U = (U^1, U^2, \ldots, U^r),$$

then 6.52 implies that U is a square matrix of the same order $k=p(r)$ as the matrix X of ordinary characters (cf. 12.41). Thus we can write 6.55 in the form

6.56
$$X = U\Phi$$

where

$$\Phi = \begin{bmatrix} (\phi^{\nu}_{(1)}) & & & & 0 \\ & (\phi^{\nu}_{(2)}) & & & \\ & & \cdot & & \\ & & & \cdot & \\ 0 & & & \cdot & (\phi^{\nu}_{(t)}) \end{bmatrix}$$

Since X is non-singular, so also is U and $|U| \neq 0$.

We are now in a position to prove that:

6.57 THEOREM. *The number $l'(b)$ of modularly irreducible representations of $\mathfrak{S}_n$ $(n=a+bp)$ which belong to a block of weight b is independent of the p-core and is given by*

$$l'(b) = \sum p(b_1)\,p(b_2)\ldots p(b_{p-1}) \quad \left(\sum_{i=1}^{p-1} b_i = b, 0 \leqq b_i \leqq b\right).$$

Proof. Since the representations $[\lambda]$ of $\mathfrak{S}_n$ fall into blocks $\mathbf{B}_1, \mathbf{B}_2, \ldots, \mathbf{B}_m$ it follows from 6.56 that the matrix U breaks up into m matrices $U_1, U_2, \ldots, U_m$ down the diagonal. The matrix U_i corresponding to $\mathbf{B}_i$ must be square, since $|U| \neq 0$, with $l(b)$ rows and columns for the appropriate b.

Let us now denote by $f(\omega)$ the number of modularly irreducible representations of $\mathfrak{S}_n$ in a block of weight ω with core $[\tilde{\lambda}]$. It follows from 6.56 that

$$l(b) = \sum_{\omega=0}^{b} p(b-\omega) f(\omega).$$

Since a p-core $[\lambda]$ is modularly irreducible and constitutes a block by itself, $f(0)=l'(0)=1$. With this as basis, we make the inductive assumption that $f(\omega)=l'(\omega)$ for all $\omega<b$, irrespective of the core.

Since U_i is square, we have from 6.56

$$\begin{aligned} f(b) &= l(b) - \sum_{\omega=0}^{b-1} p(b-\omega) f(\omega) \\ &= l(b) - \sum_{\omega=0}^{b-1} p(b-\omega)\, l'(\omega), \end{aligned}$$

by our inductive assumption. But we are subtracting from $l(b)$ just those terms which correspond to partitions of b into p parts so that $f(b)=l'(b)$ as desired. Moreover, this result is independent of the p-core $[\tilde{\lambda}]$.

Combining 6.57 with 6.37 we conclude that:

6.58 THEOREM. *The number of ordinary p-regular representations of* $\mathfrak{S}_n$ *in any p-block* **B** *is equal to the number of modularly irreducible representations in* **B**.

The results of 6.57 and 6.58 are profusely illustrated in the Appendix. For example, in Table 3-8 there are nine ordinary representations in each of the blocks of weight 2 with 3-cores [2], $[1^2]$ respectively, five of which are regular. The regular representations in the block with core [2] are:

$$[8],\ [5, 3],\ [5, 2, 1],\ [4, 3, 1],\ [3^2, 1^2],$$

and in the block with core $[1^2]$ they are:

$$[7, 1],\ [6, 2],\ [4^2],\ [4, 2^2],\ [3, 2^2, 1].$$

We shall see in the following chapter that it is possible to establish a 1-1 correspondence between such regular representations in a given block **B** and the modular irreducible representations of **B**, which is an improvement upon 6.58.

It is worth remarking in conclusion that the alternative argument given in the preceding section could be completed by substituting 6.55 in the character relations 11.372 to yield

$$\sum_{\lambda} u^{i}_{\lambda\nu}\, u^{j}_{\lambda k} = 0 \qquad j \neq i,$$

where we restrict attention to a single block **B**. Setting $i=1$ we have

6.59 $$\sum_{\lambda} d_{\lambda\nu} u^{j}_{\lambda k} = 0 \qquad j \neq 1$$

Since the U-matrix for **B** is non-singular, these relations satisfied by the rows of D are linearly independent and form a complete set of $l(b)-l'(b)$ identities. Since this number is independent of the core we have a proof of Lemma 6.44.

CHAPTER SEVEN

THE INDECOMPOSABLES OF $\mathfrak{S}_n$

Introduction. Our aim in the present chapter is to construct the *D*-matrices of $\mathfrak{S}_n$. To this end we begin by studying the problem in those cases where simple arguments yield complete results, i.e. in blocks of weight 1 (§ 7.1) and in the block of weight 2 (§ 7.2) of $\mathfrak{S}_{2p}$. In § 7.3 we introduce the 'admitted permutation' first used by D. E. Littlewood, and in § 7.4 and § 7.5 show how these are related to the raising operator.

If we confine our attention to a single block, the Fundamental Theorem in the form 5.43 implies the restriction given in 7.42 that the residue class of a node must remain invariant under every application of the raising operator *R*. In consequence of this restriction, every standard tableau obtainable from a given one under *R* will lead to the same admitted permutation. In this way we can relate the admitted permutations to the standard tableaux associated with the modularly irreducible components in each of their 'incarnations', and so define *r*-inducing and restricting to apply to these as well as to the indecomposables of the regular representation of $\mathfrak{S}_n$. The proof of the validity of our construction of the *D*-matrix is left for the following chapter.

Though the method of obtaining them was tentative, most of the Tables in the Appendix (excepting Tables A, B) appeared in the Thesis of J. H. Chung and are published here for the first time. Likewise also, much of the material §§ 7.4-7.7 has not heretofore appeared in print and is the joint work of O. E. Taulbee and the author.

Throughout this book an effort has been made to distinguish those results which depend on the primeness of the fixed integer *q*. This became critical in §§ 5.2 and 5.3 and again in §§ 6.4 and 6.5. Throughout Chapter Seven we assume that $q=p$ so as to avoid the necessity of continually clarifying the point, but none of the *processes* involved requires it. It is when we come to interpret the significance of the rows and columns of the matrix in terms of the modularly irreducible representations and indecomposables of the regular representation of $\mathfrak{S}_n$ that we must assume that $q=p$.

7.1 The *D*-matrix of a block of weight 1 of $\mathfrak{S}_n$. Since the regular representation of $\mathfrak{S}_n$ is obtained by inducing (§§ 11.5 and 12.6) on the regular representation of $\mathfrak{S}_{n-1}$, we conclude that inducing on an indecomposable of $\mathfrak{S}_{n-1}$ yields an indecomposable or a sum of indecomposables of

$\mathfrak{S}_n$. Now an ordinary irreducible representation $[\lambda]$ of $\mathfrak{S}_{p-1}$ is also irreducible modulo p and constitutes a block by itself (12.58). Only the hook representations of $\mathfrak{S}_{p-1}$ will yield hook representations of $\mathfrak{S}_p$ so that we have the following two cases to consider:

7.11 $$[r, 1^{p-r-1}] \overset{0}{\uparrow} [r, 2, 1^{p-r-2}] \qquad r = 2, 3, \ldots, p-1,$$

in which the right side is a p-core, and

7.12 $$[r, 1^{p-r-1}] \overset{r}{\uparrow} [r+1, 1^{p-r-1}]+[r, 1^{p-r}], \qquad r = 1, 2, \ldots, p-1.$$

Since the character of a p-cycle must vanish in any indecomposable representation (12.42) we conclude that *both* representations on the right of 7.12 must belong to the same indecomposable by 4.11, one being of even leg length and the other of odd leg length, for any value of r. Thus:

7.13 *If the representations* $[\lambda]$ *of* $\mathfrak{S}_p$ *in a block of weight* 1 *are arranged in dictionary order the corresponding D-matrix has p rows and* $p-1$ *columns, with* 1*'s in the leading diagonal and sub-diagonal and zeros elsewhere.*

In order to extend this result we observe that for any representation $[\lambda]$ of $\mathfrak{S}_n$ of weight 1

7.14 $$d = \tilde{d}.$$

Thus complementation consists of adding $d=\tilde{d}$ r-nodes, successively to $[\lambda]$ for suitably chosen r's, and so determining from a given $[\lambda]$ of weight 1 a unique $[\lambda^*]$ with p-core $[\tilde{\lambda}^*]$, of weight 1. Though the residue class of the single removable p-hook will change according to 6.26, nevertheless, *its leg length will remain unaltered.* Taking this in conjunction with 6.19, we conclude that:

7.15 *There is one and only one diagram* $[\lambda]$ *with p-core* $[\tilde{\lambda}]$ *of weight* 1 *in which the removable p-hook has leg length* $l\,(0, 1, \ldots, p-1)$. *Moreover all such diagrams are obtainable from* $[p-l, 1^l]$ *by successive complementation.*

This invariance of the leg length under complementation makes it possible to distinguish the disjoint constituents of the p-quotient $[\lambda]_p$ according to the leg length of the last removable p-hook rather than by the residue class, as in 4.47. However, such a procedure does not seem to be useful except in the case $b=1$ under discussion.

Consider now the meaning of *complementation* so far as the notion of an indecomposable is concerned. In view of 7.14, r-inducing d times on $[\lambda]$ yields $[\lambda^*]$ with multiplicity $d!$, and if $[\lambda]+[\bar{\lambda}]$ constitutes an indecomposable of the block with p-core $[\tilde{\lambda}]$ of weight 1 of $\mathfrak{S}_n$ then, $d!([\lambda^*]+[\bar{\lambda}^*])$ must be a sum of indecomposables of the block with p-core $[\tilde{\lambda}^*]$ of weight 1 of $\mathfrak{S}_{n+d}$. We conclude from 12.49 that $\lambda^*+\bar{\lambda}^*$ by itself is an indecomposable of $\mathfrak{S}_{n+d}$.

Thus, starting from the indecomposables defined in 7.13 and complementing in all possible ways we obtain the indecomposables of weight 1 associated with any core $[\tilde{\lambda}]$, by 6.18. Since 7.15 implies the preservation of dictionary order we have, for any value of n:

7.16 *If the representations* $[\lambda]$ *of* $\mathfrak{S}_n$ *in a block of weight* 1 *are arranged in dictionary order the corresponding D-matrix has p rows and* $p-1$ *columns, with* 1*'s in the leading diagonal and sub-diagonal and zeros elsewhere.*

7.2 The *D*-matrix of a block of weight 2 of $\mathfrak{S}_{2p}$. It is of interest to press the character argument used in determining the indecomposables of the blocks of $\mathfrak{S}_p$ of weight 1 one stage further, As before, it is necessary and sufficient to consider blocks of $\mathfrak{S}_{2p-1}$ with hook-cores of the form

7.21 $$[r, 1^{p-r-1}] \qquad r = 1, 2, \ldots, p-1,$$

or

7.22 $$[p, 1^{p-1}].$$

With each core 7.21 is associated $p-1$ indecomposables by 7.16 which we may write out explicitly as follows:

7.211 $$[p+r, 1^{p-r-1}]+[p, r+1, 1^{p-r-2}] \qquad r \neq p-1$$

7.211*a* $$[2p-1]+[(p-1)^2, 1] \qquad r = p-1$$

7.212 $$[p-s, r+1, 2^s, 1^{p-r-s-2}]+[p-s-1, r+1, 2^{s+1}, 1^{p-r-s-3}] \qquad s = 0, 1, \ldots, p-r-3$$

7.213 $$[r+2, r+1, 2^{p-r-2}]+[r^2, 2^{p-r-1}, 1]$$

7.214 $$[r, r-t, 2^{p-r-1}]+[r, r-t-1, 2^{p-r-1}, 1^{2+t}] \qquad t = 0, 1, \ldots, r-3$$

7.215 $$[r, 2^{p-r}, 1^{r-1}]+[r, 1^{2p-r-1}] \qquad r \neq 1$$

7.215*a* $$[3, 2^{p-2}]+[1^{2p-1}] \qquad r = 1.$$

r-inducing as before yields the sets of representations of $\mathfrak{S}_{2p}$:

(7.211) $\overset{r}{\uparrow}[p+r+1, 1^{p-r-1}]+[p+r, 1^{p-r}]+[p, r+2, 1^{p-r-2}]$
$+[p, r+1, 1^{p-r-1}]$

(7.211a) $\overset{r}{\uparrow}[2p]+[2p-1, 1]+[p, p-1, 1]+[(p-1)^2, 2]$

(7.212) $\overset{r}{\uparrow}[p-s, r+2, 2^s, 1^{p-r-s-2}]+[p-s, r+1, 2^s, 1^{p-r-s-1}]$
$+[p-s-1, r+2, 2^{s+1}, 1^{p-r-s-3}]$
$+[p-s-1, r+1, 2^{s+1}, 1^{p-r-s-2}]$
$s = 0, 1, 2, \ldots, p-r-3$

(7.213) $\overset{r}{\uparrow}[(r+2)^2, 2^{p-r-2}]+[r+2, r+1, 2^{p-r-2}, 1]$
$+[r+1, r, 2^{p-r-1}, 1]+[r^2, 2^{p-r}]$

(7.214) $\overset{r}{\uparrow}[r+1, r-2, 2^{p-r-1}, 1^{1+t}]+[r, r-2, 2^{p-r}, 1^t]$
$+[r+1, r-t-1, 2^{p-r-1}, 1^{2+t}]+[r, r-t-1, 2^{p-r}, 1^{1+t}]$
$t = 0, 1, 2, \ldots, r-3.$

(7.215) $\overset{r}{\uparrow}[r+1, 2^{p-r}, 1^{r-1}]+[r, 2^{p-r+1}, 1^{r-2}]+[r+1, 1^{2p-r-1}$
$+[r, 1^{2p-r}]$

(7.215a) $\overset{r}{\uparrow}[3^2, 2^{p-3}]+[3, 2^{p-2}, 1]+[2, 1^{2p-2}]+[1^{2p}]$.

In the case of weight 1 the vanishing of the character of the p-singular elements was both necessary and sufficient to define the indecomposables. This situation holds here also, but is more complicated since these are p-singular elements containing cycles of length p and also $2p$. Since all the cases arising from 7.21 are similar it will be sufficient to examine that arising from 7.211 in detail by constructing the following table:

7.23

	$[p]$	$[r+1, 1^{p-r-1}]$	$[r, 1^{p-r}]$	$[\phi]$
$[p+r+1, 1^{p-r-1}]$	.	1	.	$(-1)^{p-r-1}$
$[p+r, 1^{p-r}]$	.	.	1	$(-1)^{p-r}$
$[p, r+2, 1^{p-r-2}]$	$(-1)^{p-r-2}$	-1	.	
$[p, r+1, 1^{p-r-1}]$	$(-1)^{p-r-1}$	.	-1	

in which the entry in a given place is the character of the hook representation to be removed from the diagram associated with the row to yield as residue the diagram associated with the column. Thus $\chi(v)$ in 6.53 is the same for each entry in a column and 6.59 becomes

7.24 $$\sum_{\lambda} d_{\lambda\nu}(-1)^l = 0.$$

The orthogonality relations 7.24 must be satisfied by every column of the D-matrix and also by every column of the above table so that all four representations of $\mathfrak{S}_{2p}$ must belong to the same indecomposable.

In the remaining case arising from 7.22 we have

7.221 (7.22) $\overset{0}{\uparrow} [p+1, 1^{p-1}]+[p, 2, 1^{p-2}]+[p, 1^p]$

with the corresponding table:

	$[p]$	$[1^p]$	$[\phi]$
$[p+1, 1^{p-1}]$	.	1	$(-1)^{p-1}$
$[p, 2, 1^{p-2}]$	$(-1)^{p-2}$	-1	.
$[p, 1^p]$	$(-1)^{p-1}$	.	$(-1)^p$

so that the same argument applies. Thus (cf. Tables 2-4, 3-6, 5-10):

7.25 *The D-matrix of the block of* $\mathfrak{S}_{2p}$ *of weight* 2 *has* $l(2)=\frac{1}{2}p(p+3)$ *rows and* $l'(2)=\frac{1}{2}(p-1)(p-2)$ *columns. Each column which corresponds to the result of r-inducing upon one of* (7.211)-(7.215*a*) *contains four* 1's *while the single column corresponding to the result of* 0*-inducing upon* (7.22) *has three* 1's, *the remaining entries being zeros.*

Proof. By 5.18 the number of ordinary representations of $\mathfrak{S}_{2p}$ of weight 2 is

$$l(2) = 2p+\tfrac{1}{2}p(p-1) = \tfrac{1}{2}p(p+3)$$

as required. The number of indecomposables in the block, i.e. the number of columns of the D-matrix, is

$$l'(2) = 2(p-1)+\tfrac{1}{2}(p-1)(p-2) = \tfrac{1}{2}(p-1)(p+2)$$

by 6.37, and it only remains to show that each of these has been obtained. By r-inducing on (7.211)-(7.215a) we obtain $(p-1)^2$ sets of four diagrams, of which $\frac{1}{2}(p-2)(p-3)$ are duplicates, so that, counting the one arising from 7.22, we have

$$(p-1)^2+1-\tfrac{1}{2}(p-2)(p-3) = \tfrac{1}{2}(p-1)(p+2)$$

distinct indecomposables, as required.

In Table 5-10 the corresponding values of r are listed with the duplications which arise in the $\frac{1}{2}(p-2)(p-3)=3$ cases for $p=5$.

7.3 Standard tableaux. In § 2.4 we replaced all the symbols in the ith *row* of a standard tableau t by a_i and by reading these off in order $1, 2, \ldots, n$ we obtained a *lattice permutation* π of the a_i. Fundamentally, the condition 2.41 implies that $\lambda_i \geqq \lambda_{i+1}$ for all i so that 2.41 is the *constructibility condition* that the a_i can be added according to π to yield t. The number of such ways of building $[\lambda]$ is f^λ so that there are f^λ lattice permutations of the a_i.

If instead of identifying the symbols in the rows of $[\lambda]$ we identify them in the *diagonals* we obtain the graph $\boldsymbol{G}[\lambda]$ and a permutation P from each tableau. Standardness implies constructibility as before, and conversely. The *content* $\boldsymbol{G}^\lambda$ uniquely determines $[\lambda]$ if and only if 4.35 is satisfied.

When we replace each g_{ij} by its p-residue, setting $x=0$, we obtain the p-graph $\boldsymbol{G}_p[\lambda]$ whose content no longer characterizes a unique representation (5.43) but a *block* **B**. Again, each standard tableau t of $[\lambda]$ yields a permutation P of the residues appearing in $\boldsymbol{G}_p[\lambda]$ and we shall say that $[\lambda]$ *admits* the permutation P. In general, other diagrams $[\bar{\lambda}]$ belonging to **B** will also admit P and there is a certain ambiguity in reconstructing $[\lambda]$ from the permutation P. The study of this ambiguity will concern us in the remainder of this chapter. The following Example 7.31 illustrates these important ideas.

7.31 *Example.* Let us write out the permutation P of the residues modulo 5 corresponding to the standard tableaux of the representations of weight 1 of $\mathfrak{S}_5$, arranging the table to illustrate the effect of the *raising operator* of Chapter II.

$[\lambda]$	$\boldsymbol{G}_5[\lambda]$				
[5]	01234				12345
[4, 1]	0123 4			1235 1245 1345 4 3 2	1234 5
$[3, 1^2]$	012 4 3		125 135 145 3 2 2 4 4 3	123 124 134 4 3 2 5 5 5	
$[2, 1^3]$	01 4 3 2	15 2 3 4	12 13 14 3 2 2 4 4 3 5 5 5		
$[1^5]$	0 4 3 2 1	1 2 3 4 5			
admitted permutations		04321	01432, 04132, 04312	01243, 01423, 04123	01234

The underlined permutations arise from the standard tableaux

1 ,	12 ,	123 ,	1234 ,
2	3	4	5
3	4	5	
4	5		
5			

which being first in their respective dictionary ordering for each $[\lambda]$, may be called *initial* tableaux. The raising operator when applied to such a tableau, with the restriction that the residue class of the raised node should remain invariant, will necessarily yield a standard tableau. In fact the same operator applied to each standard tableau in the same column yields the one above it. Though this simple situation does not hold in general, nevertheless, it suggests a means of constructing the D-matrix of 7.13 (if the columns are written in reverse order).

Instead of the raising operator we could have constructed the D-matrix of 7.31 by using the admitted permutations. E.g. the only diagrams which admit $P_1=04321$ are those in the first column; the only diagrams which admit $P_2=01432$ are those in the second column, etc. We could have chosen P_i to be any P admitted by the diagrams contributing to the ith column, and in this sense each such permutation is *characteristic* but this is not true in general. In fact, our chief concern will be to prove the existence of a characteristic permutation (7.54) for each column of the D-matrix.

7.4 The raising operator. There is one further remark which we can make with reference to the ideas presented in §§ 6.1 and 6.2 which is pertinent here:

7.41 *The number of nodes which can be added to any* $[\lambda]$ *is always one more than the number which can be removed.*

Proof. Certainly this is true for the null diagram $[\phi]$. Let us assume it for any $[\lambda]$ of $\mathfrak{S}_{n-1}$ and prove it for $\mathfrak{S}_n$.

The effect on the defect u and the affect v of adding a node to $[\lambda]$ is either

(i) no change occurs in either u or v; or

(ii) both u and v are increased or decreased by 1.

Since neither (i) nor (ii) alters the difference $u-v$, and every diagram of $\mathfrak{S}_n$ is obtainable in this way, the induction hypothesis is verified and the proof is complete.

If we denote by u_r the r-defect and by v_r the r-affect of a fixed $[\lambda]$ then 7.41 implies that

7.411 $$\sum_{r=0}^{p-1} (u_r - v_r) = 1.$$

Consider now what meaning could be attached to setting $p=1$. In such a case, the p-graph would consist entirely of zeros and would not distinguish between the different nodes of $[\lambda]$. The notion of *core* would evaporate, or alternatively, we could say that every $[\lambda]$ had the same null core $[\phi]$. Thus every $[\lambda]$ of $\mathfrak{S}_n$ would belong to the same 'block' of which $[n]$ would be the *head* and $[1^n]$ the *foot* diagram.

We have examined this limiting case since the raising operator R_{ik} of § 2.2 when applied to $[1^n]$ yields all the irreducible components of the regular representation of $\mathfrak{S}_n$. The suggestion is obvious that the restriction introduced by $G_p[\lambda]$ for $p \neq 1$ should be capable of interpretation as a restriction on R_{ik} and one might hope to *generate* an indecomposable from its foot (or its head) diagram. We state the required restriction by 5.43 as follows:

7.42 *The residue class of any node must remain invariant under every application of the raising operator.*

Standardness must be preserved, and the admitted permutation P remains unchanged also, as a result of 7.42 (cf. Example 7.31).

As in the case $p=1$, interchanging rows and columns leaves standardness invariant, but here this implies changing $r \neq 0$ into $p-r$ and *lower* in the block **B** becomes *higher* in the block **B**′. Considered with reference to **B**, however, raising in **B**′ is lowering in **B**. If the core $[\tilde{\lambda}]$ of **B** is self-conjugate then the feet in **B** are the conjugates of the heads in **B**. For $p=2$ this is always the case; 0, 1 are unaffected by replacing $r \neq 0$ by $p-r$, and the admitted permutation P remains unchanged.

Thus the 'raising' operator establishes a correspondence, valid both 'up' and 'down' with reference to the dictionary ordering of diagrams $[\lambda]$, and in this sense we shall relate the standard tableaux of the different $[\lambda]$ belonging to **B** (cf. Example 7.31).

If we define the *initial* tableau (a_{ij}) associated with $[\lambda]$ to be the first in dictionary order then the sequence 1, 2, 3, . . . appears in the form

$$a_{11}, a_{12}, \ldots, a_{1\lambda_1};\ a_{21}, a_{22}, \ldots, a_{2\lambda_2};\ \ldots;\ a_{h1}, a_{h2}, \ldots, a_{h\lambda_h},$$

and

7.43 *Every tableau obtained by applying the raising operator to an initial tableau is standard.*

Defining a *foot* diagram F as one in which no p columns are of equal length, let s be the initial tableau of F and s' a second standard tableau of F. Applying the raising operator R to s we obtain the standard tableau t of some $[\lambda]$; if we also apply R to s' the result may no longer be standard. However, by permuting the symbols of s' subject to 7.42, we may be able to achieve standardness. The situation is best described by the following diagram:

7.431
$$\begin{array}{cccc} & & q=\rho p & \\ [\lambda] & t & \longrightarrow & t' \\ & R\uparrow & & \uparrow R' \\ F & s & \longrightarrow & s' \\ & & p & \\ & P & & P' \end{array}$$

where P is the permutation admitted by s and t and P' by s' and t'. We may write

7.432 $$qPq^{-1} = P', \qquad pPp^{-1} = P',$$

with $R' = R(\rho) = (\rho)R$, where

7.433 $$\rho P' \rho^{-1} = \rho(pPp^{-1})\rho^{-1} = qPq^{-1} = P'.$$

The effect of 7.42 on the raising operator is fundamental for all our subsequent work and we must study it in detail. In particular, we prove the following significant result:

7.44 (i) *Every initial tableau t_1^λ of a non-foot $[\lambda]$ is obtainable by applying the raising operator $R'=R(\rho)$, subject to 7.42 to a standard tableau t^F of some foot diagram F.* (ii) *The initial tableau t_1^F of F is not obtainable in this manner from a standard tableau of any other foot.*

We remark first that if $\lambda_1 < p$, $[\lambda]=F$ and the initial tableau t_1^F is uniquely described by the admitted permutation P. Since each symbol is placed as low as possible, this proves 7.44(ii) in this case, using 7.42. When $\lambda_i \geqq p$ ambiguities enter in and we consider them with reference to the following

7.441 *Construction*†. Assuming that $\lambda_1 \geqq p$, let us write the symbols $1, 2, \ldots, p-1$, followed by $p, \ldots, 2p-1$ with p beneath 1, and so on

† For $p=2$ this amounts to considering the conjugate tableau obtained by interchanging rows and columns in $[\lambda]$.

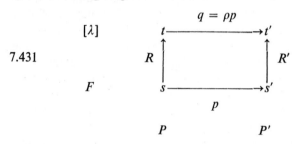

in natural order to yield a proper tableau T_1 having $p-1$ columns. This construction is certainly allowable since the residues attached to the new positions are the same as before. Then take the symbols in the second row of $[\lambda]$ and add the first $p-1$ symbols at the end of the first row of T_1, the next $p-1$ at the end of the second row of T_1 and so on. If $\lambda_1-\lambda_2 \geqq p-1$ the result will be a proper tableau T_2. If $\lambda_1-\lambda_2<p-1$ the last row may have a gap in it; if this happens the last symbols from the second row of $[\lambda]$ can be placed below those immediately above them in $[\lambda]$ to yield a proper tableau T_2.

Proceeding thus with each subsequent row of $[\lambda]$, so long as $\lambda_i \geqq p-1$, we obtain in succession $T_1, T_2, \dots$ making sure at each stage that the result is a proper tableau. If some $\lambda_j<p-1$, so will all subsequent λ_{j+s} and no further application of the construction is possible. This 'tail' of $[\lambda]$ can then be added to T_i. We may write schematically:

$$T\quad \begin{array}{l|l|c|l|} a_{11}\ a_{12}\dots a_{1,p-1} & a_{21}\ a_{22}\dots a_{2,p-1} & \dots & a_{h1}\ a_{h2}\dots a_{h,p-1}\\ a_{1p}\ \dots\ a_{1,2p-1} & a_{2p}\ \dots\ a_{2,2p-1} & & \dots\ a_{h\lambda_h}\\ a_{1,2p}\dots & a_{2,2p}\dots & & \\ \dots\ a_{1\lambda_1} & \dots\ a_{2\lambda_2} & & \end{array}\ .$$

If no improper tableau arises $T=T_h$, provided $\lambda_h \geqq p-1$. Moreover, T and $[\lambda]$ overlap so as to define the permutation

$$\rho = (a_{1p}, a_{21})(a_{1,p+1}, a_{22})\dots(a_{1,2p-1}, a_{2,p-1})\dots \text{etc.}$$

Symbols which do not overlap are free to be lowered subject to 7.42, and *the permutation P admitted by t_1^{λ} is also admitted by T.* We illustrate the construction in the following

7.45 *Example.* Take $[\lambda] = [7, 6]$ and $p = 5$:

$$t_1^{\lambda}:\ \begin{array}{ccccccc} 1 & 2 & 3 & 4 & 5 & 6 & 7\\ 8 & 9 & 10 & 11 & 12 & 13 & \end{array} \qquad T_1:\ \begin{array}{cccc} 1 & 2 & 3 & 4\\ 5 & 6 & 7 & \end{array}$$

$$T_2:\ \begin{array}{cccccccc} 1 & 2 & 3 & 4 & 8 & 9 & 10 & 11\\ 5 & 6 & 7 & & & & & \\ 12 & 13 & & & & & & \end{array}$$

If instead we apply the construction beginning in the second row we obtain

$$t_1^{F}:\ \begin{array}{ccccccc} 1 & 2 & 3 & 4 & 5 & 6 & 7\\ 8 & 9 & 10 & 11 & & & \\ 12 & 13 & & & & & \end{array}$$

By lowering 11 in T_2 we obtain the tableau

$$T_2': \begin{array}{ccccccc} 1 & 2 & 3 & 4 & 8 & 9 & 10 \\ 5 & 6 & 7 & 11 \\ 12 & 13 \end{array}$$

of $F = [7, 4, 2]$, where $\rho = (5, 8)(6, 9)(7, 10)$ and

$$t_1^\lambda = R_{23}^2\, t_1^F = R_{23}^2\,(5, 8)(6, 9)(7, 10)\, T_2',$$

illustrating 7.44(i).

The significance of the construction 7.441 is that when $\lambda_i - \lambda_{i+1} \geqq p$, i.e. when $[\lambda]$ is a non-foot, it removes the restriction on the lowering process due to standardness, which, in reverse, is in accordance with the rules of application of the raising operator. Moreover, the permutation ρ is well defined. Thus we can actually construct a standard tableau t^F belonging to some foot F such that $R' = R(\rho)$ and

$$t_1^\lambda = R'\, t^F,$$

proving 7.44(i). One further example of the construction will suffice.

7.46 *Example.* Take $[\lambda] = [4, 1^3]$ with $p = 3$ and

$$t_1^\lambda: \begin{array}{cccc} 1 & 2 & 3 & 4 \\ 5 \\ 6 \\ 7 \end{array}, \quad T_2: \begin{array}{ccc} 1 & 2 & 5 \\ 3 & 4 \end{array}, \quad t^F: \begin{array}{ccc} 1 & 2 & 5 \\ 3 & 4 \\ 6 \\ 7 \end{array}$$

so that $t_1^\lambda = R_{12}(3, 5)t^F$.

The proof of 7.44(ii) follows from the fact that even though we could remove some of the restrictions to the lowering of symbols due to the standardness condition, the vacant r-positions are not available, since each $\lambda_i - \lambda_{i+1} < p$.

7.5 Head and foot diagrams. In 6.58 we proved that the number of p-regular diagrams in a block **B** of weight b is equal to the number of modular representations in **B**. We have called such p-regular diagrams *heads* in **B**, denoting them

$$H_1, H_2, \ldots, H_{l'(b)}.$$

We shall assume that H precedes H_{i+1} in dictionary order, so that H_i is *higher* than H_{i+1} in **B**.

In the conjugate block **B**$'$ the conjugate of H_i is a *foot* F_i' and F_i' is *lower* than F_{i+1}'. Similarly, we may distinguish the heads H_u' in **B**$'$

and if we arrange them in dictionary order then their conjugates will be feet in **B**:

$$F_1, F_2, \ldots, F_{l'(b)}$$

where F_j is *lower* than F_{j+1}. Clearly the number of feet in **B** is equal to the number of heads in **B**. It can of course happen that a diagram appears as a head and also as a foot in **B**.

In order to complete the story we must prove the following complement of 7.44:

7.51 *If by applying a raising operator R subject to* 7.42, *to the initial tableau s of a foot diagram F we obtain a standard tableau t of* $[\lambda]$, *then there exists a permutation ρ such that applying the operator $R'=R(\rho)$ to the standard tableau s' of F yields a unique standard tableau t' of* $[\lambda]$. *The choice of s' is subject to the restriction that it had not similarly been obtained from a lower foot than F.*

Proof. We proceed by induction. As can be easily verified, the theorem is true for the block of weight 1 of $\mathfrak{S}_p$, since no admitted permutation contains a repeated residue and $\rho=1$ (cf. Example 7.31).

If $\bar{s}'$ is the standard tableau obtaining by removing n from s', we assume that $\bar{s}'$ is chosen in the required manner in the block **B** of $\mathfrak{S}_{n-1}$ and that there is a uniquely defined standard tableau $\bar{t}'$ of $[\bar{\lambda}]$ which is obtainable by applying the operator $\bar{R}'=\bar{R}(\bar{\rho})$ to $\bar{s}'$. If we write $P'=\bar{P}r$, then the final residue r (i.e. n) can be added to $\bar{s}'$ and $\bar{t}'$ in well-defined positions to yield s' and t'. Also, we can write

7.511 $$R' = \bar{R}(\bar{\rho}) \cdot R^+$$

where R^+ describes the raising, or lowering, of n from the position it occupies in s' to that it occupies in t'. If n occupies in t' a position previously occupied in s' by m, then interchanging m and n in s' and applying $\bar{R}(\bar{\rho})$ we see that m would occupy the position in t' occupied by n in s'. Thus there must be a factor R^- of $\bar{R}$ which affects m and $\bar{R}=RR^-$, so that

$$R' = \bar{R}(\rho)\, R^+ = RR^-\, R^+(\bar{\rho}).$$

Setting $R^-R^+=(m, n)$ and $\rho=\bar{\rho}\,(m, n)$ we have the required expression $R'=R(\rho)$. Of course if n does not occupy a position in t' which is occupied by $m<n$ in s' then $R^+=I$ and cancellation of operators does not arise; $\rho=\bar{\rho}$ and

$$R' = \bar{R}R^+(\bar{\rho}) = R(\rho).$$

The uniqueness of t' follows from the fact that both $\bar{R}$ and R must be *raising* operators.

We shall illustrate these ideas by an

7.512 *Example.* Let $p=3$ and choose $F=[1^4]$, $\lambda=[2^2]$. Then

$$\bar{s}' = \begin{matrix} 1 \\ 2 \\ 3 \\ 4 \end{matrix} \quad \xrightarrow{\bar{R} = R_{13}R_{24}} \quad \begin{matrix} 1 & 3 \\ 2 & 4 \end{matrix} = \bar{t}'$$

and

$$s' = \begin{matrix} 1 & 5 \\ 2 & \\ 3 & \\ 4 & \end{matrix} \quad \xrightarrow{R' = R(\rho)} \quad \begin{matrix} 1 & 3 \\ 2 & 4 \\ 5 & \end{matrix} = t'$$

$$R^+ = R_{31},\ R' = R_{13}R_{24} \cdot R_{31} = R_{24}(R_{13}R_{31}) = R(3, 5).$$

The alternative case where n in t' does not occupy the position of $m<n$ in s' is illustrated by:

$$s' : \begin{matrix} 1 & 4 \\ 2 & \\ 3 & \\ 5 & \end{matrix} \quad \xrightarrow{R'} \quad \begin{matrix} 1 & 4 \\ 2 & 5 \\ 3 & \end{matrix},$$

so that $R'=R_{24}$.

We may amplify 7.44 by the remark:

7.513 *If F is a p-core no raising is possible and each standard tableau corresponds to itself alone.*

If we apply 7.44 and 7.51 in succession to the feet $F_1, F_2, \ldots, F_{l'(b)}$ of **B** we can establish a 1-1 correspondence between the standard tableaux of those $[\lambda]\subset\mathbf{B}$ which *overlap* subject to the raising operator. Consider first the standard tableaux of F_1; each of these gives rise to an admitted permutation P_1 which is admitted by each $[\lambda]$ obtainable by applying the raising operator to F_1, subject to 7.42. Denote by B_1 the set of all these permutations P_1. By 7.44 the initial tableau of F_2 has not already appeared and we may again apply the raising operator. By 7.51, each standard tableau of F_2 not previously related to a standard tableau of F_1 gives rise to a permutation P_2 and these permutations P_2 constitute the set B_2. By 7.44, B_2 is not vacuous, though some of the

P_2's may have already appeared as members of B_1. Proceeding thus we may construct the set of admitted permutations B_i, each one of which is admitted by every $[\lambda]$ obtainable from F_i by applying the raising operator, subject to the proviso that the corresponding standard tableau has not already been counted. A given $[\lambda]$ may well appear with multiplicity greater than 1, along with distinct sets of its standard tableaux each of which yields the permutations of B_i, when $[\lambda]$ is obtained from F_i by means of distinct raising operators (see Tables for $p=2, 3$).

7.52 *The highest diagram in the block* **B** *to admit all the permutations of* B_i *must be a head H.*

Proof. By 7.51 it is sufficient to consider the effect of raising on an initial tableau of F_i, and the result follows from the construction of 7.441 applied to the conjugate block.

As we have remarked B_i and B_j $(j \neq i)$ may have permutations in common. It remains to show the existence in each B_i of a permutation P_i which is *not* contained in any other B_j $(j \neq i)$. Such a permutation will be called *characteristic*. The following lemma is important:

7.53 *If the lowest removable node of F is of residue class r then removing the highest r-node below which no r-position is vacant in F will yield a uniquely determined* $\bar{F}$, *and no two distinct F yield the same* $\bar{F}$.

Proof. The block **B** is uniquely determined by 5.43. That we obtain a unique $\bar{F}$ follows from the conjugate of Fig. 6.6. The proof of the last statement is left to the reader.

7.54 *Every* B_i *contains at least one characteristic permutation.*

Proof. Clearly this theorem is true for a p-core, in which case every admitted permutation is characteristic, and for a block of weight 1 of $\mathfrak{S}_p$, as we have already remarked. We shall assume it for any block $\bar{\mathbf{B}}$ of $\mathfrak{S}_{n-1}$ and prove it for any block **B** of $\mathfrak{S}_n$.

If now we assume that $\bar{F}_i$ has been constructed according to 7.53 from F_i, then we may assume that there exists a characteristic permutation $\bar{P} \subset \bar{B}_i^{(r)}$. Moreover, we may assume that $\bar{P}$ ends (i) in $s \neq r$, or (ii) in r, according as r is the lowest removable node of F_i or the highest r-node below which no r-position is vacant in F_i.

In case (i), since $\bar{P}$ is characteristic for $\bar{B}_i^{(r)}$, all raising operators are valid for n occupying the lowest removable r-position of F_i, so that $P=\bar{P}r$ is characteristic.

In case (ii), if the r-node removed from F_i to yield $\bar{F}_i$ has below it only the lowest removable node, then $\bar{P}$ ends in r and is characteristic. Thus in $P=\bar{P}r$, $n-1$ and n occupy r-positions and may be interchanged, so that we may assume that n occupies the lowest removable position. Thus all raising operators applicable to it are valid and unambiguous; repeating the argument, $P=\bar{P}r$ is characteristic in every case.

From the above construction

7.541 $$\bar{B}_i^{(r)}\, r \subset B_i,$$

and also

7.542 $$\bar{B}_i^{(r)} r \not\subset B_j. \qquad (j \neq i).$$

Combining 7.541 and 7.542, and noting that the sets

$$\bar{B}_i^{(r)} r,\ \bar{B}_j^{(s)} s,\ \ldots$$

constructed according to 7.53, are all distinct and are distributed amongst the B_i in a 1-1 manner, we have proved the existence of at least one characteristic permutation in each B_i.

Cases in which $\bar{B}_i^{(r)} r$ is *not* constructed according to 7.53 and does belong to two distinct B_i are to be found in Table B. In particular the set

$$\bar{B}_i^{(0)} 0 :\quad 0122010 \text{ (twice)},\ 0212010,\ 0120210,$$

which is contained in B_4 and B_5 is a case in point, where the set $\bar{B}_i^{(0)} = B_5$ in Table A.

If B_i contains β_i permutations (counting repetitions) we have seen that each $[\lambda]$ in **B** either admits all these β_i permutations or none of them. If we denote by M_i the set of diagrams $[\lambda]$, each of which admits every permutation of B_i, then:

7.55 *The set of diagrams M_i which admit all permutations of B_i could equally well be defined as all those that admit any given characteristic permutation of B_i with appropriate multiplicity.*

The following example illustrates the construction of 7.53.

7.56 *Example.* Consider the block of $\mathfrak{S}_7$ with $p=3$ and core [1] (Table 3-7, also Tables A, B), whose foot diagrams are respectively:

F_1	F_2	F_3	F_4	F_5
$[1^7]$	$[2^2, 1^3]$	$[2^3, 1]$	$[3, 2, 1^2]$	$[4, 2, 1]$
0	0 1	0 1	0 1 2	0 1 2 0
2	2 0	2 0	2 0	2 0
1	1	1 2	1	1
0	0	0	0	
2	2			
1				
0				

with corresponding $\bar{F}_i$:

$\bar{F}_1$	$\bar{F}_2$	$\bar{F}_3$	$\bar{F}_4$	$\bar{F}_5$	
$[1^6]$		$[2^3]$	$[3, 1^3]$		$r = 0$
				$[4, 2]$	$r = 1$
	$[2^2, 1^2]$				$r = 2$

Just as M_i has a foot F_i as lowest diagram so it has a head H_i as highest diagram. The argument we have used to establish the existence of a characteristic permutation in each B_i could have been applied equally well to the conjugate block $\mathbf{B}'$ in which *lowest* and *highest*, *below* and *above*, would be interchanged in 7.53. The highest removable r-node of H_i may be the same as the lowest removable r-node of F_i in which case no new characteristic permutations arise. This always happens for $p=2$ since $H_i = F_i$. However, it may be different as the values of r listed at the foot of Table 5-10 show, so that 7.53 may lead to two sets of characteristic permutations.

It is important to emphasise that F_i and H_i each appear in M_i with multiplicity 1.

Combining these ideas we have the important result:

7.57 *Each set M_i in the block* $\mathbf{B}$ *of $\mathfrak{S}_n$ is obtainable in at least one way, independently of every other M_j $(j \neq i)$, by r-inducing upon some $\bar{M}_i$ of $\mathfrak{S}_{n-1}$ for r chosen according to 7.53.*

While no other M_j $(j \neq {}_i)$ will be involved, yet the multiplicity of $\bar{M}_i$ may well be greater than 1 as the following example shows:

7.571 *Example.* Referring to Table 3-7 and Tables A, B we take

$$\bar{M} = [4, 1^2]+[3, 2, 1]+[3, 1^3]$$
$$M = [4, 2, 1]+[4, 1^3]+[3, 2, 1^2]$$

where

$$\bar{M} \overset{0}{\uparrow} 2M.$$

The permutations which characterize $\bar{M}$ are

012210 (twice), 012120, 021210, 021120 (twice)

which all arise from

$$[3, 1^2] \overset{0}{\uparrow} \bar{M}.$$

It is interesting to pick out the characteristic permutations in the Tables A and B.

More generally:

7.58 *If r-inducing upon any set* $\bar{M}$ *of* $\mathfrak{S}_{n-1}$ *yields a set* M *of* $\mathfrak{S}_n$ *then* (i) $M=mM_i$ *or* (ii) $M=M_i+M_j+\dots$.

Proof. If we r-induce upon a set $\bar{M}$ of $\mathfrak{S}_{n-1}$ either the result is vacuous or we obtain a set M. If $\bar{B}r$ contains a characteristic permutation P of M_i, where F_i is the lowest diagram in M, then $M=mM_i$, otherwise M will contain M_i and other sets M_j as well, according as $\bar{B}r\subset B_j$.

7.59 *Example.* The proof of 7.58 could be phrased in terms of standard tableaux. We illustrate in the case $p=3$:

$$\bar{M} \overset{0}{\uparrow} M_i+M_j,$$

where

$$\begin{bmatrix} 123+123+1235+12356 \\ 45 \quad 456 \quad 4 \quad\quad 4 \\ 6 \quad\quad\quad\quad 6 \end{bmatrix}$$

$$\overset{0}{\uparrow} \quad \begin{bmatrix} 123+1235+1235 \\ 45 \quad 4 \quad\quad 47 \\ 6 \quad\; 6 \quad\quad 6 \\ 7 \quad\; 7 \end{bmatrix} + \begin{bmatrix} 1237+1237+12356 \\ 45 \quad\quad 456 \quad 47 \\ 6 \end{bmatrix}$$

The sets of standard tableaux in brackets are uniquely associated by means of the raising operator and can be taken to represent the corresponding irreducible representations (cf. Tables A, B).

7.6 The Nakayama reciprocity formulae. Our aim in the following chapter will be to prove that the M_i do actually constitute the indecomposables of the regular representation of $\mathfrak{S}_n$, and also to show how the β_i permutations of the set B_i determine the irreducible modular component which is common to each of the ordinary representations contained in M_i. We conclude the present chapter by showing that the Nakayama Reciprocity Formulae do in fact hold for the B_i and the M_i if r-reducing and restricting are properly defined.

Let us begin by rephrasing 7.58:

7.61 *If P is any permutation of the set B_i and M is the totality of diagrams which admit P, then* (i) $M = M_i$ *or* (ii) $M = M_i + M_j + \ldots$. *In case* (ii) *P is also contained in B_j, for all j.*

This suggests that we put the question the other way and ask in what sets $\bar{B}_u$ does a permutation $\bar{P}$ appear if $\bar{P}r = P$ is contained in B_i? If we set

7.62 $$\bar{M}_i \overset{r}{\uparrow} \sum a_{ij} M_j,$$

we may also write

7.63 $$B_j \underset{r}{\downarrow} \sum a_{ij} \bar{B}_i,$$

and these two formulae correspond to the two parts of the Nakayama reciprocity formulae 12.61 *as applied to a single block.*

Just as we r-induced on the set $\bar{M}$ by adding an r-node in every possible way, so we can *r-restrict* on the set M by removing an r-node in every possible way. We prove the following result:

7.64 *If r-restricting on a set M_s of $\mathfrak{S}_n$ yields a set $\bar{M}$ or $\mathfrak{S}_{n-1}$ then*

$$M_s \underset{r}{\downarrow} \bar{M} = \sum b_{st} \bar{M}_t.$$

Proof. By definition, the set M_s contains every diagram $[\lambda]$ of $\mathfrak{S}_n$ which admits any characteristic permutation $P \in B_s$. In removing an r-node from each $[\lambda] \in M_s$ we must consider also the position it occupies in P, so that removing it yields a diagram admitting one of

$$\bar{P}, \bar{P}', \bar{P}'', \ldots.$$

Conversely, every diagram admitting one of these truncations of P must appear in the set $\bar{M}$, and if a diagram admits more than one such truncation it will appear in $\overline{M}$ with the proper multiplicity. If $\overline{P}$ is characteristic then the set admitting it will be $\overline{M}_i$; if not, this set will consist of two or more *complete* sets $\overline{M}_i+\overline{M}_j+\ldots$ by 7.61, proving the theorem.

It may help to clarify the above argument to remark that all the standard tableaux of each $[\lambda]\subset M_s$ are obtained by adding n in each available r-position to *all* the appropriate standard tableaux of $\mathfrak{S}_{n-1}$. If we denote such a tableau of $[\lambda]$ by t' then there exists a permutation p such that (cf. 7.432)

$$pPp^{-1} = P',$$

where s is a standard tableau of $[\lambda]$ yielding P. If $P'=\overline{P}'r$, it follows that *all* possible diagrams of $\mathfrak{S}_{n-1}$ which admit $\overline{P}'$ must be found amongst those obtained by restricting M_s. In other words all such sets are *complete*, as stated above.

We cannot be so specific concerning the values of the b's in 7.64 as we could concerning the a's in 7.62, since various *positions* in P are involved. This is the subtle distinction between r-inducing and r-restricting. As before, we may put the question in the other way, asking what sets B_s can be obtained by adding an r-node to the permutation of $\overline{B}_t$ in all possible ways? Clearly, the answer is given by

7.65 $$\overline{B}_t \overset{r}{\uparrow} \sum b_{st} B_s,$$

but one must be careful here in counting the multiplicity when $b_{st}>1$. The situation is similar to that which led to the multiplicity m in 7.58, and arises from the interchangeability of certain r-nodes on the rim of $[\lambda]$. These may be juxtaposed in P in which case no difficulty arises; if this is not the case, reference must be made to the diagrams, i.e. to 7.64. As before, the two formulae 7.64 and 7.65 correspond to the two parts of 12.62, again applied to a single block.

7.66 *Example.* It is desirable to illustrate these analogues of the Nakayama formulae in a case which is sufficiently complicated to bring out the points referred to above. Consider Table 3-9, when $p=3$ and we let M_1-M_{10} refer to the block of weight 3 of $\mathfrak{S}_9$, $\overline{M}_1$-$\overline{M}_5$ to the block of weight 2 of $\mathfrak{S}_8$ with core [2], $\overline{M}'_1$-$\overline{M}'_5$ to the conjugate block of $\mathfrak{S}_8$ with core $[1^2]$ and N_1, N_2 to the block of weight 1 of $\mathfrak{S}_8$ with core $[3, 1^2]$. Corresponding to 7.62 we have

7.661

	M_1	M_2	M_3	M_4	M_5	M_6	M_7	M_8	M_9	M_{10}	
$\overline{M}_1$	1										
$\overline{M}_2$				1							
$\overline{M}_3$					1						Core [2]
$\overline{M}_4$								1			
$\overline{M}_5$										1	
$\overline{M}'_1$		1									
$\overline{M}'_2$				1							
$\overline{M}'_3$						1					Core [1^2]
$\overline{M}'_4$							1				
$\overline{M}'_5$										1	
N_1			1								Core [3, 1^2]
N_2									1		

Corresponding to 7.64 we have:

7.662

	$\overline{M}_1$	$\overline{M}_2$	$\overline{M}_3$	$\overline{M}_4$	$\overline{M}_5$	$\overline{M}'_1$	$\overline{M}'_2$	$\overline{M}'_3$	$\overline{M}'_4$	$\overline{M}'_5$	N_1	N_2
M_1	2					1	2			1	2	
M_2	1					2					2	
M_3			1			1					3	
M_4		2					2				1	
M_5			2				1		1		2	
M_6		1		1	2			2				2
M_7			1		1				2			2
M_8				2				1				2
M_9				1					1			3
M_{10}					2					2		1
			core [2] $r = 2$					core [1^2] $r = 1$				core [3, 1^2] $r = 0$

We shall not write out the transposed matrices corresponding to 7.63 and 7.65, but it is worth while drawing attention to two points. In the first place, the restriction

$$M_1 \underset{1}{\downarrow} (\overline{M}'_1+\overline{M}'_5)+2\overline{M}'_2$$

illustrates the proof of 7.64 in that $P=012012012$, and $\overline{M}'_1$ and $\overline{M}'_5$ both admit $\overline{P}=01201202$ while $\overline{M}'_2$ admits $\overline{P}'=01202012$ as a characteristic permutation. Secondly, one can only expect the *degrees* β_i of the sets B_i to satisfy the Nakayama formulae if we consider all values of r. For example $\bar{\beta}_2=27$ so that the degree of the induced representation should be $27 \cdot 9=243$. Actually,

$$\bar{B}_2 \uparrow (2B_4+B_6)+B_0,$$

where $\beta_4=40$, $\beta_6=1$ and the corresponding B's are obtained by adding a 2-node in all possible positions to the permutations of $\bar{B}_2$. The number of permutations in the set B_0 is the number admitted by the core [5, 3, 1], i.e. $\beta_0=162$, and these are obtained from the set $\bar{B}_2$ by adding a 1-node in all possible positions.

CHAPTER EIGHT

THE MODULAR IRREDUCIBLE REPRESENTATIONS OF $\mathfrak{S}_n$

Introduction. In order to complete the proof of the validity of the construction of the decomposition matrix given in Chapter VII we must show that any given ordinary representation $[\lambda]$ splits according to the appropriate *row* of the D-matrix.

We first note the basic congruence property 8.11 on which our whole argument rests. Since the reduction is immediate for every $[\lambda]$ with $n \leqq p$, we have a start in 8.15 for the inductive construction of a transforming matrix L, such that $L[\lambda]L^{-1}$ is p-integral and in the desired modularly reduced form.

In constructing the D-matrix in the last chapter, we divided the tableaux of each $[\lambda]$ into sets Σ_j such that those lying in the same column of the D-matrix were related by means of the same raising operator. If

$$[\lambda] \downarrow [\bar{\lambda}_1] + [\bar{\lambda}_2] + \ldots,$$

we may assume that a transforming matrix $\bar{L}_i$ has been constructed in the manner to be described such that

$$\bar{L}_i\,[\bar{\lambda}_i]\,\bar{L}_i^{-1}$$

when reduced modulo p, splits into modular components corresponding to the sets of tableaux $\bar{\Sigma}_{ij}$ of $[\bar{\lambda}_i]$. Moreover, we may arrange that the modular components are the same for each i and fixed j.

Our chief problem is to discover the relationship between the sets Σ of the tableaux of $[\lambda]$ and the sets $\bar{\Sigma}_{ij}$ of the tableaux of the $[\bar{\lambda}_i]$. In § 8.2 we define a *partial order* amongst the Σ's which is based on the 2×2 matrices of 2.17 which 'cross over' between Σ's, and in 8.24 we prove that the Σ's form a *lattice* $\mathscr{L}$. It is necessary to show that $\mathscr{L}$ is consistent with each $\bar{\mathscr{L}}_i$ and this requires us to analyse further the significance of the raising operator.

The first step in the construction of L is to construct the matrix

$$\bar{L} = \bar{L}_1 \dot{+} \bar{L}_2 \dot{+} \ldots$$

and to rearrange the tableaux, and so the matrices $\bar{L}_i$, according to the sets Σ of $[\lambda]$. Under such rearrangement the essential order relations of the $\bar{L}_i$ are preserved and we denote the resulting matrix by $\bar{\bar{L}}$. In order that the transposition matrix $(n-1, n)$ be p-integral, we transform each 2×2 matrix of 2.17 in which p appears in the denominator according to 8.13. This is accomplished by the matrix L_n which commutes with $[\lambda]$ restricted to $\mathfrak{S}_{n-2}$. L_n will in general cut across the sets Σ_{ij} but, according to 8.21, it relates tableaux of a given Σ_k of $[\lambda]$ which are associated by the raising operator for $\mathfrak{S}_{n-1}$. If such tableaux belong to sets $\bar{\Sigma}_{i_1 j}$ and $\bar{\Sigma}_{i_2 j}$, both contained in Σ_k, it may well happen that not all the tableaux of these two sets are so related because of the appearance of a permutation (ρ). Thus to describe the raising operator completely we must supplement L_n by another matrix L_R. The construction of L_R is explained in § 8.3 and it is shown that

$$L = L_R L_n \bar{\bar{L}}$$

transforms $[\lambda]$ in the desired manner. Several examples are worked out to show the construction of L and the results of transformation and reduction modulo p.

In § 8.4 we state our main theorem which, by relating the construction of the D-matrix by columns in Chapter VII to the reduction of $[\lambda]$ by L, justifies the procedure used. The reduction has the added interest of showing the radical of the group algebra in an explicit form.

The final section of the chapter reverts to the notion of an r-Boolean algebra and shows how these ideas explain certain repetitions of D-matrices which occur in the Tables.

Except for 8.11, none of the material in this chapter has appeared in print; §§ 8.1-8.3 are based on the Thesis of Miss Diane Johnson who considered the reduction of $[\lambda]$'s having two rows only, in detail. These ideas are complicated and it may well be that much more remains to be said, but the general features of the picture seem to be clear.

8.1 Congruence properties.

The following result is fundamental:

8.11 *In Young's semi-normal representation, the quantities* $1/\rho$ *and* $1/\rho'$, *calculated with reference to associated tableaux in the matrices representing* $(m-1, m)$ *in any two* $[\lambda]$, $[\lambda'] \in M_i$, *are congruent modulo* p *for every* m $(l < m \leqq n)$.

Proof. Since

$$\frac{1}{\rho} = g_{ij} - g_{kl}, \qquad \frac{1}{\rho'} = g'_{tu} - g'_{vw},$$

and $g_{ij} \equiv g'_{tu}$, $g_{kl} \equiv g'_{vw}$ (mod p) by 4.42, we conclude that

$$\frac{1}{\rho} \equiv \frac{1}{\rho'} \pmod{p}$$

for every transposition $(m-1, m)$ of $[\lambda]$ and $[\lambda'] \in M_i$.

In the application of 8.11 to the modular reduction of $[\lambda]$ we are concerned primarily with representations of $\mathfrak{S}_{n-1}$ which differ only in the position of a single node. Since the proof of 12.13 can be modified to yield p-integers instead of rational integers, we know at least that:

8.12 *There exists a linear transformation L such that $L[\lambda]L^{-1}$ is p-integral for every ordinary irreducible representation $[\lambda]$ of $\mathfrak{S}_n$.*

The question remains, can this transformation L be chosen so as to bring the modular reduction of $[\lambda]$ into evidence, ensuring that every modular component has the same form in each of its 'incarnations'?

In Example 12.15 we constructed a transformation which put the modular splitting of [3, 2] into evidence for $p=2, 3$ simultaneously; moreover, all the coefficients were rational integers. It is not hard to see that this is too much to expect in the general case, so that we shall confine our attention to a single prime $p \leqq n$. Besides 12.152 we have the simpler transformation

8.13
$$\begin{bmatrix} 1 & -\dfrac{m-1}{m} \\ 0 & 1 \end{bmatrix} \begin{bmatrix} -\dfrac{1}{m} & \dfrac{m^2-1}{m^2} \\ 1 & \dfrac{1}{m} \end{bmatrix} \begin{bmatrix} 1 & \dfrac{m-1}{m} \\ 0 & 1 \end{bmatrix} = \begin{bmatrix} -1 & 0 \\ 1 & 1 \end{bmatrix}$$

whose use we shall illustrate in the following

8.14 *Example.* If we transform the transposition matrices of [4, 1] for $p=3$, taking the tableaux in the order of Table 3-5,

$$(12)\begin{bmatrix} 1 & & & \\ & 1 & & \\ & & -1 & \\ & & & 1 \end{bmatrix},\ (23)\begin{bmatrix} 1 & & & \\ & -\frac{1}{2} & \frac{3}{4} & \\ & 1 & \frac{1}{2} & \\ & & & 1 \end{bmatrix},\ (34)\begin{bmatrix} -\frac{1}{3} & \frac{8}{9} & & \\ 1 & \frac{1}{3} & & \\ & & 1 & \\ & & & 1 \end{bmatrix},\ (45)\begin{bmatrix} \frac{1}{4} & & & 1 \\ & 1 & & \\ & & 1 & \\ \frac{15}{16} & & & -\frac{1}{4} \end{bmatrix}$$

by the matrix

$$L = \begin{bmatrix} 1 & -\frac{2}{3} & & \\ & 1 & & \\ & & 1 & \\ & & & 1 \end{bmatrix}$$

and reduce modulo 3, we obtain:

$$(12)\begin{bmatrix}1&&&\\&1&&\\&&-1&\\&&&1\end{bmatrix},\ (23)\begin{bmatrix}1&1&1&0\\&1&0&0\\&1&-1&0\\&&&1\end{bmatrix},\ (34)\begin{bmatrix}-1&0&0&0\\1&1&0&0\\&&1&0\\&&&1\end{bmatrix},\ (45)\begin{bmatrix}1&1&0&1\\&1&0&0\\&0&1&0\\&1&0&-1\end{bmatrix}.$$

On the other hand, if we transform the transposition matrices of [3, 2] in Example 12.15 by

$$L=\begin{bmatrix}1&-\frac{2}{3}&&&\\&1&&&\\&&1&&\\&&&1&\\&&&&1\end{bmatrix}$$

and similarly reduce modulo 3 we obtain:

$$(12)\left[\begin{array}{cccc|c}1&&&&\\&1&&&\\&&-1&&\\&&&1&\\\hline&&&&-1\end{array}\right],\qquad (23)\left[\begin{array}{cccc|c}1&1&1&0&\\&1&0&0&\\&1&-1&0&\\&&&1&\\\hline&&&1&-1\end{array}\right],$$

$$(34)\left[\begin{array}{cccc|c}-1&0&0&0&\\1&1&0&0&\\&&1&0&\\&&&1&\\\hline&&&&-1\end{array}\right],\qquad (45)\left[\begin{array}{cccc|c}1&1&0&1&\\&1&0&0&\\&0&1&0&\\&1&0&-1&\\\hline&&1&0&-1\end{array}\right]$$

and the identity of the common modular component is clear.

In order to obtain the transformation L in general we proceed by induction, noting first that:

8.15 *Every ordinary irreducible representation* $[\lambda]$ *of* $\mathfrak{S}_n$ $(n \leq p)$, *constructed according to* 2.17, *is p-integral as it stands and reduction modulo p when* $n=p$ *exhibits the irreducible modular components in accord with the decomposition matrix of* 7.13.

Proof. The only representations we need consider are of the form $[p-s, 1^s]$ and only in the matrix representing $(p-1, p)$ will $1-\rho^2 \equiv 0 \pmod p$. This situation can only arise when $p-1$ and p occupy positions at the ends of the first row and column of the tableau. No transformation is necessary and the modular reduction is in accord with 7.13.

The reduction of $[3, 1^2]$ for $p=5$ in Example 7.31 illustrates 8.15.

8.2 The transforming matrix L. We record the following properties of the raising operator:

8.21 *If $n-1$ and n both occupy r-positions in t_u^λ and t_v^λ, then $\rho=1/kp$ in that part of the matrix representing $(n-1, n)$ constructed according to* 2.17(iii)(*a*); *both t_u^λ and t_v^λ belong to the same set Σ of $[\lambda]$.*

8.22 *If $n-1$ occupies an r-position and n an s-position in t_u^λ, where r and s are neither equal nor successive residues modulo p, then that part of the matrix representing $(n-1, n)$ constructed according to* 2.17(iii)(*a*) *is p-integral and t_u^λ and t_v^λ both belong to the same set Σ of $[\lambda]$.*

Proof. The first part of each Theorem is obvious. To prove the second parts, it is necessary to generalize 7.431 slightly, setting

$$s = t_u,\ t = t_u^\lambda = R(\rho)t_u;\quad s' = t_v,\ t' = t_v^\lambda = R(\rho')t_v.$$

By going around the diagram in two different ways, it follows that $\rho' p = q\rho$ and we are interested in the case $p = q = (n-1, n)$. It follows that (i) $\rho = \rho' = I$, or (ii) if $\rho \neq I$, then $\rho' = p\rho p^{-1} \neq I$.

Conversely, if t_u and t_v belong to the last set Σ of F and if $t_u^\lambda = R(\rho)t_u$, then $n-1$, n can be interchanged so that t^λ is a standard tableau and $p = q = (n-1, n)$. Moreover, $t_v^\lambda = R(\rho')t_v$, so that t_u and t_v belong to the same set Σ of $[\lambda]$.

8.23 *If t_u^λ and t_v^λ belong to distinct sets Σ of $[\lambda]$ then the residues of $n-1$ and n must be consecutive, so that $1-\rho^2 \equiv 0$ (mod p) in those parts of the matrix representing $(n-1, n)$ constructed according to* 2.17(iii)(*a*).

Proof. That the residues must be consecutive is the only possibility left by 8.22 and 8.23.

While 8.23 provides a *necessary* condition for t_u^λ and t_v^λ to belong to different sets Σ, the condition is not sufficient as can easily be seen from Table 3-5. The fundamental property of the tableaux in this case where the residues of $n-1$ and n are successive is that $n-1$ and n may be juxtaposed:

8.241 $$(n-1)n, \qquad \begin{matrix}(n-1)\\ n\end{matrix}.$$

When this happens $n-1$ and n *cannot be interchanged* because of the standardness condition. While this juxtaposition may occur in one Σ in a column of the D-matrix, the situation can change under the raising operator. It is just such a discontinuity in the applicability of the raising operator which separates the sets Σ of $[\lambda]$.

Let us now assume that

8.242 $$[\lambda] \downarrow [\bar{\lambda}_1]+[\bar{\lambda}_2]+\ldots$$

and that the tableaux of each $\bar{\Sigma}_j \subset [\bar{\lambda}]$ are arranged in the order assigned by the raising operator in the D-matrix of $\mathfrak{S}_{n-1}$. If we denote by $\bar{\Sigma}_{ij}$ the set of tableau on the ith row and the jth column of the D-matrix containing $[\bar{\lambda}_i]$, then by § 7.6,

8.243 $$\Sigma \downarrow \sum \bar{\Sigma}_{ij}$$

for each $\Sigma \subset [\lambda]$. We wish to study the order relation which can be based on 8.23 and which relates the various $\Sigma \subset [\lambda]$.

By our construction, all those tableaux which belong to a given Σ are subject to the same raising operator, and when we cross over from Σ to Σ' this operator changes its 'potential'. For the tableaux in question, such a change can only be the result of interchanging $n-1$ and n. Since the raising operator is applied first to the second row, then to the third row of $[\lambda]$, and so on, the immediate raising potential is greater when n is *lower* than $n-1$ since the possibilities 8.241 are not ruled out. Since the same statement holds when the tableaux differ by the interchange of any $r-1$ and r $(1<r\leqq n)$, we conclude that when such cross-overs exist between Σ and Σ' *they must all be in the same direction.* Thus Σ and Σ' are assigned a definite order relation which is consistent with that which we assume to have similarly been defined for the $\bar{\Sigma}_{ij}$.

If we denote each $\Sigma \subset [\lambda]$ by a node and if two Σ's are ordered by a cross-over transposition, let us join their corresponding nodes and so construct a Hasse diagram H. Since $[\lambda]$ is irreducible over the rational field, H must be a connected graph. If we 'accumulate' the tableaux which are connected by such order relations we obtain a *lattice* $\mathscr{L}$ with the natural inclusion relation, whose element 0 is that set Σ which contains the initial tableaux of $[\lambda]$ while the element I of $\mathscr{L}$ contains all the standard tableaux of $[\lambda]$. By 8.243 and our preceding argument, it follows that $\mathscr{L}$ is consistent with each $\bar{\mathscr{L}}_i$. Thus we have:

8.244 *With each* $[\lambda]$ *and every* $p\leqq n$ *is associated a partial ordering of the sets* $\Sigma \subset [\lambda]$ *which may be represented by a Hasse diagram H. Interpreting this order relation as set addition we obtain a lattice* $\mathscr{L}$ *with the natural inclusion relation.*

It will help if we illustrate the situation with the following

8.245 *Example.* If we take $p=3$ and $[\lambda]+[4, 2, 1]$ as in Table B, then $[\bar{\lambda}_1] = [4, 2]$, $[\bar{\lambda}_2] = [4, 1^2]$, $[\bar{\lambda}_3] = [3, 2, 1]$. Taking the $\bar{\Sigma}_{ij}$ in the order they appear in the Tables, we have the following Hasse diagrams:

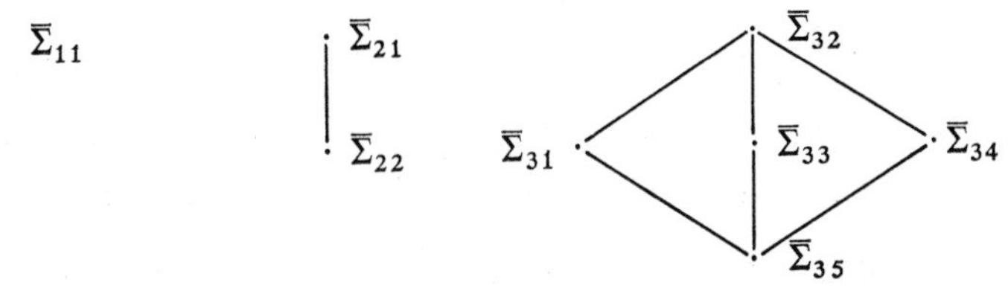

H_1 H_2 H_3

with H of the form:

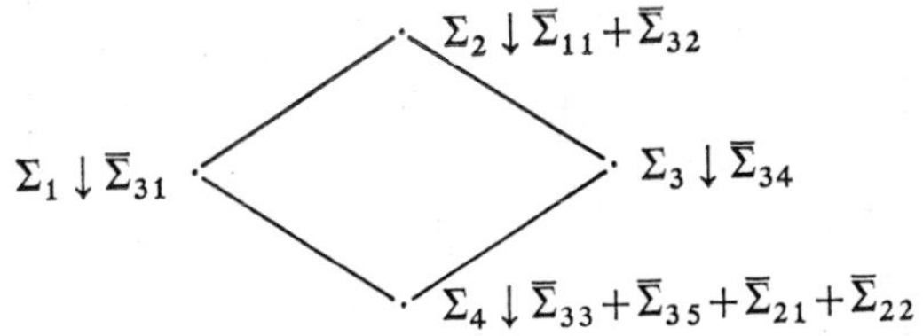

H

Note that the new order relations introduced by the transposition $(n-1, n)$ cannot interfere with those of $\mathfrak{S}_{n-1}$, though they may make one or more such relations insignificant by including the corresponding sets $\bar{\Sigma}$ in the same Σ.

Finally, we may convert the partial order of 8.244 into a linear order in at least one way, which proves the following important corollary of the preceding result:

8.246 *If $r-1$ and r have consecutive residues in t_x^λ and t_y^λ which differ only by their interchange, and if $t_x^\lambda \in \Sigma_k$ and $t_y^\lambda \in \Sigma_l$, then the Σ's may be arranged so that if r is lower than $r-1$ in t_x^λ then $k<l$ for any $r(1<r\leqq n)$.*

This ordering Theorem is the basis for our construction of the transforming matrix L. Taking the sets $\bar{\Sigma}$ in the order determined by 8.24 we may construct a matrix L_n according to 8.13 such that $L_n\,(n-1, n)\,L_n^{-1}$ is p-integral. Moreover, L_n will not 'cross over' between sets Σ. But the situation is not simple since we already have transformed $[\lambda]$ by $\bar{L}$. Thus we set

$$L = L_R L_n \bar{L},$$

where L_R completes L_n in describing the raising operator as applied to sets $\bar{\Sigma}$ of $\mathfrak{S}_{n-1}$. In the next section we consider the construction of L_R in general and the effect of transforming $(n-1, n)$ by L rather than by L_n. In the remainder of this section we consider one aspect of the problem suggested by the following

8.25 *Example.* Take $[\gamma] = [4, 2]$ with $p=3$, so that $[\bar{\lambda}_1] = [4, 1]$ and $[\bar{\lambda}_2] = [3, 2]$ in Table 3-5. Since we shall assume the reduction of Example 8.14 it is only necessary to write out the matrix representing (56) in [4, 2], taking the standard tableaux in the order:

1235	1245	1345	1234	;	1236	1246	1346	1256	;	1356
46	36	26	56		45	35	25	34		24

$$
(56):\ \left[\begin{array}{cccc|cccc|c}
-\frac{1}{3} & & & & \frac{8}{9} & & & & \\
& -\frac{1}{3} & & & & \frac{8}{9} & & & \\
& & -\frac{1}{3} & & & & \frac{8}{9} & & \\
& & & 1 & & & & & \\
\hline
1 & & & & \frac{1}{3} & & & & \\
& 1 & & & & \frac{1}{3} & & & \\
& & 1 & & & & \frac{1}{3} & & \\
& & & & & & & 1 & \\
\hline
& & & & & & & & 1
\end{array}\right]
$$

The appropriate transforming matrix L is constructed from those of [4, 1] and [3, 2], modified so that (56) becomes 3-integral, as indicated below.

$$
L = \underbrace{\left[\begin{array}{cccc|cccc|c}
1 & & & & & & & & \\
& 1 & & & & & & & \\
& & 1 & & & & & & \\
& & & 1 & & & & \frac{1}{3} & \\
\hline
& & & & 1 & & & & \\
& & & & & 1 & & & \\
& & & & & & 1 & & \\
& & & & & & & 1 & \\
\hline
& & & & & & & & 1
\end{array}\right]}_{L_R}
\underbrace{\left[\begin{array}{cccc|cccc|c}
1 & & & & -\frac{2}{3} & & & & \\
& 1 & & & & -\frac{2}{3} & & & \\
& & 1 & & & & -\frac{2}{3} & & \\
& & & 1 & & & & & \\
\hline
& & & & 1 & & & & \\
& & & & & 1 & & & \\
& & & & & & 1 & & \\
& & & & & & & 1 & \\
\hline
& & & & & & & & 1
\end{array}\right]}_{L_n}
\underbrace{\left[\begin{array}{cccc|cccc|c}
1 & -\frac{2}{3} & & & & & & & \\
& 1 & & & & & & & \\
& & 1 & & & & & & \\
& & & 1 & & & & & \\
\hline
& & & & 1 & -\frac{2}{3} & & & \\
& & & & & 1 & & & \\
& & & & & & 1 & & \\
& & & & & & & 1 & \\
\hline
& & & & & & & & 1
\end{array}\right]}_{\bar{L} = \underline{L}}
$$

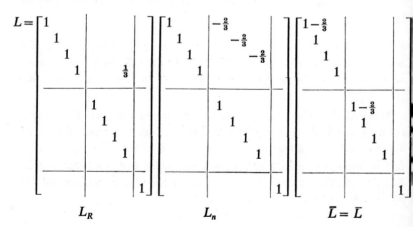

$$
= \left[\begin{array}{cccc|cccc|c}
1 & -\frac{2}{3} & & & -\frac{2}{3} & \frac{4}{9} & & & \\
 & 1 & & & & -\frac{2}{3} & & & \\
 & & 1 & & & & -\frac{2}{3} & & \\
 & & & 1 & & & & +\frac{1}{3} & \\
\hline
 & & & & 1 & -\frac{2}{3} & & & \\
 & & & & & 1 & & & \\
 & & & & & & 1 & & \\
 & & & & & & & 1 & \\
\hline
 & & & & & & & & 1
\end{array}\right]
$$

After transformation and reduction modulo 3, we obtain:

$$
(12)\ \left[\begin{array}{cccc|cccc|c}
1 & & & & & & & & \\
 & 1 & & & & & & & \\
 & & -1 & & & & & & \\
 & & & 1 & & & & & \\
\hline
 & & & & 1 & & & & \\
 & & & & & 1 & & & \\
 & & & & & & -1 & & \\
 & & & & & & & 1 & \\
\hline
 & & & & & & & & -1
\end{array}\right]
\qquad
(23)\ \left[\begin{array}{cccc|cccc|c}
1 & 1 & 1 & 0 & & & & & \\
 & 1 & 0 & 0 & & & & & \\
 & 1 & -1 & 0 & & & & & \\
 & & & 1 & & & & & \\
\hline
 & & & & 1 & 1 & 1 & 0 & \\
 & & & & & 1 & 0 & 0 & \\
 & & & & & 1 & -1 & 0 & \\
 & & & & & & & 1 & \\
\hline
 & & & & & & & 1 & -1
\end{array}\right]
$$

$$
(34)\ \left[\begin{array}{cccc|cccc|c}
-1 & 0 & 0 & 0 & & & & & \\
1 & 1 & 0 & 0 & & & & & \\
 & & 1 & 0 & & & & & \\
 & & & 1 & & & & & \\
\hline
 & & & & -1 & 0 & 0 & 0 & \\
 & & & & 1 & 1 & 0 & 0 & \\
 & & & & & & 1 & 0 & \\
 & & & & & & & 1 & \\
\hline
 & & & & & & & & -1
\end{array}\right]
\qquad
(45)\ \left[\begin{array}{cccc|cccc|c}
1 & 1 & 0 & 1 & 1 & -1 & 0 & 0 & \\
 & 1 & 0 & 0 & 0 & 1 & 0 & 1 & \\
 & & 1 & 0 & 0 & 0 & 1 & 0 & 1 \\
 & 1 & 0 & -1 & 1 & 0 & 0 & 1 & \\
\hline
 & & & & 1 & 1 & 0 & 1 & \\
 & & & & & 1 & 0 & 0 & \\
 & & & & & & 1 & 0 & \\
 & & & & & 1 & 0 & -1 & \\
\hline
 & & & & & & 1 & 0 & -1
\end{array}\right]
$$

$$(56)\quad \left[\begin{array}{cccc|cccc|c}
-1 & & & & & & & & \\
 & -1 & & & & & & & \\
 & & -1 & & & & & & \\
 & & & 1 & & & & & \\
\hline
1 & 0 & 0 & 0 & 1 & & & & \\
 & 1 & 0 & 0 & 0 & 1 & & & \\
 & & 1 & 0 & 0 & 0 & 1 & & \\
 & & & & & & & 1 & \\
\hline
 & & & & & & & & 1
\end{array}\right]$$

We may abstract the difficulty of the problem by considering the six skew tableaux

$$\begin{array}{ccc} & (n-3) & (n-1) \\ (n-2) & n & \end{array}\qquad
\begin{array}{ccc} & (n-2) & (n-1) \\ (n-3) & n & \end{array}\qquad
\begin{array}{ccc} & (n-3) & (n-2) \\ (n-1) & n & \end{array}$$

$$\begin{array}{ccc} & (n-3) & n \\ (n-2) & (n-1) & \end{array}\qquad
\begin{array}{ccc} & (n-2) & n \\ (n-3) & (n-1) & \end{array}\qquad
\begin{array}{ccc} & (n-1) & n \\ (n-3) & (n-2) & \end{array}$$

in which the residue classes are as follows:

$$8.26 \qquad \begin{array}{lcl} kp & \cdots & (r-1)\,r \\ \vdots & & \\ (r-1)\,r & & \end{array}$$

for any residue r modulo p. For the moment we assume that $p \neq 2$.

By considering the residues of the symbols in 8.26, it appears that $(n-1, n)$ and $(n-3, n-2)$ will require modification to become p-integral while $(n-2, n-1)$ will not. Thus both types of modification appearing in Example 8.14 will be considered. The transformation L is obtained from:

$$L_R = \left[\begin{array}{ccc|ccc}
1 & & & & & \\
 & 1 & & & & \\
 & & 1 & & & a \\
\hline
 & & & 1 & & \\
 & & & & 1 & \\
 & & & & & 1
\end{array}\right],\qquad
L_n = \left[\begin{array}{ccc|ccc}
1 & & & -\dfrac{kp-1}{kp} & & \\
 & 1 & & & -\dfrac{kp-1}{kp} & \\
 & & 1 & & & \\
\hline
 & & & 1 & & \\
 & & & & 1 & \\
 & & & & & 1
\end{array}\right]$$

8.261
$$\bar{L} = \left[\begin{array}{ccc|ccc} 1 & -\frac{kp-1}{kp} & & & & \\ & 1 & & & & \\ & & 1 & & & \\ \hline & & & 1 & -\frac{kp-1}{kp} & \\ & & & & 1 & \\ & & & & & 1 \end{array}\right]$$

By a tedious though straightforward computation:

$L\,(n-2, n-1)\,L^{-1} =$

$$L\left[\begin{array}{ccc|ccc} \frac{1}{kp+1} & 0 & 1 & & & \\ 0 & 1 & 0 & & & \\ \frac{kp(kp+2)}{(kp+1)^2} & 0 & \frac{-1}{kp+1} & & & \\ \hline & & & 1 & 0 & 0 \\ & & & 0 & \frac{-1}{kp-1} & \frac{kp(kp-2)}{(kp-1)^2} \\ & & & 0 & 1 & \frac{1}{kp-1} \end{array}\right]L^{-1}$$

8.262
$$\equiv \begin{bmatrix} 1 & 1 & 1 & 1 & 2 & 0 \\ 0 & 1 & 0 & 0 & 1 & -2 \\ 0 & -2 & -1 & -2 & -6 & 4 \\ & & & 1 & 1 & -2 \\ & & & 0 & 1 & 0 \\ & & & 0 & 1 & -1 \end{bmatrix} \pmod{p},$$

if we choose

8.263
$$a = \frac{kp-2}{kp} = \left(-\frac{kp-2}{kp-1}\right)\left(-\frac{kp-1}{kp}\right).$$

There is no difficulty in verifying that:

$$L(n-3, n-2)L^{-1} \equiv \qquad\qquad L(n-1, n)L^{-1} \equiv$$

8.264
$$\begin{bmatrix} -1 & 0 & 0 & & & \\ 1 & 1 & 0 & & & \\ 0 & 0 & 1 & & & \\ & & & -1 & 0 & 0 \\ & & & 1 & 1 & 0 \\ & & & 0 & 0 & 1 \end{bmatrix}, \quad \begin{bmatrix} -1 & 0 & 0 & & & \\ 0 & -1 & 0 & & & \\ 0 & 0 & 1 & & & \\ 1 & 0 & 0 & 1 & 0 & 0 \\ & 1 & 0 & 0 & 1 & 0 \\ & & & 0 & 0 & 1 \end{bmatrix}$$

modulo p over the tableaux 8.26.

One might well ask the explanation for the anomalous first factor of a in 8.263; the second factor is as we would expect. We notice that the two diagonal components of 8.262 differ for $p>3$ which implies that the two corresponding modular representations of $\mathfrak{S}_{n-1}$ are not identically the same. The situation is clarified by the following

8.27 *Example.* In the representations [7, 1] and [5, 3] of $\mathfrak{S}_8$ with $p=5$ the tableaux:

1234567 8	1234568 7	1234578 6	1234678 5	1235678 4	1245678 3	1345678 2
12348 567	12347 568	12345 678	12346 578	12356 478	12456 378	13456 278

are connected by the appropriate raising operator, modified for the first two by a permutation ρ (cf. the construction 7.441). To make each representation p-integral it is enough to transform by

$$L = \begin{bmatrix} 1 & & & & & & \\ & 1 & & & & & \\ & & 1 & -\frac{4}{5} & & & \\ & & & 1 & & & \\ & & & & 1 & & \\ & & & & & 1 & \\ & & & & & & 1 \end{bmatrix}$$

over the above tableaux, the remainder of L for [5, 3] being constructed as described above. It is easy to see, however, that the matrices of (67) and (78) are not congruent modulo 5, though they become so if L is replaced by

8.271
$$L' = \begin{bmatrix} 6 &&&&&&& \\ & 3 &&&&&& \\ && 1 & -\frac{4}{5} &&&& \\ &&& 1 &&&& \\ &&&& 1 &&& \\ &&&&& 1 && \\ &&&&&& 1 & \\ &&&&&&& \ddots \end{bmatrix}$$

for [5, 3]. In particular, for (78)

8.272
$$\begin{pmatrix} 6 & 0 \\ 0 & 3 \end{pmatrix}\begin{pmatrix} \frac{1}{3} & 1 \\ \frac{8}{9} & -\frac{1}{3} \end{pmatrix}\begin{pmatrix} \frac{1}{6} & 0 \\ 0 & \frac{1}{3} \end{pmatrix} = \begin{pmatrix} \frac{1}{3} & 2 \\ \frac{4}{9} & -\frac{1}{3} \end{pmatrix} \equiv \begin{pmatrix} -\frac{1}{7} & \frac{48}{49} \\ 1 & \frac{1}{7} \end{pmatrix} \pmod 5$$

and also

8.273
$$L'\,(67)\,L'^{-1} \equiv L\,(67)\,L^{-1} \pmod 5,$$

the L.H.S. over the above tableaux of [5, 3] and the R.H.S. of [7, 1].

Thus, while 8.11 guarantees the congruence of the diagonal terms in 2×2 matrices of 2.17, the other two terms may be incongruent. In order to correct this situation we utilize the two *multiplicative* parameters μ, ν which are available and, subject to 8.11, we have for $1<t\neq 0 \pmod p$

8.281
$$\begin{pmatrix} \mu & 0 \\ 0 & 1 \end{pmatrix}\begin{pmatrix} (kp-t)^{-1} & 1 \\ 1-(kp-t)^{-2} & -(kp-t)^{-1} \end{pmatrix}\begin{pmatrix} \mu^{-1} & 0 \\ 0 & 1 \end{pmatrix}$$
$$\equiv \begin{pmatrix} -(kp+t)^{-1} & 1-(kp+t)^{-2} \\ 1 & (kp+t)^{-1} \end{pmatrix} \pmod p$$

so that $\mu\equiv 1-t^{-2} \pmod p$ as in 8.272. Corresponding to 8.273 we require that

8.282
$$\begin{bmatrix} \nu && \\ & 1 & -(kp-1)/kp \\ && 1 \end{bmatrix}\begin{bmatrix} 1/(kp-1) & 0 & 1 \\ 0 & 1 & 0 \\ 1-1/(kp-1)^2 & 0 & -1/(kp-1) \end{bmatrix}\begin{bmatrix} \nu^{-1} && \\ & 1 & (kp-1)/kp \\ && 1 \end{bmatrix}$$
$$\equiv \begin{bmatrix} 1 && \\ & 1 & -(kp-1)/kp \\ && 1 \end{bmatrix}\begin{bmatrix} -1/(kp+1) & 1-1/(kp+1)^2 & 0 \\ 1 & 1/(kp+1) & 0 \\ 0 & 0 & 1 \end{bmatrix}\begin{bmatrix} 1 && \\ & 1 & (kp-1)/kp \\ && 1 \end{bmatrix} \pmod p$$

so that $\nu \equiv -2 \pmod{p}$ as in 8.271. Note that we may set $\nu = 1$ for $p=3$, as in Examples 8.14 and 8.25. Note also that the order of the tableaux in 8.28 conforms with Example 8.27, so that if the *last* 1 in the diagonal of $\bar{\bar{L}}$ in 8.261 were replaced by the appropriate ν, then

$$a = \left(-\frac{kp-2}{kp-1}\right)\left(-\frac{kp-1}{kp}\right) \equiv \nu\left(-\frac{kp-1}{kp}\right) \pmod{p}$$

and the interpretation of the raising operator for the construction of L would be consistent over all the tableaux in question.

If we set $p=2$ certain modifications of the skew tableaux 8.26 are possible:

(i) $\begin{array}{ccc} & (r-1) & r \\ (r-1) & r & \end{array}$ and its dual $\begin{array}{cc} & (r-1) \\ (r-1) & r \\ r & \end{array}$

(ii) $\begin{array}{llll} 2k & \cdots & (r-1) & r \\ \vdots & & & \\ (r-1) & r & & \end{array}$ and its dual $\begin{array}{lll} 2k & \cdots & (r-1) \\ & & r \\ \vdots & & \\ (r-1) & & \\ r & & \end{array}$

(iii) the self-dual skew tableaux $\begin{array}{llll} 2k & \cdots & (r-1) & r \\ \vdots & & & \\ (r-1) & & & \\ r & & & \end{array}$ and $\begin{array}{lll} 2k & \cdots & (r-1) \\ & & r \\ \vdots & & \\ (r-1) & r & \end{array}$

There are only five skew tableaux in case (i) as in $[3, 2]$ and $[2^2, 1]$ with $p=2$; $L_R = I$ in each case and it may be easily verified that the desired reduction is obtained by setting $L = L_n \bar{\bar{L}}$. Cases (ii) and (iii) are trivially different from the general case and the reduction of 8.27 modulo 2 yields the desired result.

8.29 *Example.* It is an interesting exercise to reduce the representation $[3, 1^2]$ modulo 2, taking the tableaux in the order:

$$\begin{array}{llllll} 123\,, & 124\,, & 134\,, & 125\,, & 135\,, & 145\,, \\ 4 & 3 & 2 & 3 & 2 & 2 \\ 5 & 5 & 5 & 4 & 4 & 3 \end{array}$$

and compare the reduction with that of $[3, 2]$ and $[2^2, 1]$ in Table 2-5.

8.3 The raising operator. In Chapter II we introduced the raising operator on the basis of Young's formula 2.23. In Chapter VII we saw this same operator yield what were believed to be the indecomposables of the regular representation of $\mathfrak{S}_n$, subject to 7.42. We now define the matrix L_R in terms of the appropriate raising operator as it affects the modular components of $\mathfrak{S}_{n-1}$ and $\mathfrak{S}_n$.

8.31 If $(n-1, n)$ and $(n-2, n-1)$ are both p-integral $\bar{L}$ would not have been modified and $\bar{L}(n-1, n)\,\bar{L}^{-1}=(n-1, n)$. The matrix representing $(n-2, n-1)$ might, however, have off-diagonal elements as we shall see below.

8.32 If *one* of $(n-1, n)$ and $(n-2, n-1)$ is p-integral while the other is not we could have the interference pattern 8.262 associated with the tableaux of $[\lambda]$. More generally, we should consider all six possible tableaux of the form

8.321
$$\begin{array}{ccc} & q & \cdots\ s \\ & \vdots & \\ y\,p & \cdots\ r & \\ \vdots & & \\ r & & \end{array}$$

where we assume that q is not congruent to zero modulo p.

From 8.23 we might expect a 'cross-over' between the Σ's of $\mathfrak{S}_n$ for $q\equiv\pm1 \pmod p$, and to put this in evidence we take the skew tableaux which are significant in this connection in the order:

8.322
$$\begin{array}{cccccc} \;\;n-2 & \;\;n-2 & \;\;n-1\,, & \;\;n-1 & \;\;n & \;\;n \\ \;n-1 & \;n & \;n & \;n-2 & \;n-2 & \;n-1 \\ n & n-1 & n-2 & n & n-1 & n-2 \end{array}$$

The transforming matrix L is given by:

$$L = \begin{bmatrix} 1 &&&&& \\ & 1 &&&& \\ && 1 &&& \\ && -u & 1 && \\ &&&& 1 & \\ &&&&& 1 \end{bmatrix}\begin{bmatrix} 1 & -u &&&& \\ & 1 &&&& \\ && 1 &&& \\ &&& 1 && \\ &&&& 1 & \\ &&&&& 1 \end{bmatrix}\begin{bmatrix} 1 &&&&& \\ & 1 &&&& \\ && 1 &&& \\ &&& 1 && \\ &&&& 1 & -u \\ &&&&& 1 \end{bmatrix}$$

$$= \begin{bmatrix} 1 & -u &&&& \\ & 1 &&&& \\ && 1 &&& \\ && -u & 1 && \\ &&&& 1 & -u \\ &&&&& 1 \end{bmatrix}$$

Where $u=(yp-1)/yp$, and it may be easily verified that:

$$L(n-1,n)L^{-1} \equiv \left[\begin{array}{ccc|ccc} -1 & 0 & 0 & 0 & 0 & 0 \\ 1 & 1 & 0 & 0 & 0 & 0 \\ 0 & 0 & \frac{-1}{q} & 0 & 0 & \frac{q^2-1}{q^2} \\ \hline 0 & 0 & \frac{-1}{q^2} & \frac{-1}{q} & \frac{q^2-1}{q^2} & \frac{-2}{q^3} \\ 0 & 0 & 0 & 1 & \frac{1}{q} & \frac{1}{q^2} \\ 0 & 0 & 1 & 0 & 0 & \frac{1}{q} \end{array}\right] \pmod{p}, \tag{8.323}$$

$$L(n-2,n-1)L^{-1} \equiv \left[\begin{array}{ccc|ccc} \frac{-1}{q} & \frac{1}{q^2} & \frac{2}{q^3} & \frac{q^2-1}{q^2} & 0 & 0 \\ 0 & \frac{-1}{q} & \frac{q^2-1}{q^2} & 0 & 0 & 0 \\ 0 & 1 & \frac{1}{q} & 0 & 0 & 0 \\ \hline 1 & 0 & \frac{-1}{q^2} & \frac{1}{q} & 0 & 0 \\ 0 & 0 & 0 & 0 & -1 & 0 \\ 0 & 0 & 0 & 0 & 1 & 1 \end{array}\right] \pmod{p}. \tag{8.324}$$

By way of illustration, one might take the tableaux 8.322 to be

125	125	126 ,	126	127	127
36	37	37	35	35	36
4	4	4	4	4	4
7	6	5	7	6	5

of $[3, 2, 1^2]$ in Table B with $p=3$.

8.33 If *neither* $(n-2, n-1)$ *nor* $(n-1, n)$ is p-integral, each must be modified by L. The significant skew tableaux are of the form

$$\begin{array}{lll} zp \; . \; . \; . & xp \; . \; . \; . & r \\ \cdot & \cdot & \\ \cdot & \cdot & \\ \cdot & \cdot & \\ yp \; . \; . \; . & r & \\ \cdot & & \\ \cdot & & \\ \cdot & & \\ r & & \end{array} \qquad z = x+y$$

and may be taken in the order:

8.331
$$\begin{array}{cccccc} (n-2) & (n-1) & (n-2) & (n-1) & n & n \\ (n-1) & (n-2) & n & n & (n-2) & (n-1) \\ n & n & (n-1) & (n-2) & (n-1) & (n-2) \end{array}$$

If we use the suggestion that L_R should compensate for the deficiencies of L_n, in the sense that together they must give effect to the raising operators which connect the three different representations of $\mathfrak{S}_{n-1}$ contributing to the skew tableaux 8.331, it would be natural to set:

8.332
$$L_R = \left[\begin{array}{cc|cc|cc} 1 & & 0 & 0 & +s & 0 \\ & 1 & 0 & -u & 0 & -t \\ \hline & & 1 & & -v & 0 \\ & & & 1 & 0 & 0 \\ \hline & & & & 1 & \\ & & & & & 1 \end{array}\right], \quad L_n = \left[\begin{array}{cc|cc|cc} 1 & & -\frac{yp-1}{yp} & 0 & 0 & 0 \\ & 1 & 0 & 0 & -\frac{zp-1}{zp} & 0 \\ \hline & & 1 & & 0 & 0 \\ & & & 1 & 0 & -\frac{xp-1}{xp} \\ \hline & & & & 1 & \\ & & & & & 1 \end{array}\right],$$

$$\bar{L} = \left[\begin{array}{cc|cc|cc} 1 & -\frac{xp-1}{xp} & & & & \\ & 1 & & & & \\ \hline & & 1 & -\frac{zp-1}{zp} & & \\ & & & 1 & & \\ \hline & & & & 1 & -\frac{yp-1}{yp} \\ & & & & & 1 \end{array}\right]$$

and to study the matrices $L(n-2, n-1)\,L^{-1}$ and $L(n-1, n)\,L^{-1}$.

Though the details are complicated, straightforward computations lead to the result:

8.333
$$L(n-2,n-1)L^{-1} = \left[\begin{array}{cc|cc|cc} -1 & 0 & 0 & 0 & 0 & 0 \\ 1 & 1 & \left(\frac{yp-1}{yp}-u\right) & 0 & \star & 0 \\ \hline & & -1 & 0 & 0 & 0 \\ & & 1 & 1 & \left(v-\frac{xp-1}{xp}\right) & 0 \\ \hline & & & & -1 & 0 \\ & & & & 1 & 1 \end{array}\right]$$

so that it is natural to set:

8.334
$$u = \frac{yp-1}{yp}, \qquad v = \frac{xp-1}{xp}, \qquad w = \frac{zp-1}{zp},$$

with $\star = -s+uv-t+2w$.

8.335
$$L(n-1,n)L^{-1} = \left[\begin{array}{cc|cc|cc} -1 & (s-vw) & 0 & 0 & 2(s-vw) & 0 \\ 0 & -1 & 0 & t-uw & 0 & 0 \\ \hline 1 & 0 & 1 & 1 & 0 & 0 \\ 0 & 0 & 0 & -1 & 0 & 0 \\ \hline 0 & 1 & 0 & 0 & 1 & 0 \\ 0 & 0 & 0 & 1 & 0 & 1 \end{array}\right]$$

and we set

8.336
$$s = vw, \qquad t = uw$$

so that $\star = -s+uv-t+2w = 1$ in 8.333, using the relation $z = x+y$.

The determination of u and v in 8.334 conforms with our expectation based on the raising operator, and that of s and t in 8.336 completes the definition of the matrix L_R. It should be remarked that our discussion applies to all $p \leqq n$, and the forms of the matrices 8.333 and 8.335 are in accord with 8.21.

In conclusion we consider the transform of $(n-3, n-2)$ by L when $n-3$ occupies any given position removed by q places from, say, the central node of 8.331. In addition to 8.331 we must consider:

8.337
$$\begin{matrix} n-3 & n-1 & n-3 & n-1 & n & n \\ n-1 & n-3 & n & n & n-3 & n-1 \\ n & n & n-1 & n-3 & n-1 & n-3 \end{matrix}$$

with $n-2$ and $n-3$ interchanged. If we arrange the tableaux 8.337, the first to follow the first of 8.331, the second tableau of 8.337 to follow the second of 8.331, etc., when the matrix L becomes

$$L' = L\times\begin{pmatrix}1 & 0\\ 0 & 1\end{pmatrix}$$

we have:

$L'(n-3, n-2)L'^{-1} =$

$$\left[\begin{array}{cc|cc|cc} A_1 & v(A_1-A_2) & 0 & \alpha & 0 & 0 \\ & A_2 & 0 & u(A_2-A_3) & 0 & 0 \\ \hline & & A_1 & w(A_1-A_3) & v(A_1-A_2) & \beta \\ & & & A_3 & 0 & 0 \\ \hline & & & & A_2 & u(A_2-A_3) \\ & & & & & A_3 \end{array}\right]$$

where $\alpha = uv(A_1-A_2)-uw(A_1-A_3)$, $\beta = vw(A_1-A_3)-vu(A_2-A_3)$, and

$$A_1 \equiv A_2 \equiv A_3 \equiv \begin{bmatrix} -\frac{1}{q} & \frac{q^2-1}{q^2} \\ 1 & \frac{1}{q} \end{bmatrix} \pmod p,$$

$$v(A_1-A_2) \equiv u(A_2-A_3) \equiv \begin{bmatrix} \frac{1}{q^2} & \frac{2}{q^2} \\ 0 & -\frac{1}{q^2} \end{bmatrix} \equiv w(A_1-A_3)$$

$$\alpha \equiv \begin{bmatrix} \frac{-(1+q)}{q^3} & \frac{-(2q^3+3q^2)}{q^6} \\ 0 & \frac{1+q}{q^3} \end{bmatrix}, \quad \beta \equiv \begin{bmatrix} \frac{-1+q}{q^3} & \frac{2q^3+3q^2}{q^6} \\ 0 & \frac{1-q}{q^3} \end{bmatrix}$$

for $q \not\equiv 0 \pmod p$.

In the general case, instead of terms such as $v(A_1-A_2)$ we would have terms such as

8.34 $$v(\bar{L}_1 A_1 \bar{L}_1^{-1} - \bar{L}_2 A_2 \bar{L}_2^{-1}),$$

which would remain p-integral, since $\bar{L}_1 A_1 \bar{L}_1^{-1} \equiv \bar{L}_2 A_2 \bar{L}_2^{-1} \pmod{p}$ by assumption. Similar terms would arise in the transform of $(n-4, n-3)$ and would continue to arise subject to the standardness condition.

The case in which $q \equiv 0 \pmod{p}$ requires an extension of the method of this section but no new ideas are involved, either in the modifications required or in their interpretations in terms of the raising operator. Certain special cases arise when $p=2$ as in § 8.2, one of which is illustrated in the following Example, but they present no new difficulty.

8.35 *Example.* Consider the case of [3, 2, 1] with $p=2$ and the 16 tableaux:

$$\begin{array}{ccccc} 123 & 124 & 134 & 125 & 135 \\ 45 & 35 & 25 & 34 & 24 \\ \underline{6} & 6 & 6 & 6 & 6 \end{array}; \quad \begin{array}{cccccc} 123 & 124 & 134 & 125 & 135 & 145 \\ 46 & 36 & 26 & 36 & 26 & 26 \\ \underline{5} & 5 & 5 & 4 & 4 & \underline{3} \end{array}; \quad \begin{array}{ccccc} 126 & 136 & 126 & 136 & 146 \\ 34 & 24 & 35 & 25 & 25 \\ 5 & 5 & 4 & 4 & \underline{3} \end{array}$$

The underlined tableaux correspond to the identity representation of $\mathfrak{S}_{n-1}$ appearing in the $[\lambda]=[3, 2], [3, 1^2], [2^2, 1]$, as in Table 2-5.

$$L = \left[\begin{array}{c|cc|c|cc|c|cc|c}
1 & & & -\frac{1}{2} & & & -\frac{1}{6} & & & \frac{1}{12} \\ \hline
 & M & -\frac{1}{2}M & & -\frac{1}{2}M & \frac{3}{8}M & & \frac{3}{8}M & -\frac{3}{16}M & \\
 & & M & & & -\frac{1}{2}M & & -\frac{3}{4}M & \frac{1}{4}M & \\ \hline
 & & & 1 & & & \frac{1}{3} & & & \\ \hline
 & & & & M & -\frac{3}{4}M & & -\frac{1}{2}M & \frac{1}{4}M & \\
 & & & & & M & & & -\frac{1}{2}M & \\ \hline
 & & & & & & 1 & & & -\frac{1}{2} \\ \hline
 & & & & & & & M & -\frac{1}{2}M & \\
 & & & & & & & & M & \\ \hline
 & & & & & & & & & 1
\end{array}\right]$$

$$M = \begin{pmatrix} 1 & -\frac{1}{2} \\ & 1 \end{pmatrix}$$

In order to complete our induction we recall the underlying purpose of transformation by $L = L_R L_n \bar{L}$, namely, to make $(n-1, n)$ p-integral, if necessary. Having accomplished this by means of L_n we must conform to the raising operator by introducing L_R, since in essence the transposition $(n-1, n)$ is equivalent to raising $n-1$ in some $\bar{\Sigma}$ of $\mathfrak{S}_{n-1}$. We must show that transforming by (i) $\bar{L}$ has no serious effects on $(n-1, n)$, and (ii) $L_R L_n$ has no serious effect on the reduction of $\mathfrak{S}_{n-1}$.

In 8.31-8.34 we have verified that the only consequences of transformation by L in each of (i) and (ii) above is the introduction of off-diagonal terms of the form 8.34 which are p-integral.

As regards the splitting into modular components, we have reference to 8.246 where we saw that it is possible to order the sets of tableaux Σ, defined by the raising operator of Chapter VII, so that the cross-over terms above the diagonal matrices are all congruent to zero modulo p. On the assumption of a corresponding modular splitting of each $[\bar{\lambda}]$, this situation is not changed so far as tableaux to which 8.31 applies are concerned. Since the matrices 8.323 and 8.324 similarly reduce for $q \equiv \pm 1 \pmod{p}$, and no obstructions 8.34 are introduced, the same holds true in general. One could state our conclusion by saying that the modular reduction of $[\lambda]$ after transformation by L is *coextensive* with the range of applicability of the raising operator, which is what we wished to show.

As was remarked in the Introduction to the present chapter, this situation is complicated, but the foregoing arguments seem adequate to prove the following

8.36 THEOREM. *It is possible to construct a transformation L under which any ordinary representation $[\lambda]$ of $\mathfrak{S}_n$ takes p-integral form and splits into modular components in accordance with the decomposition matrix of $\mathfrak{S}_n$ as constructed in Chapter VII. Moreover, the modular components associated with sets of standard tableaux related under the raising operator are all identical in form.*

8.4 Decomposition matrices. Let us now put together these two approaches to the D-matrix: the first through its *columns*, using the raising operator and admitted permutations as in Chapter VII; the second through its *rows* using the transforming matrix of the present chapter.

In both these approaches we have used induction; moreover, we know that the modular splitting of the representations of $\mathfrak{S}_p$ conforms to the decomposition matrices which have been proved to be correct in 7.13. Let us assume, then, that the decomposition matrix of $\mathfrak{S}_{n-1}$ is correct; that the modular components brought into evidence by the transformation L are in fact irreducible, and that the columns of the matrix do yield the indecomposables of the regular representation.

By 7.57 and 12.49, each set M_i must contain one or more indecomposables of $\mathfrak{S}_n$. Since M_i contains its head H_i and foot F_i once only, the only possibility is that M_i should contain, besides the indecomposable I_i, one or more I_j with $j>i$. From the reduction envisaged in 8.37 we conclude that the same modular component appears in each $[\lambda] \in M_i$ as appears in each H_i and F_i, and in identical form. Thus it would be impossible to remove some of the associated standard tableaux without removing them all in attempting to separate $I_j (j>i)$ from M_i. Thus no such I_j exists and $M_i = I_i$.

8.41 MAIN THEOREM. *The sets M_i of Chapter VII, as defined by the raising operator applied subject to* 7.42, *are the indecomposables of the regular representation of $\mathfrak{S}_n$. The sets of permutations B_i characterize the associated modular irreducible representations of degree β_i, which can be taken to be identical in each $[\lambda] \in M_i$, after transforming by the appropriate matrix L.*

A word is in order concerning the group algebra of $\mathfrak{S}_n$ over the field of characteristic p we have been considering. Once the modular reduction of each $[\lambda]$ has been determined, those transposition matrices which 'cross over' between modular components can be recognized and their off-diagonal elements (cf. 8.323 and 8.324) define the *radical* of the algebra. Thus *the lattice $\mathscr{L}$* of § 8.2 *is identified as that of the right ideals of* $[\lambda]$ *when this is reduced modulo p*. We have a simple illustration of this in the reduction of [3, 2] modulo 3 in Example 8.14.

8.5 *r*-Boolean algebras. In § 6.2 we studied the results of successive r-inducing on a given Young diagram $[\lambda^0]$. We now consider the special case in which $[\lambda^0]$ is a *p-core* of *r*-defect $u = \tilde{u}$, so that the unit element $[\lambda^d]$ of the algebra is also a core.

8.51 *Example.* Take $p=2$ and $[\lambda^0]=[3, 2, 1]$ with $r=1$, $u=4$. The table corresponding to that of Example 6.23 is easily constructed and the elements of the rBA of dimension v are listed as I_v below.

v	0	1	2	3	4
u	4	3	2	1	0
$\tilde{v}$	0	0	0	2	4
$\tilde{u}$	4	2	0	0	0
b	0	3	4	3	0

I_0 : [3, 2, 1]
I_1 : [4, 2, 1], [3^2, 1], [3, 2^2], [3, 2, 1^2]
I_2 : [4, 3, 1], [4, 2^2], [4, 2, 1^2], [3^2, 2], [3^2, 1^2], [3, 2^2, 1]
I_3 : [4, 3, 2], [4, 3, 1^2], [4, 2^2, 1], [3^2, 2, 1]
I_4 : [4, 3, 2, 1]

One may easily check that

$$I_0 \overset{1}{\uparrow} I_1,\ I_1 \overset{1}{\uparrow} 2I_2,\ I_2 \overset{1}{\uparrow} 3I_3,\ I_3 \overset{1}{\uparrow} 4I_4,$$

and observe that the sets I_v appear as columns in Tables 2-6 and 2-10. The significance of this observation is contained in the following theorem:

8.52 *The set I_v of all elements of dimension v of an* rBA *in which* $[\lambda^0]$ *is a p-core of $\mathfrak{S}_n$, make up a single indecomposable of $\mathfrak{S}_{n+v}$. Each set I_v coincides with one of the M_i in the appropriate block.*

Proof. Let us consider the effect of r-inducing upon $[\lambda^0]$ to obtain the set of elements of dimension 1 of the rBA. If $d=1$ there is only one such element which must be a core, i.e. an indecomposable of $\mathfrak{S}_{n+1}$. If $u>1$, then every two r-positions of $[\lambda^0]$ span a kp-hook whose removal from each of the corresponding elements of dimension 1 yields one $+1$ and one -1 in each column of a table such as 7.23. The number of entries in any given row of the table will be b_1 as in 6.21 and 6.22. Since the character of every p-singular element will vanish if and only if all elements of I_1 are included, we conclude that these elements constitute an indecomposable of the regular representation of $\mathfrak{S}_{n+1}$.

If we r-induce again upon I_1 we obtain $2I_2$; but by 12.61 this must be an indecomposable or a sum of indecomposables of $\mathfrak{S}_{n+2}$, so I_2 is itself an indecomposable by 12.49. By repeating the argument we conclude that I_v is an indecomposable of the regular representation of $\mathfrak{S}_{n+v}$ for $0<v\leqq d$, as desired.

Since $I_{v-1} \overset{r}{\uparrow} vI_v$, the permutation $P\underbrace{r\ldots r}_{v}$ is characteristic for I_v if P is characteristic for $[\lambda^0]$; since $[\lambda^0]$ is a p-core, every P has this property. Thus I_v is an M_i of $\mathfrak{S}_{n+v}$, which concludes the proof of the theorem.

As has often been remarked, interchanging rows and columns establishes a 1-1 correspondence between the representations of conjugate blocks **B** and **B′** such that indecomposables go into indecomposables. The following result establishes a more general correspondence having this same property.

8.53 *If* **B** *is a block of weight* $b \leqq g+1$, *where* g *is the grade of the corresponding p-core* $[\tilde{\lambda}]$, *then there exists an* r *such that each representation* $[\lambda] \subset$ **B** *is the zero element in an* rBA *of dimension* $d=\tilde{d}$. *The resulting correspondence between the representations of* **B** *and* **B*** *is* 1-1 *and indecomposables go into indecomposables.*

Proof. The existence of such an r follows from 6.38. Complementation amounts to adding $d\ (=\tilde{d})$ r-nodes to each $[\lambda] \subset$ **B**. But this could be thought of as successive r-inducing and such a process applied to each indecomposable of **B** will yield the same constant multiple of each indecomposable of **B***. Characteristic permutations remain characteristic so that ignoring the multiplicity according to 12.49, we have established a 1-1 correspondence between $[\lambda] \subset$ **B** and $[\lambda^*] \subset$ **B***, such that indecomposables go into indecomposables. Subject to possible rearrangement, the D-matrices of the two blocks can be taken to be the same.

In 7.16 we have the special case of this theorem for $b=1$. If $b=2$ and $p=2$ the condition $b \leqq g+1$ is satisfied for blocks with core [1] of $\mathfrak{S}_5$, [2, 1] of $\mathfrak{S}_7$, [3, 2, 1] of $\mathfrak{S}_{10}$, etc. Similarly, for $p=3$ the core $[1^2]$ is of grade 1 so that the D-matrix of the block of $\mathfrak{S}_8$ with this core is in 1-1 correspondence with that of the block of $\mathfrak{S}_{10}$ with core $[2, 1^2]$; but the block of $\mathfrak{S}_8$ with core [2] is conjugate to that of $\mathfrak{S}_8$ with core $[1^2]$, as is the block of $\mathfrak{S}_{10}$ with core [3, 1] conjugate to that with core $[2, 1^2]$, so that all these blocks have essentially the same D-matrices.

If $b>g+1$, modified complementation will be necessary in those cases for which $u>\tilde{u}$. This implies that the correspondence between $[\lambda] \subset$ **B** and $[\lambda^*] \subset$ **B*** is no longer 1-1.

NOTES AND REFERENCES

(Books are referred to by printing the author's name in bold type)

Chapter I

Part 1

11.1 The permutation representations of $\mathfrak{S}_n$ will play an important role in the sequel. For further details the reader should consult **Burnside** (chapters I and XII).

11.2 For further information consult **Littlewood** and **Van der Waerden.**

11.3 There are various methods of introducing characters: we have followed Schur (2) (cf. also **Speiser** and **Murnaghan**).

11.4 The general expression for an idempotent 11.43 involves the characters explicitly, whereas the chief interest and significance of the representation theory of $\mathfrak{S}_n$ is that this dependence upon characters is avoided 2.15.

11.5 The notion of the induced representation is important in all that follows (**Speiser**). For Lemma 11.56 cf. Osima (1), Robinson and Taulbee (1), Littlewood (14, 15).

Part 2

12.1-12.4 The modular representation theory of a finite group is based on the papers by Brauer and Nesbitt (1, 2, 3), on Nesbitt (1) and the subsequent work by Brauer (1-15). A somewhat different treatment has been given by Nagao (1) and Osima (3) which develops the ordinary and modular theories simultaneously, and it is this approach we give here. The proof of 12.49 was suggested to me by Professor Osima (cf. Brauer (14), Th. 17).

12.5-12.6 In these two sections the results of the general theory of blocks are summarized in such a way as to be readily applicable to $\mathfrak{S}_n$ (Iizuka, 1). They will be utilized first in Chapter V, at which point a reader who is meeting these ideas for the first time might well re-read Chapter I, Part 2.

Chapter II

2.1 Young's papers I-IX are difficult to read, largely because of his facility in handling permutations which is denied to most mathematicians and further, because he was primarily interested in developing invariant theory. We are indebted to D. E. Rutherford for separating out those parts of Young's work which yield the representation theory of S_n, and this book should rightly be considered a sequel to his *Substitutional Analysis* (cf. also Robinson (3), Thrall (1), Yamanouchi (1-3), Yamanouchi and Kotani (1), Jahn (3)).

Actually the pattern of nodes which gives rise to Young's 'standard tableaux' goes back to Ferrers and Sylvester (**MacMahon**, p. 124); since its significance for representation theory is wholly due to Young, we shall call such a pattern a *Young diagram*.

It is perhaps worth recording here Young's own explanation for the long gap between his papers II and III. In 1901 he knew nothing of Frobenius' work and was, moreover, unable to read German. As a country clergyman at Birdbrook, near Cambridge, he had not much time for mathematics and, with the intervention of the war (1914-1918), it was not until 1927 that the third paper on Substitutional Analysis appeared. Though he was unsuccessful in solving the problems of invariant theory, the originality and depth of his ideas have been widely recognized (**Weyl** (1, 2)). Young died in 1940 and the MSS which he left behind are now deposited in the University of Toronto Library.

2.2 Formula 2.23 is due to Young (VII, p. 199). Note that the $n!/f^{\lambda}$ cancels with the coefficient in 2.14, so that the coefficient of the identity on each side yields the equation

$$\frac{n!}{\lambda_1!\lambda_2!\ldots\lambda_h!} = \sum_{\lambda} m_h^{\lambda} f^{\lambda}$$

in the notation of 11.3, Table IV; cf. Robinson (4). Formula 2.26 should be compared with Young's I (loc. cit.).

2.3 The argument leading up to 2.33 and 2.34 is by no means new (cf. **Littlewood, Murnaghan,** Newell (1, 2)). The introduction of the notion of a *hook*, due to Nakayama (1), and of the hook length $\boldsymbol{h}_{ij}$ at this stage leads to the dramatic result 2.37 due to Frame (Frame, Robinson and Thrall (1) and Robinson (12)).

2.4 The notion of a lattice permutation is due to MacMahon and its application to representation theory is due to Littlewood and Richardson (**Littlewood** § 5.3). For the construction 2.421-6 see Robinson (6, I). These permutations were introduced independently by Yamanouchi (1-3) and are sometimes called by physicists 'Yamanouchi symbols'.

2.5 The extension of the results of 2.4 to skew diagrams $[\alpha]$—$[\beta]$ is crucial in the understanding of the process of 'removing' a hook as described by Nakayama in 1940. Littlewood uses the notation $\{\alpha \mid \beta\}$ for the corresponding Schur function. For 2.55 see **Littlewood** (p. 112) and Newell (1).

Chapter III

3.1 Robinson (6, II).

3.2 **Weyl** (1, 2). For the relations between the various symmetric functions which are involved and the characters of $GL(d)$, i.e. the Schur functions, the reader should consult **Littlewood** and **Murnaghan**. The simple formula 3.283 is due to P. Hall (cf. Robinson (13)).

3.3 The principle theorem 3.31 was stated first by Littlewood and Richardson (1) and subsequently proved by Robinson (6, I); cf. **Littlewood** (p. 94) and Murnaghan 4, 5).

3.4 Gamba and Radicati (1), Robinson and Taulbee (1), Littlewood (14, 15), and Murnaghan (19).

3.5 Many authors have studied the problem of the reduction of $[\lambda] \odot [\lambda]$ or $\{\lambda\} \times \{\mu\}$, but the situation is so complicated that only partial results have been obtained: cf. Duncan (1, 2), Foulkes (1-6), Ibrahim (1-6), Littlewood (1, 2, 5, 9, 16), Makar and Missiha (1), Murnaghan (19), Newell (3), Robinson (8, 9), Thrall (3), Todd (1, 2).

3.6 The notion of the inner product leads to the same sort of symmetrization as the outer, but it is still more intractable: cf. Littlewood (15, 16, 17), Murnaghan (21).

CHAPTER IV

4.1-4.2 Tables of characters of $\mathfrak{S}_n$ have been calculated for $n \leqq 16$; cf. **Littlewood** ($n \leqq 10$), Zia-ud-Din (1, 2, for $n=11$, 12, 13), Kondo (1, for $n=14$), Bivins et al. (1, for $n=15$, 16). Explicit formulae for some of these characters have been given by Frobenius (2) and Ingram (1). For the material in these sections cf. **Murnaghan**, Nakayama (1, 1), Robinson (6, 12) and **Littlewood** (chapter VIII). Kodama and Yamamoto (1) have shown that the number-theoretic function $\tau(n)$ is involved in this connection.

4.3 The idea of associating a residue modulo p with each node of a Young diagram is due to Littlewood (10); cf. Staal (1), Robinson (10, 12), Robinson and Thrall (1), Farahat (1-3).

4.4 Note that the term p-quotient as defined in Frame, Robinson and Thrall (1) has replaced the earlier term *star diagram* used in Robinson (6, II, III; 7), Staal (1) and Osima (10); cf. also Farahat (1-3) and Nakayama and Osima (1).

4.5 Robinson (6, III) and Thrall and Robinson (1). Cf. also Osima (9, 10).

4.6 Robinson and Thrall (1) and Farahat (3).

CHAPTER V

5.1 Thrall and Robinson (1), Robinson (10, I), Nakayama and Osima (1).

5.2 In this section the groundwork is laid for the proof of Nakayama's conjecture that the block to which a Young diagram $[\lambda]$ belongs is completely determined by its p-core. Various proofs of the fundamental result 5.21 have been given (cf. Nakayama (1), Staal (1), Robinson (7), Nakayama and Osima (1), Farahat (1)). The interesting property 5.29 of the function $\mathbf{H}^{\lambda}$ is also proved by Osima (12).

It has been conjectured that, for any group $\mathcal{G}$ and prime p, the defect group $\mathcal{D}$ of a block $\mathbf{B}$ is Abelian if and only if $\epsilon=0$ in 12.54 for every $[\lambda]\subset\mathbf{B}$. For $\mathcal{G}=\mathfrak{S}_n$, Brauer's Theorem 1 (11) shows that $\mathcal{D}$ is Abelian if and only if $\delta=b<p$, and for such values of b, $e(f_p^{\lambda})=0$ for every $[\lambda]\subset\mathbf{B}$. For $\delta>b\geqq p$, there will always be at least one $[\lambda]\subset\mathbf{B}$ for which $e(f_p^{\lambda})>0$, so that the conjecture is verified in this case.

5.3 The first proof of Nakayama's conjecture was given by Brauer (11) and Robinson (7). We follow here the argument of Nakayama and Osima (1) in the proof of necessity, agreeing with them that 'this approach helps to clarify the inner structure of the matter' (cf. also Farahat (3)). In the proof of sufficiency, however, we revert to the argument of Brauer (11). Cf. also Farahat and Higman (1).

CHAPTER VI

6.1-6.3 Robinson (10, IV, V).

6.4 Frame and Robinson (1), Osima (13).

6.5 Osima (9, II).

CHAPTER VII

7.1 Theorems 7.13 and 7.15 were first proved by Nakayama (1) for $n<2p$. The generalization to any block of weight 1 is due to Chung (1), but the proof given here is different from his.

7.2 Chung (1).

7.3 Littlewood (10). The example 7.31 sets the stage for the remainder of the chapter.

7.4-7.6 Taulbee (Thesis). The presentation given here emphasizes the significance of the raising operator applied to *standard tableaux* rather than to the graph $G_p[\lambda]$. In each case the admitted permutation is invariant, but the gain in explicitness removes the apparent redundancy of the operator noted in Robinson and Taulbee (10, VI). To say that all diagrams $[\lambda]$ admitting a characteristic permutation P belonging to B_i, amounts to saying that all raising operators applied to the set of standard tableaux of F_i in question yield the associated standard tableaux of each $[\lambda] \in M_i$, and conversely. This reconciles the two methods of constructing the set M_i.

CHAPTER VIII

8.1 Robinson (10, III).

8.2 Johnson (Thesis). Miss Johnson considered two-rowed tableaux and used Young's second tableau function (QSA VI, p. 222) to describe the elements of L. While this procedure is convenient in the two-rowed case it does not appear to generalize.

The partial ordering of the sets $\Sigma \subset [\lambda]$ to form a lattice in 8.24 implies that the modular reduction depends on the cross-overs between sets *only*, once the non-p-integral elements have been made p-integral by transformation by L.

8.3 The analysis of the different interferences which can arise is best carried through using skew tableaux. A careful study of the arrangements of the tableaux in the sets Σ of Tables A and B and Example 8.35 will greatly help the reader in this section.

8.4 The proof of 8.41 seems to require that the D-matrix be considered with reference to both its rows *and* its columns.

8.5 Robinson (10, V).

BIBLIOGRAPHY

BOOKS

E. Artin, C. J. Nesbitt and R. M. Thrall, *Rings with minimum condition* (Ann Arbor, 1944)

H. Boerner: *Darstellungen von Gruppen* (Berlin, 1955)

W. Burnside: *The Theory of Groups* (Cambridge, 1911)

C. W. Curtis and I. Reiner, *Algebras, Groups and Representations* (New York, 1961)

J. H. Grace and A. Young: *The Algebra of Invariants* (Cambridge, 1903)

M. Hall: *The Theory of Groups* (New York, 1959)

D. E. Littlewood: *The Theory of Group Characters* (Oxford, 1950)

P. A. MacMahon: *Combinatory Analysis*, vols. 1 and 2 (Cambridge, 1915)

F. D. Murnaghan: *The Theory of Group Representations* (Baltimore, 1938)

D. E. Rutherford: *Substitutional Analysis* (Edinburgh, 1948)

A. Speiser: *Theorie der Gruppen von endlicher Ordnung* (Berlin, 1937)

Van der Waerden: *Modern Algebra* (New York), vol. 1 (1953), vol. 2 (1950)

H. Weyl: (1) *Group Theory and Quantum Mechanics* (New York, 1932)
(2) *Classical Groups* (Princeton, 1946)

PAPERS

In the references to papers which follow certain journals appear so frequently that it will be convenient to make the following abbreviations:

AJM	American Journal of Mathematics
B(P,T)AMS	Bulletin (Proceedings, Transactions) of the American Mathematical Society
AM	Annals of Mathematics
PCPS	Proceedings of the Cambridge Philosophical Society
CJM	Canadian Journal of Mathematics
P(J)LMS	Proceedings (Journal) of the London Mathematical Society
MZ	Mathematische Zeitschrift
PNAS	Proceedings of the National Academy of Sciences
OMJ	Okayama Mathematical Journal
SPA	Sitzungsberichte der Preussischen Akademie der Wissenschaften
P(T)RS	Proceedings (Transactions) of the Royal Society

A. C. AITKEN

1. *The monomial expansion of determinantal symmetric functions*, PRS (Edinburgh) A, **61** (1943), 300-310.
2. *On compound permutation matrices*, Proc. Ed. Math. Soc. **7** (1946), 196-203.

F. L. BAUER

1. *Zur Theorie der Spingruppen*, Math. Am. **128** (1954), 228-256.

R. L. BIVINS, N. METROPLIS, P. R. STEIN and M. B. WELLS

1. *Characters of* $\mathfrak{S}_n$ *for* $n=15$, 16, Math. Tables and other aids to computing **8** (1954), 212-216.

R. Brauer

1. *On Modular and p-adic representations of algebras*, PNAS **25** (1939), 252-258.
2. *On the representations of groups of finite order*, ibid., 290-295.
3. *On the Cartan invariants of groups of finite order*, AM **42** (1941), 53-61.
4. *On the connections between the ordinary and modular characters*, ibid., 926-935.
5. *Investigations on group characters*, ibid., 936-958.
6. *On groups whose order contains a prime number to the first power*, AJM **64** (1942), I, 401-420; II, 421-440.
7. *On permutation groups of prime degree*, AM **44** (1943), 57-79.
8. *On the arithmetic in a group ring*, PNAS **30** (1944), 109-114.
9. *On the representation of a group of order g in the fields of the g-th roots of unity*, AJM **67** (1945), 461-471.
10. *On blocks of characters of groups of finite order*, PNAS **32** (1946), I, 182-186; II, 215-219.
11. *On a conjecture of Nakayama*, TRS (Canada) III, **41** (1947), 11-19.
12. *Application of induced characters*, AJM **69** (1947), 709-716.
13. *On the representations of groups of finite order*, Proc. Int. Congress Maths. II (1950), 33-36.
14. *A characterization of the characters of groups of finite order*, AM **57** (1953), 357-377.
15. *Zur Darstellungstheorie der Gruppen endlicher Ordnung*, I, MZ **63** (1956), 406-444; II, **72** (1959), 25-46.

R. Brauer and C. Nesbitt

1. *On the regular representations of algebras*, PNAS **23** (1937), 236-240.
2. *On the modular representations of groups of finite order*, University of Toronto Studies, **4** (1937).
3. *On the modular characters of groups*, AM **42** (1941), 556-590.

M. D. Burrow

1. *A generalization of the Young diagram*, CJM **6** (1954), 498-508.

J. H. Chung

1. *On the modular representations of* $\mathfrak{S}_n$, CJM **3** (1951), 309-327.

S. Comét

1. *Une propriété des déterminantes et son application au calcul des caractères des groupes symétriques*, K. Fys. Salls i Lund **14** (1945), 84-94.

D. G. Duncan

1. *Note on a formula of Todd*, JLMS **27** (1952), 235-236.
2. *On D. E. Littlewood's algebra of S-functions*, CJM **4** (1952), 504-512.

H. K. Farahat

1. *On p-quotients and star diagrams of* $\mathfrak{S}_n$, PCPS **49** (1953), 157-160.
2. *On the representations of* $\mathfrak{S}_n$, PLMS (3) **4** (1954), 303-316.
3. *On the blocks of characters of symmetric groups*, PLMS (3) **6** (1956), 501-517.
4. *On Schur functions*, PLMS (3) **8** (1956), 621-630.
5. *The symmetric group as a metric space*, JLMS **35** (1960), 215-220.

H. K. FARAHAT and G. HIGMAN

1. *The centres of symmetric group rings*, PRS (London) A **250** (1959), 212-221.

W. FEIT

1. *The degree formula for the skew representations of* $\mathfrak{S}_n$, PAMS **4** (1953), 740-744.

H. O. FOULKES

1. *Differential operators associated with S-functions*, JLMS **24** (1949), 136-143.
2. *Concomitants of the quintic and sextic*, JLMS **25** (1950), 205-209.
3. *Modified bialternants and symmetric function identities*, ibid., 268-275.
4. *The new multiplication of S-functions*, JLMS **26** (1951), 132-139.
5. *Monomial symmetric functions, S-functions and group characters*, PLMS (3) **2** (1952), 45-49.
6. *Plethysms of S-functions*, TRS (London) A **246** (1954), 555-593.

J. S. FRAME

1. *On the decomposition of transitive permutation groups generated by* $\mathfrak{S}_n$, PNAS **26** (1940), 132-139.
2. *The double cosets of a finite group*, BAMS **47** (1941), 458-467.
3. *Double cosets matrices and group characters*, BAMS **49** (1943), 81-92.
4. *On the reduction of the conjugating representations of a finite group*, BAMS **53** (1947), 584-589.
5. *Group decomposition by double coset matrices*, BAMS **54** (1948), 740-755.
6. *An irreducible representation extracted from two permutation groups*, AM **55** (1952), 85-100.

J. S. FRAME and G. DE B. ROBINSON

1. *On a Theorem of Osima and Nagao*, CJM **6** (1954), 125-127.

J. S. FRAME, G. DE B. ROBINSON and R. M. THRALL

1. *The hook graphs of* $\mathfrak{S}_n$, CJM **6** (1954), 316-324.

G. FROBENIUS

1. *Über Relationen zwischen den Charakteren einer Gruppe und denen ihrer Untergruppen*, SPA (1898), 501-515.
2. *Über die Charaktere der symmätrischen Gruppe*, SPA (1900), 516-534.
3. *Über die Charaktere der alternierenden Gruppe*, SPA (1901), 303-315.
4. *Über die Charakteristischen Einheiten der symmätrische Gruppe*, SPA (1903), 328-358.

A. GAMBA

1. *Sui caratteri delle rappresentazioni del gruppo simmetrico* Atti. Accad. Naz. Lincei Rend. **12** (1952), 167-169.

A. GAMBA and L. A. RADICATI

1. *Sopra un teorema per le reduzione di talune rappresentazione del gruppo simmetrico*, AttiAccad. Naz. Lincei Rend. **14** (1953), 632-634.

H. GARNIR

1. *Théorie de la représentation linéaire des groupes symétriques*, Thèse (Liège, 1950).

E. M. IBRAHIM

1. *Plethysm of S-functions*, Quart. J. Math. (2) **3** (1952), 50-55.
2. *On a Theorem of Murnaghan*, PNAS **40** (1954), 306-309.
3. *Some subgroups of the orthogonal and symplectic groups*, Proc. Math. Phys. Soc. Egypt **5** (1954), 9-15.
4. *Tables for the plethysms of S-functions*, ibid., 85-86.
5. *On D. E. Littlewood's algebra of S-functions*, PAMS **7** (1956), 199-202.
6. *Note on a paper of Murnaghan*, ibid., 1000-1001.

K. IIZUKA

1. *Note on blocks of group characters*, Kumamoto J. Sci. (A) **2** (1956), 309-321.

R. E. INGRAM

1. *Some characters of* $\mathfrak{S}_n$, PAMS **1** (1950), 358-369.

H. A. JAHN

1. *Theoretical studies in nuclear structure*—I, PRS (London) A **201** (1950), 516-544; II ibid. **205** (1951), 192-237.
2. *Direct evaluation of fractional parentage coefficients*, Phys. Rev. **96** (1954), 989-995.
3. *Hassitt-type Young operator expansions*, TRS (London) A **253** (1960), 27-53.

DIANE JOHNSON

1. *Representations of the* $\mathfrak{S}_n$. Thesis, University of Toronto, 1958.

T. KODAMA and K. YAMAMOTO

1. *Some properties of characters of* $\mathfrak{S}_n$, Mem. Fac. Sc. Kyusyu Univ. (A) **12** (1958), 104-112.

K. KONDO

1. *Tables of characters of* $\mathfrak{S}_{14}$, Proc. Phys. Math. Soc. Japan (3) **22** (1940), 585-593.
2. *Über die Zerlegung der Charaktere der alternierenden Gruppe*, Proc. Imp. Acad. Tokyo **16** (1940), 131-135.
3. *Decomposition of the characters of some groups*, Proc. Phys. Math. Soc. Japan (3) **23** (1941), 265-271.

D. E. LITTLEWOOD

1. *Group characters and the structure of groups*, PLMS (2) **39** (1935), 150-199.
2. *Some properties of S-functions*, ibid. **40** (1936), 49-70.
3. *On compound and induced matrices*, ibid., 370.
4. *Polynomial concomitants and invariant matrices*, JLMS **11** (1936), 49-55.
5. *The construction of invariant matrices* PLMS (2) **43** (1937), 226-240.
6. *Invariant Theory, tensors and group characters*, TRS (London) A, **239** (1943), 305-365.
7. *On Invariant Theory under restricted groups*, ibid., 387-417.
8. *Invariants and systems of quadrics*, PLMS (2) **49** (1947), 282-306.
9. *Invariant Theory under orthogonal groups*, ibid. **50** (1948), 349-379.
10. *Modular representations of symmetric groups*, PRS (London) A, **209** (1951), 333-352.
11. *On the Poincaré polynomials of the classical groups*, JLMS **28** (1953), 494-500.

12. *On orthogonal and symplectic group characters*, JLMS **30** (1955), 121-122.
13. *The characters and representations of isoprimitive groups*, PLMS (3) **6** (1956), 251-266.
14. *The Kronecker product of symmetric group representations*, JLMS **31** (1956), 89-93.
15. *Plethysm and the inner product of S-functions*, JLMS **32** (1957), 18-22.
16. *The inner plethysm of S-functions*, CJM **10** (1958), 1-16.
17. *Products of plethysm and characters*, ibid., 17-32.

D. E. LITTLEWOOD and A. R. RICHARDSON

1. *Group characters and algebra*, TRS (London) A **233** (1934), 99-141.
2. *Immanants of some special matrices*, Quart. J. Maths. **5** (1934), 269-282.

G. W. MACKEY

1. *On induced representations of groups*, AJM 73 (1951), 576-592.

R. H. MAKAR and S. A. MISSIHA

1. *Coefficients of S-function*, Proc. K. Accad. wet. **61** (1958), 77-86; 87-93.

F. I. MAUTNER

1. *Induced representations*, AJM **74** (1952), 737-758.

F. D. MURNAGHAN

1. *On the representations of* $\mathfrak{S}_n$, AJM **59** (1937), 437-488.
2. *The characters of* $\mathfrak{S}_n$, ibid., 739-753.
3. *On the direct product of irreducible representations of* $\mathfrak{S}_n$, PNAS **23** (1937), 288-290.
4. *The analysis of the direct product of irreducible representations of* $\mathfrak{S}_n$, AJM **60** (1938), 44-65.
5. *The analysis of the Kronecker product of irreducible representations of* $\mathfrak{S}_n$, ibid., 761-784.
6. *On the multiplication of S-functions*, PNAS **36** (1950), 476-479.
7. *On the analysis of representations of the linear groups*, PNAS **37** (1951), 51-55.
8. *The characters of* $\mathfrak{S}_n$, ibid., 55-58; Annals Acad. Bras., **23** (1951), 141-154.
9. *A generalization of Hermite's law of reciprocity*, PNAS **37** (1951), 439-441.
10. *On the Poincaré polynomial of the full linear group*, PNAS **38** (1952), 606-608.
11. *On the Poincaré polynomials of the classical groups*, ibid., 608-611.
12. *On the multiplication of representations of the linear group*, ibid., 738-741.
13. *On the invariant theory of classical groups*, ibid., 966-973.
14. *On the decomposition of tensors by contraction*, ibid., 973-979.
15. *On the Poincaré polynomials of the classical groups—addendum*, PNAS **39** (1953), 48.
16. *On the symmetry properties of powers*, PNAS **40** (1954), 822-825.
17. *On the characters of* $\mathfrak{S}_n$, PNAS **41** (1955), 396-398.
18. *On the generation of the irreducible representations of* $\mathfrak{S}_n$, ibid., 514-515.
19. *On the analysis of the Kronecker product of irreducible representations of* $\mathfrak{S}_n$, ibid., 515-518.

20. *On the irreducible representations of* $\mathfrak{S}_n$, ibid., 1096-1102.
21. *On the Kronecker product of irreducible representations of* $\mathfrak{S}_n$, PNAS **42** (1956), 95-98.

H. NAGAO

1. *On the theory of representation of finite groups*, Osaka Math. J. **3** (1951), 11-20.
2. *Note on the modular representations of symmetric groups*, CJM **5** (1953), 356-363.
3. *On groups with the same table of characters as* $\mathfrak{S}_n$, J. Inst. Polytech. Osaka City Univ. (A) **8** (1957), 1-8

T. NAKAYAMA

1. *On some modular properties of irreducible representations of* $\mathfrak{S}_n$, Jap. J. Maths. **17** (1940), I, 89-108; II, 411-423.

T. NAKAYAMA and M. OSIMA

1. *Note on blocks of symmetric groups*, Nagoya Math. J. **2** (1951), 111-117.

C. NESBITT

1. *On the regular representations of algebras*, AM **39** (1938), 634-658.

C. NESBITT and W. M. SCOTT

1. *Some remarks on algebras over an algebraically closed field*, AM **44** (1943), 534-553.

M. J. NEWELL

1. *On the quotients of alternants and* $\mathfrak{S}_n$, PLMS (2) **53** (1951), 345-355.
2. *On the multiplication of S-functions*, PLMS (2) **53** (1951), 356-362.
3. *A theorem on the plethysm of S-functions*, Quart. J. Maths. **2** (1951), 161-166.

M. OSIMA

1. *Some notes on induced representations of groups*, Jap. J. Math. **21** (1951), 191-196.
2. *On the induced characters of a group*, Proc. Jap. Acad. **28** (1952) 243-248.
3. *On the representations of groups of finite order*, OMJ **1** (1952), 33-60.
4. *On some character relations of symmetric groups*, ibid., 63-68.
5. *On the Cartan invariants of algebras*, OMJ **2** (1952), 9-12.
6. *Note on basic rings*, ibid., 103-110.
7. *On the irreducible representations of* $\mathfrak{S}_n$, CJM **4** (1952), 381-384.
8. *On the induced characters of groups of finite order*, OMJ **3** (1953), 47-64.
9. *Some remarks on the characters of* $\mathfrak{S}_n$, CJM I, **5** (1953), 336-343; II, **6** (1954), 511-521.
10. *On the representations of the generalized symmetric group*, OMJ I, **4** (1954), 39-56; II, **6** (1956), 81-97.
11. *Notes on blocks of group characters*, OMJ **4** (1954), 175-188.
12. *On blocks of characters of* $\mathfrak{S}_n$, Proc. Jap. Acad. **31** (1955), 131-134.
13. *Note on a paper by J. S. Frame and G. de B. Robinson*, OMJ **6** (1956), 77-79.
14. *On some properties of group characters*, Proc. Jap. Acad. **36** (1960), 18-21.

P. J. Redmond

1. *Calculation of fractional parentage coefficients*, PRS (A) **222** (1954), 84-93.

I. Reiner

1. *The non-uniqueness of irreducible constituents of integral group representations*, PAMS **11** (1960), 655-658.

E. D. Roe

1. *On the coefficients in the product of an alternant and a symmetric function*, TAMS **5** (1904), 193-213.
2. *On the coefficients in the quotient of two alternants*, ibid. **6** (1905), 63-74.

G. de B. Robinson

1. *A geometrical study of the alternating and symmetric groups*, PCPS **25** (1929), 168-174.
2. *A geometrical study of the hyperoctahedral group*, PCPS **26** (1930), 94-98.
3. *Group Representations*, Thesis, Cambridge, 1931.
4. *Note on an equation of quantitative substitutional analysis*, PLMS (2) **38** (1935), 414-416.
5. *On the fundamental region*, PLMS (2) **43** (1937), 289-301.
6. *On the representations of $\mathfrak{S}_n$*, I, AJM **60** (1938), 745-760; II, **69** (1947), 286-298; III, **70** (1948), 277-294.
7. *On a conjecture by Nakayama*, TRS (Canada) III **41** (1947), 20-25.
8. *On the disjoint product of irreducible representations of $\mathfrak{S}_n$*, CJM **1** (1949), 166-175.
9. *Induced representations and invariants*, CJM **2** (1950), 334-343.
10. *On the modular representations of $\mathfrak{S}_n$*, I, PNAS **37** (1951), 694-696; II, **38** (1952), 129-133; III **38** (1952), 424-426; IV, CJM **6** (1954), 486-497; V, **7** (1955), 391-400; VI (with O. E. Taulbee), PNAS **41** (1955), 596-598.
11. *On a conjecture by J. H. Chung*, CJM **4** (1952), 373-380.
12. *The degree of an irreducible representation of $\mathfrak{S}_n$*, PNAS **42** (1956), 357-359.
13. *A remark by Philip Hall*, Can. Math. Bull. **1** (1958), 21-23.

G. de B. Robinson and O. E. Taulbee

1. *The reduction of the inner product of two irreducible representations of $\mathfrak{S}_n$*, PNAS **40** (1954), 723-726.

G. de B. Robinson and R. M. Thrall

1. *The content of a Young diagram*, Mich. Math. J. **2** (1953-54), 157-167.

D. E. Rutherford

1. *On the relations between the number of standard tableaux*, Proc. Ed. Math. Soc. (2) **7** (1942), 51-54.

I. Schur

1. *Dissertation* (Berlin, 1901).
2. *Neue Begründung der Theorie der Gruppencharaktere*, SPA (1905), 406-432.
3. *Arithmetische Untersuchungen über endliche Gruppen linearer Substitutionen*, SPA (1906), 164-184.
4. *Über die Darstellung der symmetrische Gruppe*, SPA (1908), 664-678.

5. *Beiträge zur Theorie der Gruppen linearer homogenen Substitutionen*, TAMS **10** (1909), 159-175.
6. *Über die rationalen Darstellungen der allgemeinen linearen Gruppe*, SPA (1927), 58-75.

W. SPECHT

1. *Die irreducible Darstellungen der symmetrische Gruppe*, MZ **39** (1935), 696-711.
2. *Darstellungstheorie der Hyperoktaedergruppe*, MZ **42** (1937), 629-640.
3. *Zur Darstellungstheorie der symmetrische Gruppe*, ibid., 774-779.
4. *Darstellungstheorie der affinen Gruppe*, MZ **43** (1937), 120-160.
5. *Darstellungstheorie der alternierenden Gruppe*, ibid., 553-572.

R. A. STAAL

1. *Star diagrams and* $\mathfrak{S}_n$, CJM **2** (1950), 79-92.

O. E. TAULBEE

1. *Modular representations of* $\mathfrak{S}_n$, Thesis, Michigan State University, 1957.

R. M. THRALL

1. *Young's semi-normal representation of* $\mathfrak{S}_n$, Duke Math. J. **8** (1941), 611-624.
2. *On symmetrized Kronecker powers and the structure of the free Lie ring*, AJM **64** (1942), 639-657.
3. *On the decomposition of modular tensors*, I, AM **43** (1942), 671-684; II, **45** (1944), 639-657.

R. M. THRALL and C. NESBITT

1. *On the modular representations of* $\mathfrak{S}_n$, AM **43** (1942), 656-670.

R. M. THRALL and G. DE B. ROBINSON

1. *Supplement to a paper by G. de B. Robinson*, AMJ **73** (1951), 721-724.

J. A. TODD

1. *A note on the algebra of S-functions*, PCPS **45** (1949), 328-334.
2. *Note on a paper by Robinson*, CJM **2** (1950), 331-333.

B. L. VAN DER WAERDEN

1. *Der Zusammenhang zwischen der Darstellungen der symmetrische und den linearen Gruppen*, Math. Ann. **104** (1931), 92-95 and 800.

A. H. WALLACE

1. *Invariant matrices and the Gordon-Capelli series*, PLMS (3) **2** (1952), 98-127.
2. *Generalized Young tableaux*, Proc. Ed. Math. Soc. (2) **9** (1953), 35-43.

NANCY WALLS

1. *On a certain type of space-tableau*, Proc. Ed. Math. Soc. (2) **9** (1954), 82-86.

T. YAMANOUCHI

1. *On the calculation of atomic energy levels IV*, Proc. Phys.-Math. Soc. Japan **18** (1936), 623-640.
2. *On the construction of unitary irreducible representations of the symmetric group*, loc. cit. **19** (1937), 436-450.

3. *Atomic energy levels of $p^n p$ configurations*, loc. cit. **20** (1938), 547-559.

T. Yamanouchi and M. Kotani

1. *Excitation of atoms by electron collision*, Proc. Phys.-Math. Soc. Japan **22** (1940), 14-33.

A. Young

1. *Quantitative Substitutional Analysis*, PLMS (1) I, **33** (1901), 97-146; II, **34** (1902), 361-397; PLMS (2) III, **28** (1928), 255-292; IV, **31** (1930), 253-272; V, ibid., 273-288; VI, **34** (1932), 196-230; VII, **36** (1933), 304-368; VIII, **37** (1934), 441-495; IX, **54** (1952), 219-253.

M. Zia-ud-Din

1. *The characters of* $\mathfrak{S}_{11}$, PLMS (2) **39** (1935), 200-204.
2. *The characters of* $\mathfrak{S}_{12}$ *and* $\mathfrak{S}_{13}$, PLMS (2) **42** (1937), 340-355.

APPENDIX

D-Matrices (mod 2) of $\mathfrak{S}_n$

2 – 3   Core [1]

	010	011	011
010	123		
0 1 0	1 2 3		
01 1		12 3	13 2

2 – 4   Core [ϕ]

	0101	0110	0110
0101	1234		
010 1	123 4	124 3	134 2
01 10		12 34	13 24
01 1 0	14 2 3	12 3 4	13 2 4
0 1 0 1	1 2 3 4		

2 – 5

	01010		01100	01100	01100	01100	01101	01101	01011	01011
01010	12345									
010 10	123 45		124 35	134 25	125 34	135 24				
010 1 0	123 4 5	145 2 3	124 3 5	134 2 5	125 3 4	135 2 4	core [1]			
01 10 0		14 25 3	12 34 5	13 24 5	12 35 4	13 25 4				
0 1 0 1 0		1 2 3 4 5								
0101 1							1245 3	1345 2	1235 4	1234 5
01 1 0 1				core [2, 1]			12 3 4 5	13 2 4 5	14 2 3 5	15 2 3 4

2 – 6

$\beta =$	1	4	4	16	
$[6]$	1				
$[5, 1]$	1	1			
$[4, 2]$	1	1	1		
$[4, 1^2]$	2	1	1		
$[3^2]$	1	0	1		core $[\phi]$
$[2^3]$	1	0	1		
$[3, 1^3]$	2	1	1		
$[2^2, 1^2]$	1	1	1		
$[2, 1^4]$	1	1			
$[1^6]$	1				
$[3, 2, 1]$				1	

2 – 7

$\beta =$	1	12	20	6	8	
$[7]$	1					
$[5, 2]$	2	1				
$[5, 1^2]$	3	1				
$[4, 2, 1]$	3	1	1			
$[3^2, 1]$	1	0	1			
$[3, 2^2]$	1	0	1			
$[3, 2, 1^2]$	3	1	1			core $[1]$
$[3, 1^4]$	3	1				
$[2^2, 1^2]$	2	1				
$[1^7]$	1					
$[6, 1]$				1		
$[4, 3]$				1	1	
$[4, 1^3]$				2	1	core $[2, 1]$
$[2^3, 1]$				1	1	
$[2, 1^5]$				1		

2 – 8

$\beta =$	1	6	12	8	40	64	
[8]	1						
[7, 1]	1	1					
[6, 2]	2	1	1				
[6, 1^2]	3	1	1				
[5, 3]	2	1	1	1			
[5, 1^3]	3	2	1	1			
[4^2]	0	1	0	1			
[4, 3, 1]	4	1	1	1	1		
[4, 2^2]	4	0	1	0	1		
[4, 2, 1^2]	6	2	2	1	1		core [ϕ]
[4, 1^4]	3	2	1	1	0		
[3^2, 2]	2	0	0	0	1		
[3^2, 1^2]	4	0	1	0	1		
[3, 2^2, 1]	4	1	1	1	1		
[2^4]	0	1	0	1			
[2^3, 1^2]	2	1	1	1			
[3, 1^5]	3	1	1				
[2^2, 1^4]	2	1	1				
[2, 1^6]	1	1					
[1^8]	1						
[5, 2, 1]						1	core [3, 2, 1]
[3, 2, 1^3]						1	

2 – 9

$\beta =$	1	24	76	16	40	8	32	128
[9]	1							
[7, 2]	3	1						
[7, 1^2]	4	1						
[6, 2, 1]	5	1	1					
[5, 4]	2	1	0	1				
[5, 3, 1]	6	1	1	1	1			
[5, 2^2]	4	0	1	0	1			
[5, 2, 1^2]	9	2	1	1	1			
[5, 1^4]	6	2	0	1	0		core [1]	
[4^2, 1]	4	1	0	1	1			
[4, 2, 1^3]	9	2	1	1	1			
[3^3]	2	0	0	0	1			
[3^2, 1^3]	4	0	1	0	1			
[3, 2^3]	4	1	0	1	1			
[3, 2^2, 1^2]	6	1	1	1	1			
[3, 2, 1^4]	5	1	1	0				
[3, 1^6]	4	1		0				
[2^4, 1]	2	1		1				
[2^2, 1^5]	3	1						
[1^9]	1							
[8, 1]						1		
[6, 3]						2	1	
[6, 1^3]						3	1	
[4, 3, 2]						1	1	1
[4, 3, 1^2]			core [2, 1]			3	2	1
[4, 2^2, 1]						3	2	1
[4, 1^5]						3	1	0
[3^2, 2, 1]						1	1	1
[2^3, 1^3]						2	1	
[2, 1^7]						1		

N

2 – 10

$\beta =$	1	8	24	32	16	192	168	160	128	768
[10]	1									
[9, 1]	1	1								
[8, 2]	3	1	1							
[8, 1^2]	4	1	1							
[7, 3]	3	2	1	1						
[7, 1^3]	4	3	1	1						
[6, 4]	2	2	1	1	1					
[6, 3, 1]	11	2	2	1	1	1				
[6, 2^2]	9	0	1	0	0	1				
[6, 2, 1^2]	14	3	3	1	1	1				
[6, 1^4]	6	3	2	1	1	0				
[5^2]	2	0	1	0	1	0				
[5, 3, 2]	10	1	1	1	1	1	1			
[5, 3, 1^2]	15	3	3	2	2	1	1			
[5, 2^2, 1]	13	3	2	2	1	1	1			
[5, 1^5]	6	3	2	1	1	0	0			
[4^2, 2]	4	1	1	1	1	0	1		core	
[4^2, 1^2]	4	3	1	2	1	0	1		[ϕ]	
[4, 3^2]	2	1	0	1	0	0	1			
[4, 3, 1^3]	13	3	2	2	1	1	1			
[4, 2^3]	4	3	1	2	1	0	1			
[4, 2^2, 1^2]	15	3	3	2	2	1	1			
[4, 2, 1^4]	14	3	3	1	1	1	0			
[4, 1^6]	4	3	1	1	0	0	0			
[3^3, 1]	2	1	0	1	0	0	1			
[3^2, 2^2]	4	1	1	1	1	0	1			
[3^2, 2, 1^2]	10	1	1	1	1	1	1			
[3^2, 1^4]	9	0	1	0	0	1				
[3, 2^2, 1^3]	11	2	2	1	1	1				
[3, 1^7]	4	1	1	0	0					
[2^5]	2	0	1	0	1					
[2^4, 1^2]	2	2	1	1	1					
[2^3, 1^4]	3	2	1	1						
[2^2, 1^6]	3	1	1							
[2, 1^8]	1	1								
[1^{10}]	1									
[7, 2, 1]								1		
[5, 4, 1]								1	1	
[5, 2, 1^3]						core		2	1	
[3, 2^3, 1]						[3, 2, 1]		1	1	
[3, 2, 1^5]								1		
[4, 3, 2, 1]										1

3 – 3

	012	021
012	123	
01 2	12 3	13 2
0 2 1		1 2 3

3 – 4

	0120	0210	0122	0122	0212	0121	0211	0211
0120	1234							
01 20	12 34	13 24						
0 2 1 0		1 2 3 4						
012 2			123 4	124 3	134 2			
01 2 1						12 3 4	13 2 4	14 2 3

3 – 6

$\beta =$	1	4	6	1	4	9	9	
[6]	1							
[5, 1]	1	1						
$[4, 1^2]$	0	1	1					
$[3^2]$	0	1	0	1				
[3, 2, 1]	1	1	1	1	1			core [ϕ]
$[3, 1^3]$	0		1	0	1			
$[2^3]$	1			0	1			
$[2, 1^4]$				1	1			
$[1^6]$				1				
[4, 2]						1		
$[2^2, 1^2]$							1	

3 – 7

$\beta =$	1	13	1	20	13	6	15	15	6	
[7]	1									
[5, 2]	1	1								
[4, 3]	0	1	1							
[4, 2, 1]	1	1	1	1						
$[4, 1^3]$	0		0	1						core [1]
$[3, 2, 1^2]$	1		1	1	1					
$[2^3, 1]$	1		0		1					
$[2^2, 1^3]$			1		1					
$[1^7]$			1							
[6, 1]						1				
$[3, 2^2]$						1	1			core [3, 1]
$[3, 1^4]$							1			
$[5, 1^2]$								1		
$[3^2, 1]$								1	1	core $[2, 1^2]$
$[2, 1^5]$									1	

$\beta =$	1	27	35	7	13	7	13	1	35	27	21	21	90
$[8]$	1												
$[5, 3]$	1	1											
$[5, 2, 1]$	2	1	1										
$[5, 1^3]$	0	0	1										
$[4, 3, 1]$	1	1	1	1									
$[3^2, 1^2]$	1		1	1	1			core					
$[2^4]$	1			0	1			[2]					
$[2^2, 1^4]$				1	1								
$[2, 1^6]$				1									
$[7, 1]$						1							
$[6, 2]$						1	1						
$[4^2]$						0	1	1					
$[4, 2^2]$						1	1	1	1				
$[4, 1^4]$						0		0	1				
$[3, 2^2, 1]$						1		1	1	1			
$[3, 2, 1^3]$			core					2	1	1			
$[2^3, 1^2]$			$[1^2]$					1		1			
$[1^8]$								1					
$[6, 1^2]$											1		
$[3^2, 2]$								core			1	1	
$[3, 1^5]$								$[3, 1^2]$				1	
$[4, 2, 1^2]$													1

$\beta =$	1	7	21	40	35	1	35	7	21	40	27	189	189	27	162	162
[9]	1															
[8, 1]	1	1														
[7, 1^2]	0	1	1													
[6, 3]	1	1	0	1												
[6, 2, 1]	2	1	1	1	1											
[6, 1^3]	0	0	1	0	1											
[5, 4]	1	0	0	1	0	1										
[5, 2^2]	2	1	0	1	1	1	1									
[5, 1^4]	0	0	0	0	1	0	1									
[4^2, 1]	1	0	0	1	1	1	0	1								
[4, 3, 2]	1	1	1	1	1	1	1	1	1							
[4, 1^5]	0	0	0		0	0	1	0	1					core [ϕ]		
[3^3]	0	0	1		0	0	0	0	1							
[3^2, 2, 1]	1	1	1		1	1	1	1	1	1						
[3^2, 1^3]	1	0			1	2	1	1	0	1						
[3, 2^3]	1	1				1	1	0	0	1						
[3, 2, 1^4]	0					2	1	1	1	1						
[3, 1^6]	0					0		1	1	0						
[2^4, 1]	1					1		0		1						
[2^3, 1^3]						1		1		1						
[2, 1^7]						1		1								
[1^8]						1										
[7, 2]											1					
[4, 2^2, 1]						core [4, 2]					1	1				
[4, 2, 1^3]												1				
[5, 2, 1^2]													1			
[4, 3, 1^2]						core [2^2, 1^2]							1	1		
[2^2, 1^5]														1		
[5, 3, 1]															1	
[3, 2^2, 1^2]																1

$\beta =$	1	34	40	84	224	1	224	34	84	40	9	81	126	3
[10]	1													
[8, 2]	1	1												
[7, 3]	1	1	1											
[7, 2, 1]	2	1	1	1										
$[7, 1^3]$	0	0	0	1										
$[6, 2, 1^2]$	2	0	1	1	1									
$[5^2]$	1	0	1	0	0	1								
$[5, 2^2, 1]$	2	1	1	0	1	1	1							
$[5, 2, 1^3]$	0	0	0	0	1	0	1							
$[4^2, 1^2]$	1	0	1	0	1	1	0	1						
$[4, 3^2]$	1	0	1	1	0	1	0	0	1		core [1]			
[4, 3, 2, 1]	2	1	1	1	1	2	1	1	1	1				
$[4, 3, 1^3]$	1	0		0	1	2	1	1	0	1				
$[4, 2^3]$	1	1		0		1	1	0	0	1				
$[4, 2, 1^4]$	0			0		2	1	0	1	1				
$[4, 1^6]$	0			0		0		0	1	0				
$[3^3, 1]$	1			1		1		0	1	1				
$[3, 2, 1^5]$	0					2		1	1	1				
$[2^5]$	1					1		0		1				
$[2^3, 1^4]$						1		1		1				
$[2^2, 1^6]$						1		1						
$[1^{10}]$						1								
[9, 1]											1			
[6, 4]											1	1		
$[6, 2^2]$											2	1	1	
$[6, 1^4]$											0	0	1	
$[4^2, 2]$											1	1	1	1
$[3^2, 2, 1^2]$											1		1	1
$[3, 2^3, 1]$											1			0
$[3, 2^2, 1^3]$														1
$[3, 1^7]$														1
$[8, 1^2]$														
[6, 3, 1]														
[5, 4, 1]														
[5, 3, 2]														
$[5, 1^5]$											core $[2, 1^2]$			
$[3^2, 2^2]$														
$[3^2, 1^4]$														
$[2^4, 1^2]$														
$[2, 1^8]$														
$[5, 3, 1^2]$														
$[4, 2^2, 1^2]$														

D-Matrix (mod 5) of the Block of Weight 2 of $\mathfrak{S}_{10}$

5 – 10

$\beta =$	1	8	28	56	70	34	217	266	56	34	217	28	1	8
$[10]$	1													
$[9, 1]$	1	1												
$[8, 1^2]$		1	1											
$[7, 1^3]$			1	1										
$[6, 1^4]$				1	1									
$[5^2]$		1				1								
$[5, 4, 1]$	1	1	1			1	1							
$[5, 3, 1^2]$			1	1			1	1						
$[5, 2, 1^3]$				1	1			1	1					
$[5, 1^5]$					1				1					
$[4^2, 2]$	1						1			1				
$[4, 3, 2, 1]$						1	1	1		1	1			
$[4, 2^2, 1^2]$								1	1		1	1		
$[4, 1^6]$									1			1		
$[3^2, 2^2]$						1					1		1	
$[3, 2^3, 1]$										1	1	1	1	1
$[3, 1^7]$												1		1
$[2^5]$										1				1
$[2, 1^8]$													1	1
$[1^{10}]$													1	
r	4	3	2	1	0	3	2, 4	1, 4	4	2	1, 3	3	1	2

INDEX